George Ronald Bahá'í Studies Series

The Spirit of Agriculture

edited by
Paul Hanley

George Ronald
Oxford

George Ronald, *Publisher*
Oxford
www.grbooks.com

*A catalogue record for this book is available
from the British Library*

ISBN 978-0-85398-501-3

Contents

Five Project Summaries

Introduction

Agriculture and Religion: A Necessary Unity

Paul Hanley

Agriculture and religion have been closely associated for 12,000 years and since the dawn of the Neolithic period have played complementary and crucial roles in the formation and development of civilization. Their ongoing, reciprocal role in sustaining an ever-advancing civilization is the theme of this book.

The Bahá'í Faith is unique among religions in the emphasis it places on agriculture. For Bahá'u'lláh, who established the religion in the latter half of the 19th century, agriculture was a 'vital and important matter' (Bahá'u'lláh, *Tablets* 90). His commitment to agriculture is evidenced in his own agricultural endeavours and those of his son and successor, 'Abdu'l-Bahá, and in their extensive discourse on the topic.

Agriculture was to have a fundamental part in the new social order Bahá'u'lláh aimed to establish. His overarching objective was to effect a transformation in world civilization through the application of a set of spiritual principles that, while consistent with the core values of earlier faiths, corresponded more closely to the needs of the modern world.

Foremost among these is the principle of human unity. Only its recognition would put an end to the prejudices dividing people along racial, ethnic, religious, gender, class and national lines. One's primary loyalty, he said, is to the human race. By setting aside hatreds and prejudices, humanity would free itself to pursue the processes of personal and social development required to ensure the rights and dignity of all.

In 1891, in the Tablet of the World, Bahá'u'lláh outlined 'that which is conducive to the advancement of mankind and to the reconstruction of the world' (ibid. 89). He identified several principles that would contribute to achieving social order, including international cooperation and disarmament; a new ethos of universal fellowship, epitomized by the adoption of a common auxiliary language; the training and education of children; and agricultural development. Bahá'u'lláh stated that 'special regard must be paid to agriculture', as 'unquestionably' it precedes the other principles in importance (ibid. 90).

Why this 'special regard' for agriculture? Why should it take precedence over the promotion of international peace or human fellowship or universal education? An obvious answer is that food is the prerequisite of human development: What could be more basic to human dignity than an adequate diet? Can we have peace or even fellowship while multitudes starve? Is education possible when children are malnourished?

Human beings, said Bahá'u'lláh, have been created 'to carry forward an ever-advancing civilization' (Bahá'u'lláh, *Gleanings* 215) and a properly functioning food and agriculture system, which provides sufficient nutrition for all on a sustainable basis, is clearly essential to this purpose. And since 'The fundamental purpose animating the Faith of God and His Religion is to safeguard the interests and promote the unity of the human race . . .' (Bahá'u'lláh, *Tablets* 168), religion has been and must continue to be involved in the development of agriculture.

But what does it really mean for religion to be involved in agriculture? What can a religion contribute, in a practical sense, to its development? What does the Bahá'í Faith have to offer farmers, agronomists, agricultural economists or policy-makers? This collection of articles aims to answer these questions.

By way of introduction this chapter offers a context in which to frame this perspective. First, it examines present agricultural conditions and what they are likely to be in the future. This immediately points to a need to radically transform the food and agriculture system and its operating principles. Second, it considers the role we can expect agriculture to play in an industrial or post-industrial and global society. Will it be so significant that agriculture deserves the emphasis it received in the Bahá'í writings in the late 19th and early 20th centuries? Third, it explores the nature of the relationship between religion and agriculture. By looking at history and prehistory we will see that these two civilizing forces are intrinsically and necessarily linked; that the realization of an effective, just and sustainable agriculture is dependent on the application of spiritual principles; and that the revitalization of religion is the means by which the transformations necessary to ensure an ever-advancing civilization become possible. Finally, it touches briefly on the process of transformation itself.

The Problem of Success

India's Silicon Valley, the city of Bangalore in the southern state of Karnataka, has become a symbol of the global sweep of the new economy. Its laptop-toting yuppies, software firms and trendy malls contrast sharply with stereotypes of poverty-stricken India. To some, Bangalore's improbable rise to economic prominence signals the advent of a new prosperity emerging from the explosion of high tech innovation and the opening of transnational markets.

Outside Bangalore the prospect is less bright. In Karnataka, 65 per cent of the 52 million citizens still depend on agriculture for a living and while the capital's educated class plugs into the global economy, the rural poor sink into despair. Their desperation has been made tragically evident in a disturbing string of suicides. In one three-month period late in 2001, for example, a hundred farmers killed themselves (Madhavan, 'Farmers' suicides').

'Farm activists say rural folk are trapped in the grip of moneylenders who demand high interest,' reported journalist Narayanan Madhavan. 'Farm leaders say crop failures because of drought and pests are compounded by inadequate credit, a patchy crop insurance system, high input costs, subsidy cuts, and low support prices offered by state-run procurement agencies.'

The resulting unrest among farmers has translated into major political tension for both Karnataka and its technology rival and neighbouring state Andhra Pradesh. In Andhra Pradesh there have also been hundreds of farmer suicides: in 1998–9 more than five hundred farmers killed themselves, many by drinking pesticides.

In addition to high input costs, resulting from government subsidy cuts, loans were cited as the major problem for these farmers. Many rely on private lenders who charge three times the 12 per cent bank rate. Interest charges grow faster than crops, said one activist, who blamed the World Trade Organization for low commodity prices which make life difficult if not impossible for farmers caught in a cost-price squeeze.

The 'new prosperity' has had little effect in rural areas around Bangalore or in Andhra Pradesh. Like their counterparts throughout India and the 'developing world', small producers and farm labourers continue to be under-compensated for their efforts and unappreciated for their primary contribution to society. And as political power weakens in the rural areas owing to urbanization, their already tenuous standing is further diminished.

Such desperate conditions among rural people are symptomatic of a wider malaise in the world's agricultural system. This malaise is seen in the social and economic status of farmers and the rural poor, the prevalence of undernourishment in the face of inadequate food supplies and a deep-seated ecological crisis. Ironically, these problems arise in the face of the overall success of agriculture.

Great Successes, Tragic Failures

The world's food and agriculture system is arguably the greatest achievement of civilization.

When plants were first domesticated just 12,000 years ago, it is estimated that some five million people were feeding themselves by hunting, fishing and gathering. Today, agriculture provides more than 94 per cent of the protein and 99 per cent of the calories for six billion people (Wood, *Pilot Analysis* 4). Most of the human population explosion has occurred in the past hundred years. Population has almost quadrupled since 1900, when there were 1.6 billion people. Since 1960 it has doubled, from three billion to over six billion. Yet agriculture has more than kept pace. On average, food supplies are 24 per cent higher per person today than in 1961 and real prices are 40 per cent lower (ibid.).

Despite this success, extreme food deprivation is widespread. Some 792 million people in developing countries – 18 per cent of their population – are chronically undernourished (FAO 'Mobilizing' Executive Summary). Even in the developed nations, 34 million are in the same condition. This incongruity was highlighted in the UN Food and Agriculture Organization's (FAO) documents for the 27th session of the Committee on World Food Security in November 2001:

> Looking back on the century . . . future historians are likely to point to the anomaly that hunger should have coexisted on a vast scale with more than adequate

aggregate global food supplies. The simultaneous persistence of widespread extreme food deprivation and plentiful food supplies in a world with excellent means of communications and transport, can only suggest that there are fundamental flaws in the way in which nations are functioning and the relationships between them are governed and managed (FAO, 'Fostering' no. 12).

Farm Crisis Worldwide

'Fundamental flaws' are also evident in the conditions facing producers. Ironically, farmers have effectively been penalized for their ever-increasing productivity, in that higher production has led to lower food prices. Frequently, farmers are caught in a squeeze between falling prices and rising costs.

It is important to recognize that the global forces governing farming in Karnataka and the rest of the developing world also affect farmers in the industrial world. While the consequences are radically different for an Indian farmer compared to, say, a Canadian, the dynamics that result in instability for the farm economy are remarkably similar. Consequently, the 'farm crisis' is not confined to Karnataka; in my own province of Saskatchewan, in affluent Canada, the agriculture department maintains 'suicide lines' which offer farmers telephone counselling to deal with farm-related stress.

Saskatchewan offers a useful illustration of the farm crisis in an industrial nation. Although situated in a country consistently ranked number one or two on the United Nations Development Index, its farm sector is far from healthy.

Saskatchewan is a little larger than France, Belgium and the Netherlands combined but with a population of less than one million it is almost entirely dependent on export markets for its main agricultural products – grain, oilseed and livestock. Farming has long been its mainstay but this is changing. Between 1935 and the late 1990s the numbers of farms dropped from 142,000 to fewer than 50,000 as farm size increased and in the last four years it is estimated that 26,000 farmers and farm workers have quit.

As a result of rural depopulation, the number of rural communities has diminished dramatically. Of the 600 communities in Saskatchewan in 1995, 500 had less than 175 inhabitants and only a handful have a full array of services. The provincial grain handling system is also disappearing: in 1975 there were 2,309 primary grain buying and storage facilities; by 1996 the number had fallen to 656. The decline of rural communities creates substantial problems for those remaining. In addition to the loss of family and friends, there is a considerable burden involved in maintaining a substantial infrastructure for so few people. Saskatchewan has more kilometres of roads per capita than any other jurisdiction in the world, for example, and the maintenance of these roads is further challenged as the network of railways are abandoned in favour of heavy trucks. With its rural population ageing (the average age of a farmer is now 60) and significantly reduced in size, the tax base required to maintain the system of roads, power, gas and telephone grids, schools and hospitals has evaporated (Fung, *Saskatchewan*).

The forces causing rural depopulation are similar to those found throughout North America and the world.

In 1997 Saskatchewan accounted for just two per cent of world production of wheat but about ten per cent of the world trade. The average net price of wheat in 1920 (in Canadian dollars) was US$2.63 per bushel (US$96.64 per tonne). Today it averages US$4.00 per bushel (US$150.00 per tonne) for an average grade. However, the net price is much lower; owing to the elimination of government transportation subsidies, costs rose from US$16.30 per tonne to deliver grain in 1984 to US$76.33 today. This puts the net price of grain lower than it was many years ago. Meanwhile, costs have risen dramatically. Capital investment on the average farm, for instance, now averages more than US$500,000.

A primary factor in chronically low prices for agricultural commodities is farm subsidies paid by the US and European governments. Canada blames these subsidies for distorting world grain markets; the solution, it says, is to reduce subsidies, which would lead to lower levels of production, pushing grain prices higher – and in turn eliminate the need for subsidies.

Like their counterparts in India, many of Saskatchewan's farmers are mired in debt and see little hope of a brighter future – if they stay on the farm. Unlike India's farmers, they have the option to pursue opportunities in the prosperous cities of a fully industrialized nation.

The complexities of the farm economy involve a strange paradox: The problems facing farmers result from their own success. The agricultural revolution of the 20th century has led to stunning increases in labour and land productivity which have been reflected in a progressive fall in real international grain prices, benefiting the average food consumer. As farmers produce more and more food, meeting the needs of a burgeoning urban population, prices go down, undermining their income, but there is no corresponding downward pressure on costs. In much of the world an informal 'cheap food policy' serves the interests of the urban consumer but the costs of machinery, capital, fuel and other inputs are out of control. Subsidies moderate the effects of the cost-price squeeze but few nations can afford them.

The Rural Poor

While farmers find themselves in difficult straits, their efforts are gradually improving world food security. True, more than 800 million are undernourished today but that number has fallen from 960 million in 1970. At that point the overall population of the developing world was 2.6 billion, compared to 4.5 billion today, meaning that 37 per cent of the population was undernourished 30 years ago, compared to 18 per cent today (FAO, 'Mobilizing' no. 8)

These encouraging statistics mask critical disparities, however. Average Dietary Energy Supply (DES) in the developing countries grew from 2110 to 2650 kilocalories per caput (26 per cent) between 1969 and 1998 but this improvement was concentrated in 37 countries, including seven with populations of over 100 million. Hunger actually increased in 59 countries (FAO, 'Mobilizing' no. 10; Homer-Dixon, *Ingenuity* 32).

Undernourishment typically results from poverty, not a lack of available food. The number of people living on less than one dollar a day in the developing world is about 1.3 billion, meaning that on average about 30 per cent of the population of these countries live in absolute poverty (Homer-Dixon, *Ingenuity* 33). For a majority of these people this means chronic hunger.

Poverty in developing countries is overwhelmingly concentrated in rural areas and urban poverty is often a consequence of migration from rural areas. Amongst rural populations, small farmers' families are usually among the poorest and most undernourished. The implications of this nutritional deficit for human development are considerable: poor nutrition affects the ability to work and to learn and is a primary cause of ill health, substantially undermining human potential and contributing to the vicious cycle of poverty. Conversely, adequate nutrition is a key to economic development: this point was forcefully argued by the economist Robert Fogel, whose research shows that improved nutrition accounted for 50 per cent of British economic growth between 1790 and 1980 (ibid. 383).

Hunger is not Necessary

Bringing the benefits of prosperity to the poorest of the poor is certainly not beyond human capacity, either technically or financially. It has been estimated that boosting the caloric intake of the 800 million most in need through direct food aid would cost just US$13 per head per year or US$10.4 billion (FAO, 'Mobilizing' Executive Summary). This level of spending is within the reach of a small number of individuals, let alone nations, given that the combined wealth of the 225 richest people in the world is more than the combined annual income of 2.5 billion of the world's poorest. In fact, the combined wealth of the three richest families alone is now greater than the combined GDP of the 48 poorest countries.

Disparities between rich and poor are growing. In 1960 the income of the richest 20 per cent of the world's population was 30 times that of the poorest 20 per cent; in 1998 it was 82 times greater. Nowhere are these disparities more evident than in Africa: while consumption has risen dramatically in much of the world over the last 25 years, average household consumption in Africa actually dropped by 20 per cent (Homer-Dixon, *Ingenuity* 33–4).

Food aid is a necessary part of any strategy to feed the poor but more important is a process of development that assists people to obtain resources needed to increase their incomes or, in the case of the estimated one billion subsistence farmers, their productivity. Evidence indicates that improvements to income and productivity are entirely feasible given the political will to support processes of development. In other words, extreme hunger and poverty are not an unavoidable aspect of the human condition. They are symptomatic of conditions that can be changed.

Thailand's successful campaign against malnutrition makes this point.

Over three decades ago Thailand decided to address malnutrition through a community-driven rural development programme. Improving the nation's nutritional status was reframed as an investment instead of an expense. A national rural development plan was created, involving rural job creation, village development projects, complete coverage of basic services for the community and an expansion of food production (with an emphasis on improving the quality of the diet). Among the reasons for Thailand's success in eradicating moderate to severe malnutrition in a single decade (1982–91) was its investment in human capital. A community–government partnership was developed and fostered through broad-based social mobilization strategies. Volunteer facilitators, selected by the community, became responsible for mobilizing the community to engage in nutrition-relevant actions that maximized the potential of local resources (FAO, 'Fostering' no. 54)

This example shows that a combination of social, economic and technical methods can result in significant improvements in productivity and nutrition. While providing grounds for optimism, such examples raise serious questions about the underlying reasons for persistent underdevelopment. How can poverty and hunger be tolerated when methods of their eradication are well established?

The Problem of Permanence

Economic insecurity is one side of the agricultural dilemma; environmental insecurity is the other.

Agriculture has kept pace with population growth over the past few centuries mainly by converting forests and natural grasslands to agriculture. Between farming and forestry, managed ecosystems now constitute half of the planet's ice-free land, while human-mobilized material and energy flows now rival those of nature (Homer-Dixon, *Ingenuity* 35). Since the limits of agriculture's geographic expansion were reached many years ago in most densely populated areas, increasing the productivity of existing farmland has become a necessity. In some regions, particularly in Asia, this has been achieved primarily by growing multiple crops each year in irrigated agroecosystems using new, short-duration crop varieties.

Land-abundant developed countries still possess the physical capacity to increase food production through various technologies that increase yields. However, those countries most in need of this food could not afford to import it. Thus the vast majority of new food supplies will have to come from domestic production in developing countries, many of which already experience high population growth and significant stress on their agricultural resources.

As agriculture intensifies to meet demand, broad concerns emerge about related environmental impacts, especially in the developing nations:

Land degradation Soil erosion and other forms of land degradation rob the world of up to seven million hectares of farmland every year. According to the study *Pilot Analysis of Global Ecosystems: Agroecosystems*, 40 per cent of the world's agricultural land is seriously degraded. Based on the most comprehensive mapping of global agriculture to date, the study indicates that almost 75 per cent of crop land in Central America is seriously degraded, 20 per cent in Africa (mostly pasture) and 11 per cent in Asia. Although crop production can still grow on a global scale over the next several decades, the study warns that the underlying conditions of many of the world's agroecosystems are 'not good', particularly those in developing countries (*Pilot Analysis* 5, 48).

Deteriorating water resources Some 40 per cent of the world's food comes from irrigated cropland but the productivity of these lands is in jeopardy. Water tables are dropping steadily in several major food-producing regions and farmers are racking up an annual water deficit of some 160 billion cubic metres. Meanwhile, the amount of irrigated land per person has dropped five per cent since 1978 and one in five hectares of irrigated land is damaged by salt. In all, waterlogging and salinization have sapped the productivity of nearly half the world's irrigated lands; 30 million hectares have been severely damaged and an additional 1.5 million hectares are lost each year. Meanwhile, so much water is being diverted for irrigation and other uses that the lower reaches of several major rivers sometimes run dry for portions of the year, including the Yellow in China, the Indus in Pakistan, the Ganges in South Asia and the Colorado in the American Southwest.

The number of people living in water-stressed countries is projected to climb from 470 million to 3 billion by 2025. In the swathe of countries from Morocco to Iran, virtually every nation is facing water shortages. Since it takes a thousand tons of water to grow a ton of wheat, these countries import grain to meet their food needs. Last year the water required to produce the grain and other farm products imported into the region was equivalent to the annual flow of the Nile River (Postel, *Pillar*).

Agricultural chemicals Fertilizer and pesticide use has been another means of boosting productivity. Global use of nitrogen fertilizers went from five million tonnes in the 1940s to 100 million tonnes in recent years, and today about 40 per cent of all the protein in humanity's diet is dependent on the application of nitrogen fertilizer. The global use of agricultural pesticides rose from about 50 million kilograms a year in 1945 to current application rates of approximately 2.5 billion kilograms per year. Excessive use of fertilizers and pesticides can pollute surface and groundwater sources, posing a health risk, especially for infants. In some countries the use of too little fertilizer results in a form of soil mining that contributes to soil degradation (Homer-Dixon, *Ingenuity* 66).

Genetic erosion The loss of genetic diversity in both wild and domesticated plant and animal species threatens future agricultural productivity. As monocultures replace natural ecosystems and traditional crop diversity, genetic resources useful for many purposes, including crop improvement, are disappearing. It is expected that 25 per cent of the earth's biodiversity will disappear in this century.

Climate change Agriculture produces greenhouse gases linked to global warming. In addition to methane, some 30 per cent of carbon dioxide emissions result from deforestation and land use practices such as burning rangeland. Global warming is already contributing to extreme heat, storms, drought and flooding, all of which impact negatively on agriculture.

Overfishing Close to one billion people depend on fishing for most of their animal protein. About two-thirds of the world's marine fisheries are either over-exploited, depleted or at the limits of exploitation. About one half of all mangrove ecosystems, which are essential to the health of coastal fisheries, have been changed or destroyed, and coral reefs, another source of fish stock, are experiencing a massive collapse, probably as a result of climate change (Homer-Dixon, *Ingenuity* 55). Consequently, it is unlikely that we can look to the seas for additional food supplies.

The impacts of these environmental factors are already being felt in the slowing of the rate of growth in productivity. The annual increase in agricultural production per person during the years 1970 to 1990 was 0.54 per cent. Recent indications are that the rate of increase is expected to average just 0.25 per cent in the period 1990 to 2010 (Hanley, 'Constraints').

In addition to environmental factors, an important reason for the slowing of growth in productivity may simply be that many major innovations, such as improved crop varieties, have already been widely adopted. Once in place, they can no longer increase but only maintain productivity. There may still be room for wider application of these practices but those nations that have not already adopted them typically cannot afford to do so without significant outside assistance, and levels of foreign aid in agriculture are declining – official development assistance (ODA) decreased during the 1990s from 0.33 per cent to 0.25 per cent of the GNP of OECD countries (FAO, 'Fostering' no. 15).

Nevertheless, in the near term technical innovation is likely to succeed in offsetting the trends threatening food security but the challenge of meeting human food needs is likely to grow ever more difficult over time as the agricultural environment deteriorates and population rises. The world's population will increase by up to 50 per cent by 2050 and almost all the three billion new mouths to feed will be found in developing countries.

Denial, Cynicism and Hope

Alarming data about the food, agriculture and environmental crisis tend to overwhelm people, resulting in denial. Many not directly affected by the crisis are not aware of its extent at all – so long as food continues to appear on the table there *is* no problem. Others with a stake in maintaining the status quo may contribute to mass denial. As Bahá'u'lláh observed, the world is in a strange slumber.

For those who are aware, many believe these problems can be overcome through technological fixes or market measures. Often the recommended solution is a more aggressive application of the technologies that cause environmental problems, such as more fertilizers, pesticides, irrigation or monocultures. On the other hand, some take the cynical approach that such problems result from a fundamental flaw in human nature or in civilization that is irreparable, at least without abandoning modernity.

But the fact is neither rural poverty nor the deterioration of the means of agricultural production is unavoidable. Alternative methods of agriculture that are productive and more environmentally sensitive have been identified and are being used with impressive results. A recent, comprehensive study undertaken by Jules Pretty and Rachel Hine at the University of Essex shows that sustainable farming methods adopted in the 1990s delivered extraordinary yield improvements. The researchers carried out the largest ever survey of worldwide sustainable agriculture, involving nine million farmers in 52 countries using sustainable agriculture practices and technologies on 29 million hectares, which represented at least three per cent of the land area of the countries involved. Of the 91 projects that report data on yield changes, proportional yield increases were generally 50 to 100 per cent for rain-fed crops, though considerably greater in a few cases, and five to ten per cent for irrigated crops.

Such research supports the idea that there are solutions to agriculture's problems but it also begs the question: 'Why are they not being universally supported, promoted and adopted?'

A Moral Crisis

In 1996 the Food and Agriculture Organization of the United Nations assembled the world's heads of state in Rome for the World Food Summit. The intention was to muster sufficient political will to set the world on a course to food security. The Summit Declaration reaffirmed 'the fundamental right of everyone to be free from hunger' and the leaders pledged their 'political will and . . . common national commitment to . . . an ongoing effort to eradicate hunger in all countries . . .' With a sentiment remarkably similar to that expressed by Bahá'u'lláh 105 years earlier in the Tablet of the World, their declaration included commitments on peace, poverty reduction, equality, sustainability and fair trade (FAO, 'Fostering' nos. 5, 7).

By 2001 the FAO frankly admitted that the political will necessary to end hunger had not been mustered. The Committee on World Food Security noted the moral implications of this failure:

> That some 792 million people in developing countries and 34 million in the developed world remain chronically hungry in spite of the success of farmers in generating enough food to meet everyone's needs and that there is widespread evidence of land degradation, imply that there are serious imperfections in the way in which we are handling our responsibilities to each other and exercising our stewardship over global resources. Inequity in access to food and technology, the damage to natural resources associated with some farming methods and scientific advances, erosion of biodiversity, threats to the sustainability of ocean fisheries and trade restrictions which prevent countries from exercising and benefiting from their comparative advantages all have important ethical dimensions. Looking at

these issues from an ethical and human rights standpoint may contribute to the development of a consensus on how they can be better addressed in the common interest of humanity, capturing important considerations which may not be given sufficient weight when decisions are taken principally on technical or economic grounds or left to market forces alone (FAO, 'New Challenges' no. 58).

In recognizing 'serious imperfections' in collective human behaviour towards each other and the natural world, and in expressing its obvious frustration with the lack of political will to achieve food security, the committee was drawn to a moral argument. Significantly, linking food security to human rights and ethical values, and placing it in the context of 'the common interest of humanity', is precisely the standpoint advocated by Bahá'u'lláh. The human cost of ignoring his message over the course of the past century has been immense.

Recognizing that the world's 'prevailing order' was 'lamentably defective', Bahá'u'lláh said that the solution to the world's problems would only be found in an ethical approach as expressed in the spiritual principles of the world's religions and reiterated in his writings (Bahá'u'lláh, *Tablets* 171). In a statement addressed to the world's leaders, Bahá'u'lláh described religion as 'the chief instrument for the establishment of order in the world and of tranquillity amongst its peoples' (Bahá'u'lláh, *Tablets* 63–4). Food security would be a consequence and a sign of achieving an ordered and tranquil world and Bahá'u'lláh stated that realizing these conditions would depend of the recognition of the fundamental principle of human unity: 'The well-being of mankind, its peace and security, are unattainable unless and until its unity is firmly established' (Bahá'u'lláh, *Gleanings* 286). Until we accept that all people, regardless of ethnicity, gender, class or national status, are equal members of one human family, each with unalienable rights – and act out of that belief – we are likely to overlook the obscene disparities that now divide humankind into rich and poor.

In *The Prosperity of Humankind*, the Bahá'í International Community pointed out that 'Justice is the one power that can translate the dawning consciousness of humanity's oneness into a collective will . . .' (Bahá'í International Community, *Prosperity* 9) and in a remarkable statement in the 'Words of Paradise' Bahá'u'lláh, quoting the Qur'án, espouses justice as the underlying solution to poverty and hunger. 'The light of men is Justice', he said. '. . . were mankind to be adorned with this raiment, they would behold the daystar of the utterance, "On that day God will satisfy everyone out of His abundance" [cf. Qur'án 4:129], shining resplendent above the horizon of the world' (Bahá'u'lláh, *Tablets* 66–7). This idea is implied in the 'The Right to Food' endorsed by the World Food Summit; the Committee of World Food Security notes that:

The right to food is recognized in legally binding international instruments, including, most fully, the International Covenant on Economic, Social and Cultural Rights . . . Under the Covenant, States parties are obliged to take all appropriate steps, to the maximum of available resources, to progressively achieve the right to food for all . . . Under international law, the State is accountable for the enjoyment of human rights within its territory . . . it remains incumbent on the State to ensure that those who are unable to do so for themselves are adequately provided for, so that as a minimum, no one suffers from hunger (FAO, 'Fostering' no. 30).

Economist and Nobelist Amartya Sen has observed there has never been a famine in a democratic nation. His observation underlines the idea that food security is primarily about justice. Extreme poverty and hunger result from the willingness, deliberately or through neglect, to permit inequalities within or between nations to be perpetuated. The Bahá'í teachings assert that hunger will be eliminated when people and governments embrace justice as an operating principle; when permitting poverty and inequality to degrade any human life is understood to be an assault on the dignity of the entire human race; when the oneness of humanity is the pivotal value around which human relationships are organized.

Justice is also key to solving environmental problems associated with agriculture, according to the Bahá'í teachings. Bahá'u'lláh calls on human beings to be 'the embodiments of justice and fairness amidst all creation' (Bahá'u'lláh, *Kitáb-i-Aqdas*, para. 187), implying that the circle of unity must be expanded to encompass the myriad species with which we cohabit this planet – and the planet itself. Though revealed before the term ecology had been coined, the Bahá'í teachings offer a distinctly ecological perspective which requires our species to treat the natural world with respect and to act as its trustee, answerable to its Creator for its sustainable development.

From the Bahá'í perspective, these and other spiritual principles offer means by which we can address the root causes of a very complex and entrenched agricultural crisis. This perspective underlies the articles presented in this book.

The Centrality of Agriculture

Arguably, a spiritually informed approach to human development is nowhere more important than in agriculture which, as 'Abdu'l-Bahá points out, is the 'fundamental basis of the community' ('Abdu'l-Bahá, *Promulgation* 217).

In *The Centrality of Agriculture: Between Humankind and the Rest of Nature*, environmental historian Colin Duncan contends that 'the central place in every culture should be occupied by agriculture' (Duncan, *Centrality* xv). He acknowledges this will seem naive or heretical to most living economists, though it was accepted in the past. In his influential *Wealth of Nations*, published in 1776, Adam Smith called the modern order in which industry and foreign trade take precedence over agriculture 'unnatural and retrograde'.

> According to the natural course of things, the greater part of the capital of every growing society is, first, directed to agriculture, afterwards to manufactures, and last of all to foreign commerce . . . But . . . this natural order of things . . . has, in all the modern states of Europe, been, in many respects, entirely inverted (quoted in ibid. 49).

While there have obviously been benefits to this inversion, Duncan and others argue that – viewed globally and with an eye to the future – many social and most environmental consequences of this sea change have been negative. Duncan believes that no sustainable human future can be conceived unless and until the centrality of agriculture is properly recognized and new economic institutions are developed that will encourage people to take care of their lands.

Agriculture is a unique activity. In agriculture we make products mainly by working *with* living systems and renewable resources. In industry we mainly use 'dead' matter and non-renewable materials. Agriculture works primarily with plants that are the only primary producers of products that we can consume directly, or indirectly through the consumption of animal products.

Strictly speaking, agriculture refers to cultivating plants and rearing livestock. There are of course various branches of agriculture – field-cropping, horticulture, floriculture, apiculture, aquaculture, sericulture, animal agriculture, the production of medicinal plants or fibres such as cotton, and so on. It would be appropriate, however, for the purposes of this discussion to broaden our definition to include many other activities in which people work with natural systems to produce products, such as fishing, forestry, silviculture and other means of using renewable resources. It is significant, for example, that 40 per cent of the people on the planet use fuelwood, charcoal, straw or dung as their main source of energy and 50 to 60 per cent for at least some of their energy requirements. A billion people rely on fishing for a large part of their protein requirements (Homer-Dixon, *Ingenuity* 31). Some 3.5 billion people in developing countries rely on plant-based medicine for their primary health care. In all, it has been estimated that rural residents of developing countries depend on plant resources for up to 90 per cent of their total material needs. Plants also furnish oils, latexes, gums, fibres, timbers, dyes, essences and other products used in industry (Tuxill, *Cornucopia*). All these activities might fit generally under the rubric 'agriculture'; the fact that the FAO oversees forestry suggests that an inclusive definition is not unreasonable.

We can then reframe our topic by pointing out that the dependence of people on agriculture, i.e. methods of production that rely on nature, has not diminished in the industrial era but increased. Humans now control 25 per cent of the primary productivity, i.e. the plant growth, on the planet's land surface (Eisenberg, *Eden* 22). We use more of the products of nature than ever before, and because of higher levels of consumption, we are more dependent than ever on them. During the last hundred years, per capita resource consumption rose fourfold; the production of goods and services now requires, on average, for each person, over 80 tons of natural resources annually. And by 2050 the level of consumption of natural resources is expected to rise by an additional factor of three (Homer-Dixon, *Ingenuity* 53–4). Although some economists may say that natural resources 'aren't important anymore' (ibid. 31), humanity's ongoing and ever increasing dependence on nature and agriculture is clear.

Since agriculture – in the full sense of the word – will continue to play a central role in civilization, one of the most important things that can be done is to raise, overall, the status of agriculture. Or as Bahá'u'lláh put it, 'Special regard must be paid to agriculture'.

Currently, the status of agriculture tends to be low, whether from the point of view of government priority, cultural attitudes or religious discourse.

It is interesting that Bahá'u'lláh specifically warned the shah of Iran not to neglect agriculture. Seemingly, little has changed since the 19th century, given the share of spending on agriculture in total government expenditures is as low as 0.015 per cent in some countries and lower than ten per cent in 90 per cent of the countries for which data are available. Depending on one's point of view, it is either surprising or not at all surprising that public expenditure on agriculture is lowest in the countries with the highest prevalence of undernourishment, despite the dependence of low-income food-deficit countries (LIFDCs) on agriculture for incomes and food security (FAO, 'Mobilizing' Executive Summary).

A number of negative cultural attitudes have developed concerning agriculture and rural people. As ecologist Stan Rowe (Rowe, *Home* 168) has pointed out, negative views of rural people are evident in a rich vocabulary of put-downs: rube, yokel, hayseed, bumpkin, clodhopper, hick, peasant, rustic, heathen, pagan, savage and even 'farmer'! ('City slicker' is just about their only comeback.) Contrast this with 'Abdu'l-Bahá's assertion that farmers exceed all others in the importance of their service ('Abdu'l-Bahá, *Foundations* 39).

Agriculture has suffered from negative perceptions even in religion. The Bahá'í view of the value of agriculture and its affirmation as a form of worship is radically different from that expressed in Genesis – that farming is a divine punishment (Gen. 3:17–19; 4:11–12). The Bahá'í perspective does not deny the truth underlying this scripture; instead, it expands and deepens our understanding, resulting in a fuller, positive picture of the nature of agricultural work.

Religion can play a substantive role in raising the status of agriculture to a central position in human culture, and farming to a respected occupation, by promoting the development of agriculture to the status of a spiritual principle ordained by God. This is what Bahá'u'lláh has done. His revaluing of agriculture is consistent with the ancient roots of its association with religion.

Complementary Forces in Human Development

Looking at the roots of the Neolithic period we see that the bond between agriculture and religion is intrinsic: it can be argued that agriculture is in a sense a product of religion and that religion, if not a product of agriculture, has been substantially shaped by it.

The word 'agriculture' speaks to this connection: '*agri*' is Latin for field; 'culture' is derived from '*cult*', meaning both tillage and worship. By providing surplus food, agriculture supplied the material means for the formation of civilization – literally 'citification' (Thomas, *Unfinished* 53). Religion, from '*religio*', to bind, provided civilization with its cultural adhesives: its mythologies, moral principles, philosophies, institutions and central figures.

Cristiano Grottanelli makes the case that the influence of agriculture on religion has been immense: 'The historical roots of complex phenomena such as polytheism, the so-called gift-sacrifice, and priesthood, to name but three examples, lie in the humus prepared by the Neolithic revolution' (quoted in Eliade, *Encyclopedia* 141). Indeed, agriculture provided many of the great symbols and metaphors of religion, from the myths of Greece and China to the parables of Christ and Buddha. But religion also influenced agriculture. According to Grottanelli, religious interpretations of agricultural processes, from germination through harvest, placed farming in the context of the 'cosmogonic drama of an ordered universe'. As a result, 'all agricultural and horticultural labours [had] a ritual aspect or value . . .' (ibid. 143). Agriculture and religion merged in the ritual calendar, in the feast, in the cult of religious figures and deities, in several origin myths and in the cultural practices, taboos and laws of agricultural societies. Grottanelli comments that, 'The unity of productive and ritual activity . . . was . . . complete in all archaic communities of cultivators' (ibid. 143). Many of their archaic practices echo today in religious-cultural festivals, from Dussehra and Divali in India, to Naw-Rúz in Iran, to Easter in the Christian world.

The complementary force of agriculture and religion also influenced ecological, economic, social and political relationships and structures. The Neolithic revolution resulted in a surge in population and the concentration of people, power and capital in settlements.

'In transforming *Homo sapiens* from a mere consumer of natural goods into a producer,' writes Grottanelli, 'the development of agriculture drastically changed the role of humanity within its environment, and thus the very nature of humankind. Moreover, it permitted a vast transformation of human life and activity, involving both a demographic increase and the rise of more complex settlements and communities. Agriculture required an increasingly greater specialization, differentiation, and stratification within societies, and made possible and indeed necessary the "urban revolution" that was to follow . . .' (ibid. 140–1).

Agriculture created village and city life because it produced abundant, storable and transportable human energy stores, especially grain (Thomas, *Unfinished* 33). Again, the close association of religion and agriculture can be seen in the word 'cereal', derived from the name Ceres, a Mediterranean goddesses of agriculture.

Agriculture's Roots in Religion

Religion played a key role in the invention and development of agriculture. How far this role can be traced is an interesting question. In mythology, it goes to the beginning – agriculture is explained as a divine gift. The Greeks tell that in a burst of goodwill, Demeter, their goddess of crops, bestowed wheat seeds on a trusted priest, who then crisscrossed the planet in a dragon-drawn chariot, sowing the dual blessings of agriculture and civilization.

Science does not deny a role for religion in the Neolithic revolution but gives precedence to other factors. The currently accepted theory is that climatic, demographic and ecological factors combined to create conditions that favoured the adoption of agriculture, initially in the Near East, whence agriculture diffused through the Mediterranean region, Europe, North Africa and Western Asia. Independent centres of origin cropped up in several regions, including China, Meso and South America and Africa, and possibly Southeast Asia, Eastern North America, and Papua New Guinea (Diamond, *Guns* 131–56). Some research suggests that agriculture sprang up independently in many locations, including the American tropics (Pringle, *Neolithic*).

Another theory, from French archaeologist Jacques Cauvin, is put forward in *The Birth of the Gods and the Origins of Agriculture*. Following 20 years of work on the origins of the Neolithic in the Near East, Cauvin – Director of Research emeritus of the CRNS, France's national centre for scientific research – concluded that the climatic and ecological conditions conducive to agriculture were in place several millennia before agriculture began. Quoting Levi-Strauss, he explains that 'culture was not ready' for agriculture, even though 'biology' was. Before the cultivation of plants could occur in earnest, a cultural shift was required.

Cauvin believes the start of the Neolithic period was preceded or accompanied by what he calls a 'revolution in symbols'. As there are no texts from this period, the cultural record is derived entirely from remnants of the art and architecture of the late Palaeolithic period in the Near East. Excavations of early agricultural communities show that prior to the advent of farming, the art of the pre-Neolithic period went through a dramatic transformation. Whereas art objects had consisted largely of figures of various animals, the new art began to portray the human form, in particular the female form, which in some cases is clearly shown as a divinity. Other human figures have their arms up in attitudes of supplication. In addition, the figure of the bull appears for the first time.

Here we have what would be the central figures of religion in the Middle East and Europe until the rise of monotheism. Cauvin argues that their appearance signalled a transformation of human consciousness, a new way of perceiving the world: people began to see themselves as beings distinct from their environment. They identified, for the first time, opposing or complementary forces in the nurturing power of the feminine and a virile power epitomized by the bull. And human beings were now cast in a relationship with a divine force, a relationship that required a shift to a vertical model of the cosmos, indicated by the pose of supplication mentioned above. There were now powerful forces or principles identified to which people must relate as supplicants. Cauvin sees this emergent consciousness as a trigger of, on the one hand, dissatisfaction with life as it was, immersed in nature, and on the other, a creative urge to innovate. Obviously, ecological conditions were ripe for the experiments in cultivation which followed but Cauvin speculates that the new consciousness made a new kind of relationship with the environment possible – that of controller/producer. Culture was now ready for agriculture. Or as David Fromkin observed, 'for what must have been the first time a species was altering its behaviour . . . in order to satisfy, not needs, but desires. It seemed to be seizing an opportunity, not responding to a necessity' (Fromkin, *Way* 27).

Cauvin's theory provides an interesting insight into possible cultural/religious triggers of early agricultural innovation, contributing to an appreciation for the intrinsic association between religion and agriculture.

The Co-evolution of Religion and Agriculture

Several millennia passed while the Neolithic took hold. Ultimately, towns and cities grew, often around centres of religious worship, facilitating the specialization of roles and the stratification of society (Fromkin, *Way* 36). Political structures were influenced by religious interpretations of divinity. A royal class was a link between men and the divine, and monarchs thought to be incarnate gods gained moral and temporal authority. Political leaders were typically sanctioned and crowned by religious figures, a practice continued to this day in some countries. In some cases, as in Mesopotamia, the formation of leading political institutions was made possible through efforts to build great irrigation works to support intensive farming.

Religion began to articulate customs and laws designed to bring order to an increasingly complex society, a process accelerated by the monotheistic faiths. The Mosaic code, for instance, was primarily directed to establishing an ethical order in an agrarian society. Such laws also had ecological connotations, for example, a sabbatical or fallow year was prescribed to rest the land and improve its long-term value. The Hebrew prophets began to associate agricultural and ecological conditions with the moral character of the people; Isaiah, for one, attributes the deterioration of the environment to the breaking of Israel's covenant with God (Isaiah 24:4–6).

One of the most important and lasting influences of religion is its effect on the ethos of the societies it inspires. Each of the major religions has had a profound impact on the way people behave towards nature and other human beings, which even today influences the way agriculture is carried out. Religious myths, ideas and models inform people's understanding of the significance of human life and of their role in the physical world. Religions – or interpretations of religions – have fostered both sympathetic and antagonistic attitudes to nature.

While religion is often seen as antithetical to science, it is often the case that religion contributed to the development of a scientific approach in agriculture. Islamic scholars and Christian monastic orders were leaders in the advancement of agricultural practices, a tradition epitomized by the Austrian monk Gregor Mendel, who introduced the study of plant genetics in 1859.

Religion and agriculture also combined to offer a compelling, prophetic vision of the future. This has provided a moral incentive and ultimate social goal. 'Where there is no vision, the people perish' (Proverbs 29:18); religion used agricultural metaphors to supply an agrarian vision – the 'land of milk and honey', the 'Peaceable Kingdom' – in which humankind would someday live in harmony amid plenty. This bucolic vision was presented as the endpoint of God's plan for the world. So in Micah (4:1–4) we learn that

... in the last days it shall come to pass, that ... they shall beat their swords into plowshares, and their spears into pruning hooks: nation shall not lift up a sword against nation, neither shall they learn war any more. But they shall sit every man under his vine and under his fig tree; and none shall make them afraid: for the mouth of the LORD of hosts hath spoken it.

This beatific vision has echoed through social and cultural movements, fuelled secular ideologies and generated a rich literary and artistic tradition. It is again echoed in the Bahá'í principle of the unity of humankind and its ultimate product, what Bahá'u'lláh calls the Most Great Peace.

The Process of Transformation

This outline has shown that the perennial relationship between religion and agriculture is part and parcel of human culture: it would be naive to think that this relationship has come to an end simply because of the current ascendancy of an industrial mind set or a secular interpretation of reality. The vast majority of human beings still live within a world view dominated by religion (Fromkin, *Way* 55) and this is especially true of rural people, the agricultural classes, who continue to form one half of the world's population; their religious heritage has positive and negative consequences for agriculture that must be dealt with and resolved.

The Bahá'í teachings modernize the role of religion in agriculture. Bahá'u'lláh encouraged the elimination of dangerous superstitions and irrational elements that had taken hold of religion in his day and promoted the harmonization of religious beliefs with rational thought informed by science. At the same time, he warned of the dangers inherent in the careless embrace of the western model of civilization. Science unbalanced by spiritual wisdom is potentially dangerous. Without the moderating influence of a moral perspective, the economic, technological imperative threatens the very basis of civilization (Bahá'u'lláh, *Gleanings* 342–3).

He therefore counselled a balanced approach to development, including agricultural development, in which science is pursued holistically, without bias, in the public interest and with due respect to environmental constraints. This balance is best achieved when spiritual values are given a leading role. What is more, Bahá'u'lláh said that religion links humanity to the immense power of divine assistance, empowering social change.

Many leaders of thought are coming to the conclusion that it is the process of change itself that is the greatest stumbling block in the way of the world's future development. In his most recent book, *The Future of Life*, the eminent biologist Edward O. Wilson characterizes the coming century – which he calls the 'Century of the Environment' – as a bottleneck into which all the vast momentum of human culture and economy is being forced. The bottleneck is caused by the limits of the planet to supply resources and dissipate the wastes of an economy that is expanding exponentially. Our ability to make it through this bottleneck will depend, he says, not just on technological ingenuity, but also on the development of foresight and the application of sufficient moral courage to transform our behaviour. We must free our minds from past genetic programming, which favours immediate needs over long-term values, so that we can harmonize our needs with those of future generations.

'The great dilemma of environmental reasoning stems from this conflict between short-term and long-term values', says Wilson. 'To select values for the near future of one's own tribe or country is relatively easy. To select values for the distant future of the whole planet also is relatively easy – in theory, at least. To combine the two visions to create a universal environmental ethic is, on the other hand, very difficult. But combine them we must, because a universal environmental ethic is the only guide by which humanity and the rest of life can be safely conducted through the bottleneck into which our species has foolishly blundered' (Wilson, *Future* 17).

But there is a tremendous inertia evident in our collective behaviour. In a report marking the tenth anniversary of the 1992 Earth Summit, UN Secretary General Kofi Annan acknowledged that in some respects conditions are actually worse now than they were ten years ago and that no major changes have been made in unsustainable patterns of consumption and production.

A change of the nature required to meet the challenges of development and sustainability is unprecedented in human history, at least in the time available. From the Bahá'í perspective, meeting this challenge is only possible through the power of divine assistance. Just as religion animated the agricultural revolution, it can now animate the process by which humanity can change its mentality, its values, its actions. A deeper understanding of the means to access this transformative power is, ultimately, the contribution that the Bahá'í community is attempting to make and it is in this context that a Bahá'í perspective on agriculture gains its greatest relevance.

The following chapters provide an initial attempt to flesh out this perspective. They should not, however, be interpreted as a definitive 'position' of the Bahá'í Faith on agriculture but as an effort to initiate what will no doubt become an ongoing dialogue on a topic crucial to the future of an ever-advancing civilization.

Works Cited

'Abdu'l-Bahá. *Foundations of World Unity*. Wilmette, IL: Bahá'í Publishing Trust, 1945.

Bahá'í International Community. *The Prosperity of Humankind*. London: Bahá'í Publishing Trust, 1995.

Bahá'u'lláh. *Gleanings from the Writings of Bahá'u'lláh*. Wilmette, IL: Bahá'í Publishing Trust, 1983.

— *Tablets of Bahá'u'lláh*. Wilmette, IL: Bahá'í Publishing Trust, 1988.

— *The Kitáb-i-Aqdas*. Haifa: Bahá'í World Centre, 1992.

Cauvin, Jacques. *The Birth of the Gods and the Origins of Agriculture*. Trans. Trevor Watkins. Cambridge: Cambridge University Press, 2000.

Diamond, Jared. *Guns, Germs, and Steel: The Fates of Human Societies*. New York: W. W. Norton & Co., 1999.

Duncan, Colin A. M. *The Centrality of Agriculture: Between Humankind and the Rest of Nature*. Montreal: McGill–Queen's University Press, 1996.

Eliade, Mircea (ed.). *The Encyclopaedia of Religion*, vol. 1. New York: Macmillan, 1987.

Eisenberg, Evan. *The Ecology of Eden*. Toronto: Random House of Canada, 1998.

FAO (Food and Agriculture Organization of the United Nations). 'Fostering the Political Will to Fight Hunger'. Committee on World Food Security, Twenty-seventh Session, Rome, 28 May –1 June 2001.

— 'Mobilizing Resources to Fight Hunger'. Committee on World Food Security, Twenty-seventh Session, Rome, 28 May –1 June 2001.

— 'New Challenges to the Achievements of the World Food Summit Goals'. Committee on World Food Security, Twenty-seventh Session, Rome, 28 May –1 June 2001.

Fromkin, David. *The Way of the World: From the Dawn of Civilizations to the Eve of the Twenty-first Century*. New York: Alfred A. Knopf, 1999.

Fung, Ka-iu (ed.). *Atlas of Saskatchewan*. Saskatoon, SK: University of Saskatchewan, 2nd edn. 1999.

The Holy Bible. King James Version. Cleveland: The World Publishing Company.

Hanley, Paul. 'Environmental Constraints Limit Agricultural Potential'. Saskatoon *StarPhoenix*, 26 November 1996.

Homer-Dixon, Thomas. *The Ingenuity Gap*. Toronto: Knopf Canada, 2000.

Madhavan, Narayanan. 'Farmers' suicides embarrass India's tech paradise'. Reuters, 9 November 2001.

Postel, Sandra. *Pillar of Sand: Can the Irrigation Miracle Last?* Washington: Worldwatch Institute, 1999.

Pretty, Jules and Rachel Hine. 'Reducing Food Poverty with Sustainable Agriculture: A Summary of New Evidence'. SAFE-World Research Project, University of Essex, February 2001.

Pringle, Heather. 'Neolithic Agriculture: The Slow Birth of Agriculture'. *Science*, vol. 282 (1998) pp. 1446.

Rowe, J. S. *Home Place: Essays on Ecology*. Edmonton: NeWest, 1990.

Thomas, Hugh. *An Unfinished History of the World*. London: Papermac, rev. edn. 1995.

Tuxill, John. *Nature's Cornucopia: Our Stake in Plant Diversity*. Worldwatch Paper 148. Washington: Worldwatch Institute, 1999.

Wilson, Edward O. *The Future of Life*. New York: Alfred A. Knopf, 2002.

Wood, Stanley et al. *Pilot Analysis of Global Ecosystems: Agroecosystems*. Washington DC: World Resources Institute, 2000.

Section 1

Religion, Agriculture and the Bahá'í Faith:
An Overview

Agriculture in the World's Religions: An Overview

P. J. Stewart

Introduction

Concepts

Every creature must feed and the way it does helps to decide its place in the world and its impact on other living things. Our species is peculiar in the extent to which our choice of food and our means of obtaining it – like the rest of our behaviour – are learned and not innate. One of the things that most influences human food consumption and production is religion.

The word 'religion', adopted from Latin into all the major European languages, poses problems. These are not to be solved by proposing a definition, since in practice the way that people learn what a word means is by seeing what others apply it to (Lakoff, *Women, Fire and Dangerous Things*). Westerners get their idea of the meaning of 'religion' mostly from its application to Christianity and they then use the word for whatever seems similar in other societies.

Westerners tend to think of the word 'religion' as meaning essentially a system of beliefs because of the peculiar Christian concern with doctrine and orthodoxy – hence the frequent use of 'creeds' or 'faiths' as a synonym for 'religions'. In contrast, there is no word in the Hebrew Bible that can be translated as 'religion'; for its authors, worship of the sacred was an integral part of their whole life. The Quranic word *deen*, in many contexts translated 'religion', has the root meaning of 'judgement' or 'law' and to Muslims it means every aspect of Islamic life, both belief and action. Much the same is true of the Indian word *dharma*, used alike by Hindus, Buddhists and Jains; it applies to the right way of life in a community and can be translated not only as 'religion' but also as 'law' or 'nature'. In Chinese, the nearest equivalent to 'religion' is *dao* – the right way of living taught by a school of thought, which may be a secular philosophy; different *dao*s can be combined and, if they seem to contradict, that is the surface appearance of a deeper *dao*.

Certain common themes occur in the ways of living and thinking that are covered by these words in different cultures. Perhaps the most general is the claim by their followers that their way is deeper or truer or more real than other ways of seeing and acting in the world. There are two common forms that this takes: on the one hand the mystic's experience of union with everything in the cosmos; on the other the segregation of a sacred realm from the profane. These appear to contradict each other but perhaps the second is an incomplete realization of the first, since in the mystical vision everything is sacred. The antithesis of both is seeing nothing as sacred.

When the sacred is distinguished from the profane, rules are set up to keep the two separate. These can be used to divide society and to set certain classes apart from others. They can even divide the self, regarding certain parts of a person or his actions as endangering a sacred part, the 'flesh' as ensnaring the 'soul' and so on. Many societies justify food taboos on this basis. In the most extreme cases, every aspect of life is governed by laws rooted in ideas of the sacred and the profane. At the other extreme, for the secular modern West, where nothing is sacred, behaviour is governed by notions of utility.

Because the systems that we call religions differ so much from one civilization to another, we should not expect them all to influence agriculture, in the sense of affecting what crops are grown, what animals kept and what techniques used. Gods or goddesses may be held responsible for rain, fertility and harvest or for the gift of agricultural tools but if they do not cause agriculture to take specific forms, they are just an idiom for expressing what can be described as well in secular terms. It is only where a god dictates how land should be farmed that religion can be seen as a causative agent, and perhaps the only clear case of this is classical Judaism. Elsewhere, implications for agriculture may be drawn either from general attitudes to the biological world or from particular notions about what foods should or should not be eaten.

Hunters and Gatherers

Before agriculture was invented our ancestors lived like other species by gathering and hunting the foods produced by the living planet. Exactly what they thought about their world we can never know in detail. However, clues may be found in the history of its flora and fauna at that time, in the cultures of modern hunters and gatherers and perhaps also in our dim memories of early childhood.

All the scientific evidence shows that our species first appeared in Africa, though a minority still consider that modern humans evolved separately in various parts of the Old World. However that may be, it is clear that people developed in balance with other African species, for no extinctions among them have been put down to human action before the arrival of Europeans in the 19th century. Hominid populations presumably expanded and their cultures developed slowly and in balance with each other and with changes in the living systems on which their survival depended.

Things changed when modern *Homo sapiens* appeared outside Africa about 90,000 years ago. Soon after, a wave of extinctions began to spread around the world, destroying many species of large mammals and flightless birds. This began in Eurasia, continued in Australia from about 40,000 years ago, reached the Americas about 12,000 years ago and finally arrived in New Zealand and Madagascar with the Maoris and the Malagasy in the past two millennia. Climate change may have been a contributing factor but these lost species had survived two million years of ice ages and there is a close correspondence between the date at which people first arrived in a region and the date of the main extinctions (Diamond, *Third Chimpanzee*).

What seems to have happened is that when people came out of Africa they suddenly found themselves surrounded by huge natural resources for which there was no human competition. If they destroyed species – intentionally or otherwise – they had only to push over the next river or the next ridge to find more untapped reserves. Having no need for conservation, the frontiers-people lost those elements of their culture that encouraged it. Perhaps, like foxes in a henhouse, they killed far more than they needed, or perhaps they were simply careless of the impact of their growing armory of tools and techniques, but it seems that for them nothing was sacred.

This wasteful age cannot have lasted long in any one place. The wastrels moved on, leaving behind a remnant who were surrounded by other people's territories and who had to rediscover the lost African restraints. Soon they must have become like the modern hunter-gatherer societies observed by anthropologists and now, alas, mostly extinct: deeply respectful of fellow creatures, killing only what they needed, showing concern for the reproduction of prey species and using natural methods to control their own birthrate (Posey, *Cultural and Spiritual Values*).

Such behaviour was supported by myths that described the common origin of humans with other living beings, which were thought of as having souls. Cautionary tales warned against the consequences of greed, cruelty and lack of respect for animals and plants, land and water, and for their spirits. There was no fundamental separation between sacred and profane, spiritual and material: every physical thing had its ruling spirit. Like the small human societies of hunter-gatherers and the ecosystems they lived in, the spirit community was democratic or anarchic; some spirits were more powerful than others but they had to negotiate their relationships, for there was no established hierarchy.

These peoples did not write and their modern equivalents have been so much exposed to outside influence that it is often hard to be sure what is authentic. A recent example of reminiscences is given by one of the Creek Indians from Oklahoma (originally the Muskogee Nation from what is now Georgia and Alabama), Bear Heart (*Wind is My Mother*):

> We recognized a long time ago that there was life all around us – in the water, in the ground, in the vegetation. Children were introduced to the elements so that as we grew up, we were not looking down upon nature or looking up to nature. We felt a part of nature, on the same level. We respected each blade of grass, one leaf on a tree among many other leaves, everything.

From this history we may conclude that the desire to conserve life is not innate but is a culture, which has to be developed over lifetimes of experience and taught to each new generation. From the way that small children experiment, pulling the tails of pets, tearing the wings off living insects and testing the effects of fire and water on all sorts of animals, it might seem that this teaching must always start from zero. However, many people have early memories of being at one with a benign world, in which humans, animals and plants, houses, gardens and streams, sun, moon, stars and clouds all seemed to be one big family. The presence of wise and loving parents and a good environment no doubt help to create such memories but we may see in them evidence that, although reverence for life is not inborn, we are perhaps predisposed to learn it.

Religions of Agrarian Societies

Polytheism: The Near East

The first peoples whose beliefs we know in detail are the agricultural societies that invented writing some five thousand years ago in Mesopotamia and Egypt. The Egyptians have captured the public imagination with their stone temples and rock-hewn tombs, their sculptures, paintings and grave furniture; but we know far more about how the Mesopotamians thought about daily life. They did not have the accessible building stone of Egypt and their mud-brick buildings long since became hillocks but their writings on baked clay tablets have survived far better than the papyrus texts of the Nile valley.

Both these ancient civilizations believed in a pantheon of gods whose behaviour was a divine reflection of the life of the human beings below. Just as the small agricultural kingdoms were brought together into an empire with a supreme ruler assisted by his ministers and generals and regional governors, so there came to be a supreme god with one or more consorts, assisted by gods and goddesses who specialized in regulating particular aspects of the world – birth, death, love, war, crops, livestock, fire, rivers, sea, sun, moon, wind, rain, thunder and lightning. Some of these gods and goddesses were national, others local, and their relationships with each other were a complicated tangle of love and hate, kinship, alliance and rivalry.

By the time of the oldest writings there were already temples and priests in both Mesopotamia and Egypt, with land set aside to furnish them with offerings of food for the gods – which ended up feeding the temple employees. Religion had come to mean a separation of sacred and profane. The human king to some extent bridged the two, not only being the secular head of society but also having a special role in relations with the gods, and indeed being one of them (Kuhrt, *Ancient Near East*).

Events in the divine world were closely bound up with the cycle of the seasons, the surges of the great rivers and the sowing and harvesting of the crops. The Mesopotamian story of the marriage, death and rebirth of Tammuz and the Egyptian story of the death and resurrection of Osiris were re-enacted in agricultural festivals. However, one cannot say that religion shaped their agriculture but rather that it reflected it.

Concern for the impact of humans on the world is evidenced in two of the oldest works of ancient Mesopotamian literature: the story of Ziusudra (in Sumerian) or Atrahasis (in Akkadian) and the epic of Gilgamesh. The oldest fragments of these are found in tablets more than four and a half thousand years old but the most nearly complete versions are at least a thousand years younger (Dalley, *Myths from Mesopotamia*).

The story begins with the gods going on strike. They are tired of having to do all the work of digging and earth-moving and irrigation. They organize a noisy demonstration outside the palace of Enlil, king of the gods. He asks the goddess of fertility to find a solution and she creates humans to take over the work from the gods. All goes well for six hundred years but by then people have become so numerous and so rowdy that the gods get no peace.

Enlil sends a plague to get rid of the troublesome humans but Ziusudra is tipped off by his friend the god Ea and told how to save himself and his family. Enlil relents and people multiply anew until, after another six hundred years, they are again so troublesome that he makes a new attempt to destroy them, this time with a drought. Once more Ea saves Ziusudra and again the numbers build up over six hundred years, causing Enlil to attempt a final solution by sending a flood to drown the earth. Ea tells Ziusudra to build an ark and 'reject possessions, save living things'.

When the flood subsides, Enlil sees the ark, which has landed at the mouth of the Shatt al-Arab, and he realizes that he will never get rid of humans. He calls the goddess of fertility and asks her to devise a solution. She introduces a policy of birth control, afflicting some women with sterility, making others into temple virgins and increasing infant mortality. Human numbers are kept in check and the gods are satisfied. It is remarkable that within a few centuries of the beginning of city life, people were already preoccupied by problems of overpopulation and natural disaster and that birth control was already seen as part of the solution.

The hero of the epic is Gilgamesh, king of Uruk. With the help of a prostitute, he tames the wild man Enkidu and becomes his friend. Together they go beyond the frontier of civilization to a mountain with a forest over which Ellil (=Enlil) has placed the monster Humbaba as guardian. Gilgamesh kills Humbaba and they cut down trees to adorn the temple of Ellil at Nippur. After further adventures Enkidu eventually dies of a sickness, partly as punishment for the killing of Humbaba. However, it would be a comic intrusion of modern thought to say that there is a moral, condemning deforestation; rather, one of the themes of the epic is the estrangement of the wild and the tamed. The physical symbols of this contrast were the natural mountains and the artificial ones – the ziggurats – that dominated Mesopotamian cities (Eisenberg, *Ecology of Eden*).

Both these stories are concerned essentially with events in the world of humans and gods. The world of animals and plants figures only as background. The Mesopotamians did protect their fields and canals but as a matter of state policy and law rather than of religion (Postgate, *Mesopotamia*).

In the case of the Egyptians, less is known of their ideas about life than of those about death. They seem to have been the first to record the belief that people could look forward to an afterlife, though achievement of this depended on having enough wealth to prepare the corpse and provision a tomb. Some animals shared this privilege, notably the Apis bulls and certain cats. However, later peoples who took over this belief extended the afterlife to all humans and took it away from animals, driving a deep divide between us and them.

Agrarian Polytheism: Greece and Rome

The civilization of Greece first took shape under the Minoans, two thousand years after the rise of Mesopotamia and Egypt, but its sudden collapse was followed by a long eclipse, from which it reemerged at about the time that Rome was founded 28 centuries ago. The religions of these two societies were so closely similar that they virtually merged, with equations being made between the Greek and Roman gods and goddesses and with myths and practices being adopted in either direction, though mostly from east to west.

The general shape of this religion was very like that of Mesopotamia and Egypt, with which the Greeks and later the Romans were in frequent contact. There was a divine hierarchy like that of human society, with a king and queen of the gods ruling over a court and with minister gods and goddesses responsible for the same sort of functions, to the extent that many of them could be equated with their Near Eastern homologues. There was the same network of temples and priesthoods with their staff and their landed estates and their animal sacrifices.

Incarnation played an important part in Greco-Roman mythology, with gods and goddesses frequently taking human or animal form or even being embodied in plants or inanimate objects. Emperors and other prominent people were promoted to godhood on death or even during their lifetime. This meant that there was no deep gulf between the divine, the human and the animal, and the behaviour of the gods was often all too human or bestial. In the absence of an afterlife, humans were closer to animals than to gods.

The division between sacred and profane was much like that in the Near East. There were sacred places and sacred groves of trees but outside them there was no general reverence for life and whatever was edible was fair game. The menus of the ancient world gloried in such delicacies as larks' tongues and blackbirds' livers and Roman sports required a steady supply of lions, bears and other fierce creatures to be tormented for the pleasure of the crowd.

Agrarian Polytheism: India

On the other side of the Near East lie Persia and India. In the Indus Valley a civilization flourished and was devastated at much the same time as that of the Minoans. Its writing system remains undeciphered, so we do not know anything about its ideas. However, it may have contributed much to the civilization that succeeded it, whose language was Sanskrit – a close relative of Greek and Latin – which is presumed to have come in from the northwest with cattle-herding invaders. The oldest writings in this language are the Vedas, composed by unknown authors more than three thousand years ago. They give a detailed picture of an early form of Hindu belief and practice.

The Hindu concept of the divine followed the familiar pattern, with royal gods presiding over their court and priests over their temples, but there is no straightforward equation between any of their gods and those further west. At a humbler level, every village has its local goddess (it is almost always a goddess), who protects its people against disease and natural disaster or who punishes them by allowing calamity to befall them. She often looms larger than mightier gods in the minds of her people (Kinsley, *Hindu Goddesses*). There are temples and priests but a Hindu can perform an act of worship – a *pooja* – anywhere and it is common to find the traces of a recent one on the edge of a field, on a rock or at the foot of a tree.

As in Greece and Rome, the incarnation of gods in human, animal or plant form plays an important part in Indian thought. There was intermittent contact with Mesopotamia and a near eastern writing system was adapted for Sanskrit. Certain myths seem to have been adopted too, most notably the story of Manu, who combines the roles of Ziusudra and Adam. He alone survives a flood by building an ark and he then becomes the ancestor of all humans. His name, like Hebrew Adam, means 'man'. However, Hindu literature is a vast and largely autonomous creation.

It is misleading to talk of 'Hindu*ism*' in the singular, since Indian society was from the earliest times rigidly divided into hereditary social classes, each with its own preferred gods and its own *dharma*. At the summit of society were the Kshatria – the kings and nobles and warriors – and the Brahmins, who were the priests. These two still exist as castes. They are 'twice-born' because boys go through a rite of passage to manhood which is regarded as a rebirth. A third twice-born group were the Vaisya, who have since ceased to be a single recognizable entity; they were the herders, farmers and merchants. A fourth class soon came to be added, the Sudra, the aboriginal servants assimilated into Sanskrit-speaking society, who were deemed untouchable.

The Hindu *dharmas* have had a profound effect on human interaction with animals and plants, including agriculture. This can be attributed mainly to *samsara* – the belief that every living thing has an *atman*, an imperishable soul or self, which is repeatedly reborn in human, animal or plant form. Whether it moves up or down the scale at each rebirth depends on its *karma* – the sum of good or bad deeds that it has accumulated. Rebirth is not something to look forward to; on the contrary, the goal is to build up such good *karma* that the cycle is broken. This is quite different from the Egyptian idea of once-for-all promotion to an afterlife in a higher world. It draws humans close to other living things. It does not preclude killing, since the soul does not die but is merely sent on to rebirth, but it does open Hindus to the notion that animals have minds and feelings.

Although Hindu belief does not preserve all animals, it does give protection to particular species, most notably the cow, which no Hindu may kill and only the lowest may eat. Paradoxically, the effect of reverence for cattle on wild vegetation has been much the same as would have been that of a beef-eating society, for it has allowed their numbers to multiply beyond the level compatible with their health and that of their pastures.

Other species are revered because of the part they played in the life of incarnate gods, for example the Hanuman langur, the bear, the eagle, the elephant, the cobra – even in some places the rat. Brahmins are almost total vegetarians, eating only the meat of periodic animal sacrifices. The Kshatria, on the other hand, are expected to eat permitted meats to maintain their warrior character. Other castes all have their own rules but there is a widespread tendency towards vegetarianism, with obvious implications for agriculture.

Alongside this patchy respect for animals there is a general Hindu reverence for forests, which are traditionally seen as sacred places at the opposite extreme from town and village. Hindus go to the forest to seek religious enlightenment away from worldly distractions and temptations. One of the most beautiful hymns in the Vedas is a prayer to the spirit of the forest, portrayed as the gentle and generous protector of all life (O'Flaherty, *Rig Veda*):

> The spirit of the forest does not kill – not if no one else approaches. She eats sweet fruit and lies down wherever she pleases.

> Mother of wild beasts, untilled by the plough but full of food, sweet-smelling of perfume and balm – to her, the spirit of the forest, I offer my praise.

Hindu respect for the physical world is somewhat undermined by the belief that only the divine is real; everything else is *maya*, usually translated as 'illusion', to be left behind when at last the soul breaks out of the cycle of rebirth and achieves union with Brahman, the Ground of Being – the ultimate goal of Hindu striving.

The Gentle Revolution: Jains and Buddhists

India has been called 'the second Holy Land' but it might even be accounted the first, for it gave birth not only to the religion of the Hindus but also to those of the Jains, Buddhists and Sikhs. It also gave an early welcome to Parsees, Jews, Christians, Muslims and Bahá'ís.

The Jain movement was founded about 2,600 years ago by Vardhamana the Mahavira ('Great Hero'), who is seen by Jains as the 24th in a series of leaders, to be followed by 24 more. His fundamental principle was non-violence, *ahimsa*, towards all living things and accordingly Jains are complete vegetarians. There is a strong ascetic element in their tradition and many of them become monks or nuns, with inevitable effects on Jain demography. The Mahavira broke with Hinduism by rejecting the caste system and offering his teaching to all comers but he retained the Hindu belief in *atman*, *karma* and *samsara*. The same is true of his younger contemporary, Gautama the Buddha, except that he rejected belief in an imperishable *atman*.

Like the Mahavira, Gautama was born a Kshatria prince. As a young man he became concerned with suffering, which he perceived as the fundamental problem of all living things. An early biography includes a reference – rare in religious literature – to the creatures that live in the soil (Conze, *Buddhist Scriptures*):

> The ploughs had torn up the sprouting grass, scattering tufts of grass here and there, and the land was littered with tiny creatures who had been killed and injured,

worms, insects and the like. The sight of all this grieved the prince as deeply as if he had witnessed the slaughter of his own kinsmen. He observed the ploughmen, saw how they suffered from wind, sun and dust, and how the oxen were worn down by the labour of drawing. And in the supreme nobility of his mind he performed an act of supreme pity. He then alighted from his horse and walked gently and slowly over the ground, overcome with grief. He reflected on the generation and passing of all living things, and in his distress he said to himself: 'How pitiful all this!'

In search of a solution to the problem of suffering, he abandoned his wife and baby son and joined a group of yogins in the forest. After years of yogic practices he realized that the more he mortified his body the more he became conscious of its suffering, so he turned his back on his companions and left the forest. After restoring his body with food, he meditated all night at the foot of a great tree and achieved enlightenment. Returning to humanity, he went from town to town preaching his Middle Way between asceticism and self-indulgence. A growing band of monks and nuns followed him and carried his message far and wide. Unlike Jainism, which has remained almost entirely confined to India, Buddhism spread over most of East and Southeast Asia. It has a sacred canon of ancient texts, including the *sutras* – discourses attributed to the Buddha but written down long after his death.

In the course of its spread to so many societies, Buddhist ideas and practices underwent many changes. There is no priesthood or central authority but monks have performed the role of intellectual guardians and revered teachers preside over the many varieties of Buddhism. They raised complex and subtle philosophical and psychological systems on the foundations laid by the Buddha, generally with no mention of gods. At the same time, elaborate temples were built, full of beautiful paintings and sculptures, superficially little different from the temples of polytheism.

Concern with suffering makes compassion the highest virtue in the eyes of Buddhists, who must therefore avoid causing pain to any living thing. The effect of this is much the same as Jain *ahimsa* and it has had a profound effect on Buddhist agriculture. Some Buddhist countries practise no animal husbandry at all and others confine themselves to free-range grazing. Where meat is part of their traditional diet, for example in Tibet, Buddhists have shown typical human ingenuity; to avoid killing, they sell their animals to non-Buddhist butchers. By similar contortions of logic, many coastal communities practise fishing and in Japan the sea is exploited on an enormous scale.

Philosophically, Buddhists have narrowed the gap between humans and other living things by the doctrine of interdependent origination – *pratitya samutpada* – the notion that everything that happens is related to everything else. This leads to a holistic approach to life and an easy acceptance of the kinship of human and animal minds. The theory of evolution and the viewpoint of ecology have never encountered any opposition from Buddhists, and conservation movements quickly took root in countries where they predominate.

There is no general Buddhist doctrine of marriage and divorce; each society follows its own system. However, there is discouragement of promiscuity, which is seen as a form of addiction or enslavement. Celibacy is respected but monks and nuns do not take lifelong vows and it is common for people to go into a monastery for a few years, before or after raising a family. There is no great social pressure to produce children, who are seen as being born into a world of suffering, and in modern times Buddhist societies have seen rapidly declining birthrates, with consequences for the demand for food.

Religion in China and Japan

A civilization developed independently in the Yellow River Valley some four and a half thousand years ago and within a thousand years it had produced its own writing system. The oldest inscriptions, dating back over three thousand years, indicate a society with a hierarchy of gods and goddesses much like those of the other ancient agrarian societies. Great importance was attached to divination of the future, which eventually gave rise to the *I Ching* – The Classic of Change – which is the nearest Chinese equivalent to a sacred text.

The *I Ching* consists of the 64 permutations of six whole or broken lines, each of which stands for *yin* – the dark, passive, feminine – or *yang* – the bright, active, masculine. Feminine and masculine are not to be taken as equivalent to male and female, for both elements are held to be present in both sexes. These 64 combinations are held to represent all the 64 possible patterns of events in the world. Westerners either revere this book as a source of esoteric knowledge of the future or condemn it as rank superstition. However, it can be regarded as a poetic expression of the way that the complex world of the *wan wu* – the 'ten thousand things' or the 'myriad forms' – is built of simple elements.

This notion of a fundamental pattern underlying reality is present in all Chinese philosophies but its deepest expression is in the *Tao Te Ching* – The Classic of Tao and Virtue – said to have been written by Lao-Tse at the time when the Buddha was active, though it probably dates from somewhat later (Waley, *Way*). This Tao or *Dao*, which its advocates regard as *the* Great Tao (but with no definite article in Chinese), is beyond human understanding but can be approached by living in harmony with the *zi-ran* – the 'autonomous', Nature. The wise person discovers the natural flow of events and lives in accordance with it, practising *wu-wei* – 'not forcing'. The ideal for followers of the Tao was to live in a simple dwelling in a wild place, growing homely food in the garden and contemplating nature. They cultivated the arts, developing nature poetry and founding the world's first school of landscape painting.

The Tao of Lao-Tse never became the dominant philosophy of China. That role was occupied by the teachings of Confucius, who definitely *was* a contemporary of the Buddha. He was essentially a humanist, concerned with the ordering of society and the proper relations between ruler and ruled, parent and child, older brother and younger brother and so on. Later Confucians added a cosmology and a general philosophy but human relationships remained central. An exceptional reference to the human ecological impact is to be found in the book of Mencius, who lived about

300 years after Confucius. This was for centuries one of the set books for the civil service exams (Waley, *Way*):

> Bull Mountain was once covered with lovely trees. But it is near the capital of a great state. People came with their axes and choppers; they cut the woods down, and the mountain has lost its beauty. Yet even so, the day air and the night air came to it, rain and dew moistened it. Here and there fresh sprouts began to grow. But soon cattle and sheep came along and browsed on them, and in the end the mountain became gaunt and bare, as it is now. And seeing it thus gaunt and bare people imagine that it was woodless from the start. Now just as the natural state of the mountain was quite different from what it now appears, so too in every man (little though they may be apparent) there assuredly were once feelings of decency and kindness; and if these good feelings are no longer there, it is that they have been tampered with, hewn down with axe and bill.

Neither Confucian nor Taoist thought nor any of the other *daos* that competed in China's cities had much to say about gods or goddesses. For the literate classes, the old polytheism seems at an early date to have become little more than a fund of stories and metaphors that no one took very seriously. Things were different in the countryside but even there people were more interested in their village deities and in the worship of their ancestors.

Neither Confucianism nor village religion had much effect on agriculture but there is one feature of Chinese belief that has strongly influenced attitudes to living things. The notion that humans are just one of the *wu wei*, the myriad forms, on a par with the others, has given rise to a system of medicine that sees in the appropriate parts of animals and plants the source of whatever is missing in sick people. The result is a demand not only for a huge range of herbal medicines but also for such things as tiger bones, bear gall bladders, rhinoceros horns and so on. There is probably nowhere in the world where more body parts of more species can be found than in a Chinese market or traditional pharmacy.

There is much in common between Taoist and Buddhist thought, and when Buddhism came to China it developed new forms that owed much to the influence of the Tao. Chan (Japanese 'Zen') Buddhism, in particular, adopted Taoist skills and arts as an aid to enlightenment. It was Chinese rather than Indian Buddhism that was later exported to Japan and Korea (Suzuki, *Japanese Spirituality*).

Japan has repeatedly shown an extraordinary capacity to import elements from other cultures without ceasing to be distinctively Japanese. By the time Buddhism reached its shores, Confucian and Taoist ideas were already well established there but there was also a pre-existing religion – Shinto. The word is in fact Chinese – *shen-dao* 'spirit path' – but the ideas and practices are peculiarly Japanese. Shinto is in fact the only case of a hunter-gatherer type of religion that has survived more or less intact in a modern society. Instead of a hierarchy of gods and goddesses, it sees a multitude of spirits, each one attached to a particular place or object and needing to be placated in its own way. (It is possible that the religion of the Aztecs or the

Incas was a similar survival but too little detail is known of these civilizations.)

Chinese forms of Buddhism took their place in the Japanese ecology of ideas and helped to produce a unique agriculture, in which very careful tending of crops takes place with virtually no animal husbandry and with almost complete reliance on fisheries for animal protein. As a consequence, forests still cover more than two-thirds of the land area of one of the most densely inhabited industrial countries in the world.

Japan has a bad name for conservation, largely because of its continued pursuit of whaling, its wide-ranging factory fishing boats and its importation of timber from endangered tropical forests. On the other hand, it must be the only country in the world which virtually closes down when its people go out to celebrate the first blossom of springtime. A possible explanation for the paradox is that Japanese people have great difficulty in regarding humans as opposed to the natural world, of which they see themselves as very much a part.

The Revolt against Polytheism: Judaism

The revolution against Indian polytheism was as much social and intellectual as religious in character, and eventually Hindu culture absorbed elements from the Jains and Buddhists and continued to dominate. In China there was no dramatic revolt against the old gods but just a slow decline with the rise of more sophisticated ideas.

Things went differently in the Near East and in Europe, where the worship of the old gods suffered a series of frontal attacks. This started on the margins of agricultural society, though the earliest attempt to establish a form of monotheism was made at the heart of the Egyptian state by the Pharaoh Akhenaton. However, he was rapidly marginalized by his shocked ministers, and after his early and perhaps not natural death, polytheism returned in full force.

The form of monotheism that was eventually to triumph started hundreds of years before Akhenaton among the descendants of Abraham. He was a nomad who spent his life wandering over the semi-deserts and the hill country between Mesopotamia and Egypt, living in hair tents and finding grazing land for his herds of camels, sheep, goats and donkeys. His way of life was that of a typical Bedouin sheikh and he is regarded by both Arabs and Jews as their ancestor.

Judging by the pre-Islamic Bedouin of Arabia, the religion of Abraham's ancestors must have been less like the polytheism of agrarian empires than like that of the hunter-gatherers whose way of life theirs so resembled. Nomads lived in small mobile family groups and they did not have governments or priests, temples or books. They worshipped the spirits that presided over notable features of the landscape, and any idols they had were small and portable.

According to the biblical account, Abraham came to believe that his personal god was the One God. In his old age he had two sons. Before the first, Ishmael, was born to his Egyptian concubine Hagar, his God promised to his descendants 'all this land, from the river of Egypt to the great River Euphrates' (Genesis 15:18), and indeed this did come to be part of the territory of the Arabs, the children of Ishmael. Before the second son, Isaac, was born to Abraham's wife Sarah, his God made a second promise: 'I will give to you and your descendants this land in which you are now a foreigner. The whole land of Canaan will belong to your descendants for ever' (Genesis 17:8). Whatever one's attitude to the validity or meaning of these reported promises, they are remarkable – and now it seems to many regrettable – for their involvement of religion in territory and land ownership.

The territorial wars did not start immediately, for the great-grandsons of Abraham were still nomads and they migrated to Egypt, where their descendants lived for several centuries. Eventually they returned under the leadership of Moses and the struggle with the Philistines or Palestinians began. By the time the Torah or Pentateuch was written several centuries later, the Jews had been transformed from nomadic pastoralists into settled farmers.

The law of Moses is, among other things, a charter for an agricultural society. Many of its prescriptions are concerned with food and its production. The meat of certain animals is forbidden, as is any meat from which the blood has not been drained, and it is forbidden to cook meat and milk together. Farmers are required to treat their animals well and rest them on the sabbath. Cattle and donkeys even get a mention in the Ten Commandments. However, some of these laws seem to be theoretical rather than practical, for example the command to leave all land uncultivated in every seventh year; it is hard to believe that the produce of the sixth year was ever enough for two years, as promised (Leviticus 25:21–2).

The agrarian society that the Jews founded took on many of the characteristics of other Near Eastern countries, with a capital, a king, a temple and a priesthood. After the exile of two generations of their leading families in Babylon, they adopted many features of Mesopotamian culture, including its calendar, some of its mythology and, little by little, its language, Aramaic, which had by then supplanted Akkadian (and had perhaps been the language of Abraham).

As increasing numbers of Jews came to live in urban centres, the focus of the religion changed and the importance of agriculture began to be forgotten. An early example of this is to be found in The Wisdom of Jesus Son of Sirach, one of the books included in the Greek translation of the Jewish Bible but not in the final Hebrew version. Writing about two centuries before the time of Jesus of Nazareth, the author says (Eccl. 38:24–6):

A scholar's wisdom comes of ample leisure;
  if a man is to be wise he must be relieved of other tasks.
How can a man become wise who guides the plough,
  whose pride is in wielding the goad,
who is absorbed in the task of driving oxen,
  and talks only about cattle?
He concentrates on ploughing his furrows,
  and works late to give the heifers their fodder.

The tradition of farming according to Mosaic law was greatly weakened with the destruction of the Jewish kingdoms. It was lost altogether in Christian countries, where land ownership by Jews was prohibited and Judaism became a purely urban religion. The value of the experiment in reviving Jewish agriculture in Israel has been compromised by the way in which the land was obtained as well as by the completely secular ideology of many of its practitioners.

Later Judaism was greatly influenced by another form of monotheism, which had been founded on the eastern fringe of the Persian Empire at about the time when the Torah was written. Its Prophet, Zoroaster, taught that the whole world was the battleground for a struggle between light and darkness, good and evil, citizens and nomads. The Lord of Light was the creator, Ahura Mazda, and his opponent was Ahriman. After death the good would be rewarded with eternal life in Paradise (Persian *peridaizon*, a walled garden or park) and the evil would be punished in Hell.

Christianity

By the time of Jesus, belief in the Devil and in Hell and Paradise had become part of Judaism and they seem to have formed part of his teaching. Indeed, his central message appears to have been that the world was about to come to an end, to be replaced by a Kingdom of God. However, nothing was written down until a generation after his death, which has resulted in disagreement about the exact content of his teachings. Some sayings attributed to him imply that not the least letter of the law of Moses would cease to apply before the end of time (Matthew 5:18), others suggest that faith in him dispensed with the need to obey Jewish laws (Mark 2:27–8). These two versions were favoured by his Jewish and gentile followers respectively.

Eventually things came to a head at the Council of Jerusalem, about 20 years after the death of Jesus (Acts 15:4–29). The Jewish Christians demanded that gentile converts be circumcised, while Paul and Barnabas argued that in that case there would hardly be any gentile Christians. The Council ruled against the Jewish law and from then on Christians used the Jewish Bible mainly as a source of quotations to prove that Jesus was the expected Messiah. The result was that all the provisions that regulated food and agriculture were abandoned and Christianity came to be less concerned with this aspect of human activity than any other major religion.

In a celebrated essay, White ('Historical Roots') found the roots of our ecological crisis in 'Judaeo-Christian' ideas, from the Book of Genesis, where God creates man in his own image. His first words to Adam are taken as a charter, Genesis 1:28: 'Be fruitful, and multiply, and replenish the earth, and subdue it: and have dominion over the fish of the sea, and over the fowl of the air, and over every living thing that moveth upon the earth.' Jewish writers have pointed out that this cannot be read as justifying heedless exploitation if it is taken in the context of Mosaic law (Rose, *Judaism*).

Jesus had preached mainly in the villages of Galilee, and most of his parables were drawn from rural life, but within a few decades Christianity had been spread by missionaries to the great cities of the Roman Empire, where in due course its bishops established themselves. It thus became primarily an urban religion, although it took over various features of pagan spring, harvest and midwinter festivals.

The distancing of humans from the rest of the biological world was increased by the adoption of neo-Platonist philosophy, which under the influence of St Augustine in the West and St Gregory of Nyssa in the East became the dominant influence in theology. This saw the soul as exiled from the divine world of pure forms and trapped in a prison of flesh, from which it would be released by death. Humans alone had immortal souls, so human life – and *only* human life – was sacred. Our animal nature was equated with temptation, sin and spiritual death. Celibacy was seen as preferable to marriage (cf. Matthew 19:10–12 and I Corinthians 7:1–9).

Ironically, it was those who had most completely mortified the flesh, the monks, who gave the closest attention to the biological needs of plants. On the basis of their belief that *laborare orare est* – work is prayer – they developed farming and gardening to a high degree of perfection, producing food and medicinal herbs and even fine wines and liqueurs. However, although this work was motivated by religion, it would be wrong to say that it was directed by it.

At the beginning of the 13th century St Francis of Assisi founded his order of friars. He preached a universal love for all living things, which has since inspired many individuals, though it did not become the official teaching of the Church. In the next generation St Thomas Aquinas made Aristotelian philosophy acceptable in the West, reducing the intellectual dominance of neo-Platonism. However, neither of these had much immediate impact on the popular attitude towards animals (Thomas, *Man*).

A more dramatic change was brought about when Protestants started translating the Bible into modern languages. They did not start applying the Mosaic law (though many eventually proved St Paul wrong by taking up circumcision) but the fact that large numbers of ordinary people started reading it did no doubt subtly influence attitudes to agriculture, particularly in North America, to which many of the most enthusiastic Protestants migrated.

Islam

The Byzantine Emperor Theodosius outlawed all religions other than orthodox Christianity in 392 CE. From then on, almost the whole of western Eurasia was divided between the Christian Roman Empire and the mainly Zoroastrian Empire of the Sasanids in Iran and Mesopotamia. However, there was one region that neither side controlled: Arabia, in which the children of Ishmael had created a highly original society, based on a balance between pagan camel nomads and oasis farmers, many of whom were Jewish. The Bedouin were superb survivors with an intimate knowledge of the desert plants and animals, which provided the imagery for a rich oral literature.

The principal town of Arabia was Mecca. It had virtually no fields or palm groves but it was the crossroads of two major trade routes and it had an ancient shrine, the Kaaba. In the hills above the town, in about 610 CE, a prosperous businessman and head of family, Muhammad ibn Abdallah, had a vision in which he was called to restore the religion of Abraham: *islam* – 'submission [to God]'. He braved persecution and financial ruin to preach his message to the people of Mecca. The rich who dominated the town feared that he would drive the polytheist pilgrims away from the Kaaba and they resented his demand for justice towards widows, orphans, slaves and the poor.

In 622 CE Muhammad and his followers migrated to the wealthy agricultural oasis of Medina. The Meccans attacked with Bedouin allies, and the main Jewish tribes of Medina made the mistake of siding with them, to their own great cost. The Meccans were defeated and eventually Mecca itself fell to the Muslims. By the time Muhammad died in 632 CE he was virtually the ruler of all Arabia. He left behind him the Qur'án – the divine message to humanity, of which Muslims regard him as the transmitter, not the author, and which was written down in his lifetime by his secretaries. There are also several large collections of his reported words and actions, which are the source of much of the detail of Islamic law.

The Qur'án repeatedly invites people to see the signs of God's benevolence in the wonders of nature and in the way that human needs are provided for, for example 6:99:

> He it is who sends down from the sky rain, from which you drink and from which grows the vegetation for your grazing.

> He produces with it for you corn, olive-trees, date-palms, grapes and every kind of fruit. Truly in that is a sign for those who think.

Because he came from a city and moved to an oasis and was also in intimate contact with Bedouin, Muhammad had to deal with the problems of townsmen, farmers and nomadic grazers, and this is reflected in the vast body of Islamic law that was built up in succeeding centuries. Like Jewish law, it forbids the meat of the pig and any meat from which the blood has not been drained but there is no hint of vegetarianism in Islam.

An innovation that has had increasingly negative consequences in modern times is the obligation to sacrifice a suitable animal – usually a ram – in the course of the pilgrimage. The tradition grew up, without clear Quranic authority, that this was obligatory not just for the pilgrims but for every household all over the Muslim world. This created a huge demand for grazing land, which is only now beginning to abate (Stewart, *Unfolding Islam*).

The most important provision regarding land use is the distinction between 'living land', which is cultivated, and 'dead land', which is not. 'Dead land' cannot be individually owned but a person who brings it under cultivation can thereby establish ownership. This acts as an incentive to extend the area of cropland. Wildlife receives some protection from the prohibition on hunting for pleasure.

Islamic thought was influenced by neo-Platonism but never to the extent of Christianity. The Qur'án condemns celibacy and urges all Muslims to marry, so there could never be the same distancing of our animal nature that holds for many followers of the virgin son of the virgin mother. In this respect Islam is like Buddhism – a middle path between indulgence and mortification of the flesh.

Conclusion

From this brief survey of the major religions in their classical form, it would seem that Judaism is alone in having specific rules for agriculture. Others influence it indirectly either through dietary restrictions or through general attitudes to animals and plants. Christianity is unusual in having no clear implications for the use of living things. This is not to deny that later generations, especially in very recent times, have developed ecologically sensitive attitudes.

Most of these religions of agrarian societies are of the type that separates sacred and profane. The notion that all life is sacred has been a minority view expressed by mystics, ecstatics or prophets. The main exceptions are the Indian religions and Shinto. Hindu thinking is ambivalent; although everything is a manifestation of the divine, many things are viewed as polluting. With its concept of interdependent origination, Buddhism is the tradition that most completely reveres the whole of existence.

In the past two centuries the world has been transformed by the application of science to society. The consequences have included the Industrial Revolution, with attendant pressure on resources and outpouring of pollutants. At the same time a huge growth in human populations has been followed by a sudden collapse in the birthrate in industrialized countries. Cheap travel and global communications have brought peoples face to face as never before and at the same time huge inequalities of wealth and income have added to the difficulty of such contacts, sending flocks of affluent tourists in one direction and hordes of poor migrants in the other. All over the world, social stresses have reached new levels of intensity.

One of the most striking features of this history is that the first wave of industrial societies repeated the experience of the first wave of hunter-gatherers who fanned out over the continents destroying resources. The planters and loggers, hunters and trappers, fishers and whalers of colonialist Europe spread over land and sea, moving to new sites as they exhausted the old ones. Again, proof was given that the desire to conserve is not innate but is a culture to be learnt and taught. It was only in the latter half of the 20th century that there dawned a consciousness that there are limits to physical growth.

The prehistoric wave of destruction and extinction was followed by the emergence of hunter-gatherer religions for which all things were sacred. There are signs that the excesses of industrial expansion may be leading to the rise of a new ethos of the same kind. Some ecological thinking, some 'New Age' movements, some 'anti-globalization' protests and much of the growing demand for organic foods seem to be going in this direction. It remains to be seen whether the pre-industrial religions will join this trend. Meanwhile, there is one world religion, the Bahá'í Faith, that was born in the midst of the scientific and Industrial Revolution. Its message for agriculture and conservation is the subject of the rest of this book.

A world view in which all life is sacred would practise a very particular kind of agriculture. The health and vigour of the communities of the living soil would literally be at the root of it and any techniques that reduced it would be avoided. Biological control would replace pesticides and herbicides, and mixtures of crops would be used to ensure full and balanced use of water and nutrients. Diets would change too, with much less reliance on animal protein, which would greatly reduce the area needed to feed a given size of population and would allow large areas to revert to forest and other types of self-regulating ecosystem. Such changes would come about not in order to 'protect nature against humans' but in order to promote the well-being of the living planet of which we are part.

Works Cited

Bear Heart, with Molly Larkin. *The Wind Is My Mother*. New York: Clarkson N. Potter, 1996.

Callicott, J. Baird. *Earth's Insights*. Berkeley: California University Press, 1994.

Conze, Edward (translator). *Buddhist Scriptures*. Harmondsworth: Penguin, 1959.

Dalley, Stephanie. *Myths from Mesopotamia: Creation, the Flood, Gilgamesh and Others*. Oxford: Oxford University Press, 1989.

Diamond, Jared. *The Third Chimpanzee*. London: Hutchinson, 1991.

Eisenberg, Evan. *The Ecology of Eden*. New York, Knopf, 1998.

Kinsley, David. *Hindu Goddesses*. Berkeley: California University Press, 1986.

Kuhrt, Amélie. *The Ancient Near East*. London: Routledge, 1995.

Lakoff, George. *Women, Fire and Dangerous Things: What Categories Reveal about the Mind*. Chicago: Chicago University Press, 1987.

O'Flaherty, Wendy (trans.). *The Rig Veda: An Anthology*. Harmondsworth: Penguin, 1981.

Posey, D. (editor). *Cultural and Spiritual Values of Biodiversity*. London: UN Environment Programme, 1999.

Postgate, J. N. *Mesopotamia at the Dawn of History*. London: Routledge, 1992.

Rose, Aubrey (ed.). *Judaism and Ecology*. London: Cassell, 1992.

Stewart, P. J. *Unfolding Islam*. Reading: Garnet, 1994.

Suzuki, D. T. *Japanese Spirituality*. New York: Greenwood, 1988.

Thomas, Keith. *Man and the Natural World*. Harmondsworth: Penguin, 1984.

Tucker, M. E. and D. R. Williams (eds.). *Buddhism and Ecology*. Cambridge, MA: Harvard University Press, 1997.

Waley, Arthur. *The Way and Its Power*. London: Allen and Unwin, 1934.

White Jr., Lynn. 'The historical roots of our environmental crisis'. *Science* 155 (1967): 1203–7.

P. J. Stewart graduated in Arabic and Hebrew at the University of Oxford in 1962 and in Forestry in 1965. After a year with the Food and Agriculture Organization he worked in forest management and rural development in Algeria from 1967 to 1974. Since returning to Oxford to teach, he has researched the influence of religious beliefs and aspirations on interaction with the natural world. Of his own convictions he prefers to say with Lao-Tse, 'A way that can be known is not the eternal Way.'

This Vital and Important Matter:
A Survey of the Bahá'í Writings on Agriculture

Paul Hanley

In most mythologies, the means of human development are depicted as gifts from God. Quetzalcoatl, for instance, stole corn from the ants and gave it to the people of Meso-America, while Hou Chi, Lord Millet, sent down the 'lucky grain', the black, double-kernelled millet for the Zhou tribe. These cereals provided the basis for early Mexican and Chinese civilizations (Thomas, *Unfinished History* 71).

Myths of the divine origins of civilization may be little more than quaint but many scholars accept the idea that the invention of agriculture was – if not a gift of God – at least associated with religion (Thomas, *Unfinished History* 30–6; Eliade, 'Agriculture' 139–49; Cauvin, *Birth* 67–72). Bahá'u'lláh confirmed this. He said technological discoveries such as agriculture have been inspired by the Word of God, revealed in each age by the founders and prophets of religions – some of whom predate the historical record (Bahá'u'lláh, *Gleanings* 141–2). This revelation, he said, is 'the supreme animating power for the advancement of the world and the exaltation of its peoples' (Bahá'u'lláh, *Tablets* 86). 'Every bounty conferred by the Creator upon man, be it material or spiritual' is a 'gift of Divine Revelation.' 'It is, in its essence, and will ever so remain, the Bread which cometh down from Heaven' (Bahá'u'lláh, *Gleanings* 195).

While the purpose of the revealed religions is primarily spiritual – to enable us to know our Creator – achieving this purpose depends on material means. Consequently, the prophets address themselves to both spiritual and practical matters. Generally, their discourse holds that God is the Creator and Master of the physical universe; that nature, while a sign of its Creator, is incomplete; that nature is evolving to higher states of complexity and unity; that of all species, human beings have a unique, God-given potential for higher consciousness; that God wishes this potential to be discovered and developed; that the realization of this potential completes and gives meaning to the physical world; that the development of human consciousness is dependent on the establishment of civilization, which is intended as a milieu for our physical, intellectual and spiritual progress; that the function of religion is to foster this progress; and that its goal is a Golden Age or Great Peace in which humanity acknowledges its Creator and Earth comes to mirror the beatific unity of the divine world.

As agents of the development process, the founders of religions have a twofold purpose; the first, in the words of Bahá'u'lláh, is 'to liberate the children of men from the darkness of ignorance, and guide them to the light of true understanding. The second is to ensure the peace and tranquillity of mankind, and provide all the means by which they can be established' (Bahá'u'lláh, *Gleanings* 79–80). Spiritual education and material means are complementary elements of a single process of human development, and in this context, the material realm is understood to be sacred.

A Special Regard for Agriculture

Agriculture is the most important means of material development. Its invention initiated a cultural transformation that launched civilization and freed the human species from an animal-like dependence on nature. This material transformation is also part of a spiritual process since, as Masanobu Fukuoka put is, 'The ultimate goal of farming is not the growing of crops, but the cultivation and perfection of human beings' (Fukuoka, *Straw Revolution* xii). This may explain the interest of each of the religions in agriculture.

While various scriptures occasionally prescribe specific agricultural practices, their main contribution has been ethics and laws governing the use of food, the use and abuse of land, plants and animals, and the organization of agrarian societies. In turn, these have led to an ethos in each civilization that influenced its social and economic arrangements and helped shape attitudes to agriculture and agricultural practices.

While agriculture has been important for all religions, the regard given it in religious discourse has gradually faded, especially in the modern era. The traditional interest of religion in agriculture has been renewed, however, in the Bahá'í Faith. This may seem curious if we consider that the Bahá'í Faith is the first of the revealed religions to emerge in the modern period, in the 19th and 20th centuries, an era defined by industrialization and urbanization. Nevertheless, as farming and village life were eclipsed by manufacturing and cities in the industrial nations, the Bahá'í discourse on social and economic issues gave precedence to agriculture and the conditions of rural people. Bahá'u'lláh urged that 'special regard' be paid to agriculture, which was assigned a central role in a 'new world order' he prescribed.

In innumerable writings, Bahá'u'lláh and 'Abdu'l-Bahá addressed the social and physical condition of the global order taking shape in the 19th century and in the process articulated a new social–physical model that aimed to harmonize the spiritual and material requirements of life. Bahá'u'lláh proposed a set of spiritual principles to guide human development and specifically recommended attention to agriculture as a 'fundamental principle'. In one of his 'most noteworthy' writings (Shoghi Effendi, *God Passes By* 216), the Tablet of the World, he lists a number of administrative principles for the reorganization of the world and gives precedence to agricultural considerations:

Whilst in the Prison of 'Akká, We revealed in the Crimson Book that which is conducive to the advancement of mankind and to the reconstruction of the world. The utterances set forth therein by the Pen of the Lord of creation include the following which constitute the fundamental principles for the administration of the affairs of men:

First: It is incumbent upon the ministers of the House of Justice to promote the Lesser Peace so that the people of the earth may be relieved from the burden of exorbitant expenditures. This matter is imperative and absolutely essential, inasmuch as hostilities and conflict lie at the root of affliction and calamity.

Second: Languages must be reduced to one common language to be taught in all the schools of the world.

Third: It behoveth man to adhere tenaciously unto that which will promote fellowship, kindliness and unity.

Fourth: Everyone, whether man or woman, should hand over to a trusted person a portion of what he or she earneth through trade, agriculture or other occupation, for the training and education of children, to be spent for this purpose with the knowledge of the Trustees of the House of Justice.

Fifth: Special regard must be paid to agriculture. Although it hath been mentioned in the fifth place, unquestionably it precedeth the others. Agriculture is highly developed in foreign lands, however in Persia it hath so far been grievously neglected. It is hoped that His Majesty the Sháh – may God assist him by His grace – will turn his attention to this vital and important matter (Bahá'u'lláh, *Tablets* 89–90).

Given the significance of the other principles mentioned in this passage, Bahá'u'lláh's statement about the precedence of agriculture is particularly weighty.

In this article, reasons for this emphasis will be considered and various writings will be reviewed to identify elements of a Bahá'í perspective on agriculture. This perspective will be shown to apply to two crucial defects in the world's food and agricultural system. The first is its inherent injustice and inequity, which results in the destabilization of rural communities throughout the world and in widespread poverty and hunger in much of the 'developing world'. The second is its inherent unsustainability, which results in the gradual deterioration of the soil, water and genetic and other resources on which productivity depends. A Bahá'í perspective will be shown to champion principles and practices that correct these defects in a fundamental way. Furthermore, it will be shown that the Bahá'í perspective addresses the means of mustering the will required to build a new social order, one that will foster a just, equitable and sustainable agricultural system.

Principles for Agricultural Development

What did Bahá'u'lláh mean in stating that agriculture is a 'principle' for the administration of human affairs? And why is this principle so important that 'unquestionably' it precedes the others mentioned in the above text?

A principle can be defined as 'a fundamental truth or law as the basis of reasoning or action' or 'a fundamental source; a primary element'. We usually think of a principle as a guide to action and each of the five principles mentioned in the quoted text is an action statement. In the case of agriculture, the principle is that 'special regard' must be paid to it, that is, agricultural conditions and the organization and development of agricultural systems should be a *fundamental* concern of those administering human affairs.

In the quoted passage this principle is presented in the context of the neglect into which agriculture had fallen in 19th-century Persia. Having been responsible for the management of several farm estates in his native land prior to his imprisonment and exile, Bahá'u'lláh was well aware of the deplorable conditions of Persia's farms and peasantry. These conditions contrasted sharply with those in some other countries, most notably England, a nation which Bahá'u'lláh admired in several respects.

In *The Centrality of Agriculture*, environmental historian Colin Duncan describes English agriculture as experiencing a kind of Golden Age prior to and during the 19th century. Well-organized, highly productive and sustainably managed, English agriculture was then on a par with other industries; it was championed by the landed upper classes and governed by what were for the time enlightened laws and customs. In recommending that the shah turn his attention to the 'vital and important matter' of agriculture, Bahá'u'lláh endorses a progressive approach; as we survey the Bahá'í writings, we will find that the general principles of sustainable development outlined by Bahá'u'lláh and 'Abdu'l-Bahá will help us to identify elements of the progressive approach Bahá'u'lláh envisioned.

The Position of Agriculture in the World's Order

The most important element of Bahá'u'lláh's vision seems to be *recognition* of the importance of agriculture and the raising of this recognition to a matter of principle. 'Abdu'l-Bahá frequently reinforced this in his lectures and letters, stating, for example, that the 'fundamental basis of the community is agriculture . . .' ('Abdu'l-Bahá, *Promulgation* 217).

Why does agriculture have such an important place in the Bahá'í discourse? Several reasons are apparent. First is the simple fact that everyone needs food. Agriculture now supplies 99 per cent of humanity's caloric intake (Wood, *Pilot Analysis* 4). As far as we can see, agriculture is and will always be required to sustain life and will therefore continue to underlie the existence of civilization. As the human population rises to as high as 10 billion in this century, its importance can only increase.

Second is the economic value of agriculture. Directly or indirectly, the food and agriculture system is the world's single largest source of employment. Food production processes directly employ 1.3 billion people (ibid.); half the world's population rely on agriculture for their main income and of these one billion are subsistence farmers (Homer-Dixon, *Ingenuity Gap* 31). In many of the so-called developing countries the percentage is higher. Even in the industrialized nations, where as few as one in 50 are working farmers, it is estimated that some 25 per cent of the population work in various aspects of the food and related industries. Food production from agroecosystems is currently valued at more that US$1.3 trillion (Wood, *Pilot Analysis* 4) and this amount is multiplied several times in the latter stages of food processing and delivery to consumers. In addition to food, agriculture provides other products, such as fibres, and it is likely that the value of non-food products will significantly reinforce the economic importance of agriculture in the future.

Third, a broad range of activities, such as fisheries, aquaculture and forestry, are often included under the rubric 'agriculture'. Arguably, when Bahá'u'lláh refers to agriculture he includes a full range of activities involving the management of natural resources. 'Abdu'l-Bahá includes the management of a range of natural resources in his models of agricultural and rural development ('Abdu'l-Bahá, *Foundations* 38–41). An inclusive definition of agriculture would help explain the precedence given agriculture in the Bahá'í texts.

Fourth is the cultural importance of food. Students of prehistory see food-sharing as a central experience shaping human development and the formation of culture. 'Social life would have developed around the rituals of dining together,' according to Fromkin (*Way* 20.) Our most basic human relationships – parent to child, gatherings of family and friends, national, religious or ethnic feasts and festivals – are formed around food. Conversely, because of our common need, we can all empathize with hunger. Food's profound cultural significance accentuates the central role of agriculture.

Fifth, the countryside is understood to have intrinsic value. It is a place of beauty and peace and is typically experienced as a refuge from the urban world with a positive effect on the human spirit. Bahá'u'lláh also places specific value on the countryside: the country, he said, 'is the world of the soul', whereas 'the city is the world of bodies' (Bahá'u'lláh, quoted in Esslemont, *New Era* 33). Furthermore, agro-ecosystems now constitute some 40 per cent of terrestrial biological systems and are considered essential to sustaining the planet's ecological and climatic balance. Rural people, cultures and communities, which hold and carry forward essential forms of traditional knowledge, are similarly valued in the Bahá'í texts.

These are several reasons why agriculture deserves 'special regard' as urged by Bahá'u'lláh. Although Bahá'í discourse does not provide a set of agricultural policies, Bahá'u'lláh's strong endorsement raises this 'vital and important matter' to the status of *spiritual principle,* adding moral weight in support of policies and measures that would reinforce agriculture, strengthen rural life and favour conservation.

Agricultural Work as Worship and the Status of Farmers

Agriculture warrants 'special regard' but the perception of its importance seems to decrease in reverse proportion to the growth of its productive capacity. The more farmers produce, the greater the supply of products available to support a population of non-producers. People migrate to towns and cities and their interest in and sympathy for agriculture and rural people declines. They perceive cheap food to be a right but feel little responsibility for the viability of farms. As urban people become a majority on a world scale for the first time in history, rural people lose political clout and agriculture tends to be neglected. The social, economic and ecological consequences of this neglect are beyond the scope of this article.

As value shifts to cities and industry, and now to the post-industrial economy, agricultural work and those who perform it are devalued. Farmers, and rural people in general, are seen as unsophisticated and their work less important than that of other classes. Services such as education and health care are increasingly urbanized while rural services deteriorate. The rural economy is allowed to stagnate.

The Bahá'í writings strike a very different note by stressing the uniquely important role of agricultural producers. 'Abdu'l-Bahá stated that 'the peasant class and the agricultural class exceed other classes in the importance of their service' ('Abdu'l-Bahá, *Foundations* 39) and that 'the farmer is the primary factor in the body politic' (quoted in Balyuzi, *'Abdu'l-Bahá* 239). Bahá'í texts place specific value on the countryside and on country people (Esslemont, *New Era* 33).

Agricultural work, an essential service to society, is raised to the status of worship by Bahá'u'lláh. From a Bahá'í perspective, all work can be considered sacred, particularly when performed in a spirit of service.

> Thou hadst made reference in thy letter to agriculture. On this matter He hath laid down the following universal rule: that it is incumbent upon everyone, even should he be a resident in a particular land for no more than a single day, to become engaged in some craft or trade, or agriculture, and that the very pursuit of such a calling is, in the eyes of the one true God, identical with worship. This rule was exemplified by the Bahá'í community at the time when they were facing exile from Iraq, for, while they were making arrangements for their journey, they occupied themselves in cultivating the land; and when they set out, instructions were given for the fruits of their labours to be distributed amongst the friends (Bahá'u'lláh, in *Economics* no. 2).

'Abdu'l-Bahá allied work, including agricultural occupations, with spiritual attainment:

> Commerce, agriculture and industry should not, in truth, be a bar to service of the One True God. Indeed, such occupations are most potent instruments and clear proofs for the manifestation of the evidences of one's piety, of one's trustworthiness and of the virtues of the All-Merciful Lord ('Abdu'l-Bahá, in *Trustworthiness* no. 52).

On the specific value of agricultural work, he said, 'The fundamental basis of the community is agriculture, tillage of the soil. All must be producers' ('Abdu'l-Bahá, *Promulgation* 217).

In contrast, idleness, whether due to a lack of incentive or opportunity, or as a result of living from inherited wealth, is forbidden. According to Shoghi Effendi, work has 'not only a utilitarian purpose, but has a value in itself, because it draws us nearer to God, and enables us to better grasp His purpose for us in this world' (Shoghi Effendi, quoted in Bahá'u'lláh, *Kitáb-i-Aqdas* 192). It is the duty of those who are in charge of the organization of society to provide every individual with the opportunity to acquire skills and use them (ibid.). Governments have a responsibility to ensure that society is organized such that education and work are available to all, including those in rural areas. Given a worldwide deterioration in rural communities and the trend to urbanization, this principle raises important questions about policies for rural employment and education.

Vocations in Agriculture and Agricultural Education

Bahá'u'lláh places great importance on educating children and states that farmers must set aside part of their earnings for this purpose (Bahá'u'lláh, *Tablets* 90). The Bahá'í writings also place specific emphasis on the value of pursuing training in agriculture, which is identified as a 'noble science' by 'Abdu'l-Bahá ('Abdu'l-Bahá, in *Economics* no. 7). In several Tablets 'Abdu'l-Bahá expresses enthusiasm for an agricultural vocation, for both boys and girls, which he describes as a form of worship:

> . . . thou art ready to enter an agricultural school. This is highly suitable. Strive as much as possible to become proficient in the science of agriculture, for in accordance with the divine teachings the acquisition of sciences and the perfection of arts are considered acts of worship . . . What bounty greater than this that science should be considered as an act of worship and art as service to the Kingdom of God ('Abdu'l-Bahá, *Selections* 144–5).

> . . . my fervent wish . . . is that . . . he may go on to study agriculture and master its various branches, practical and theoretical. Agriculture is a noble science and, should thy son become proficient in this field, he will become a means of providing for the comfort of untold numbers of people ('Abdu'l-Bahá, in *Economics* no. 7).

The value of such an education is multiplied when it is applied in a spirit of service to humanity. 'Every child, without exception,' said Shoghi Effendi, ' must . . . devote extreme diligence to the acquisition of learning beneficial arts and skills . . . and contemporary technology' (Shoghi Effendi, in *Bahá'í Education*). However, he expressed the wish for 'such knowledge to be coupled with an intense love for the welfare of humanity' (Shoghi Effendi, letter 20 September 1929). The Universal House of Justice continues to encourage youth to consider acquiring skills and professions in areas such as rural development and agriculture, which are urgently needed in developing countries (Universal House of Justice, in *Lights* no. 2147). And whenever possible, young people should avoid taking part in military service in favour of national service programmes involving agricultural or other activities useful to humankind (ibid. no. 1358).

Agriculture and the Participation of Women

'Abdu'l-Bahá promoted the full participation and inclusion of women in all aspects of life, including agriculture and the institutions of rural communities: '. . . it is well established in history', he said, 'that where woman has not participated in human affairs the outcomes have never attained a state of completion and perfection' ('Abdu'l-Bahá, *Promulgation* 134). He applied this principle specifically to agriculture: 'Woman must especially devote her energies and abilities toward the industrial and agricultural sciences, seeking to assist mankind in that which is most needful. By this means she will demonstrate capability and ensure recognition of equality in the social and economic equation' ('Abdu'l-Bahá, *Promulgation* 283).

Education is critical to women's progress in agriculture and rural life. Bahá'u'lláh therefore 'promulgated the adoption of the same course of education for man and woman. Daughters and sons must follow the same curriculum of study, thereby promoting unity of the sexes ('Abdu'l-Bahá, *Promulgation* 175). But 'most important of all is the education of girl children, for these girls will one day be mothers, and the mother is the first teacher of the child . . . And how can a mother, herself ignorant and untrained, educate her child? It is therefore clear that the education of girls is of far greater consequence than that of boys' ('Abdu'l-Bahá, in *Bahá'í Education* 36). Further to this, the Universal House of Justice states that 'decision-making agencies . . . would do well to consider giving first priority to the education of women and girls, since it is through educated mothers that the benefits of knowledge can be most effectively and rapidly diffused throughout society' (Universal House of Justice, *Promise*, para. 34). This Bahá'í principle may be of particular importance in the rural areas of many less developed nations when educational resources are limited. 'Abdu'l-Bahá also encouraged women to pursue higher studies in agricultural colleges.

Women are primary agricultural producers in much of the world, especially in Africa, and it is only reasonable that development projects should stress their participation and leadership. Equal opportunity in the agricultural field contributes to the struggle for gender equality, which is often a precondition for elements of sustainable development, such as family planning and peace building. In fact, 'When all mankind shall receive the same opportunity of education and the equality of men and women be realized, the foundations of war will be utterly destroyed' ('Abdu'l-Bahá, *Promulgation* 175).

Agriculture and Development

The concept of social and economic development enshrined in the Bahá'í teachings presupposes a dynamic coherence between the material and spiritual aspects of life. This concept was illustrated in a talk given by 'Abdu'l-Bahá after he attended an agricultural fair in the United States. He commented that in America

> . . . agriculture and all details of material civilization have reached the highest stage of perfection, but spiritual civilization has been left behind . . . material civilization is like unto a beautiful body, and spiritual civilization is like unto the spirit of life. If that wondrous spirit of life enters this beautiful body, the body will become a channel for the distribution and development of the perfections of humanity ('Abdu'l-Bahá, *Promulgation* 11).

If the spirit is not present, however, the material civilization is lifeless, fruitless and ultimately unsustainable. The goals of development must therefore be to enlighten the human spirit as well as to raise the level of material prosperity. Both can be achieved when spiritual principles are applied to the process of material development.

Spiritual principles have direct application to the general organization of the world's food and agricultural systems and even to specific day-to-day agricultural practices. In the following section, a number of these principles are discussed.

Spiritual Principles for Agricultural Development
The Oneness of Humankind: To Eat with the Same Mouth

The oneness of humankind is a spiritual truth confirmed by all sciences. It is the principle that every person, as a result of being human, has an inherent God-given right to the benefits of membership in the human family, regardless of race, ethnicity, gender, national origin, creed, class or religious heritage. As a spiritual principle, unity is more than a legal requirement; it becomes the pivotal moral value animating the ethos of a world community. Without it, said Bahá'u'lláh, human progress is impossible: 'The well-being of mankind, its peace and security, are unattainable unless and until its unity is firmly established' (Bahá'u'lláh, *Gleanings* 286). '. . . until the minds of men become united,' said 'Abdu'l-Bahá, 'no important matter can be accomplished' ('Abdu'l-Bahá, in *Bahá'í World Faith 285).

In the age of globalization, the failure to acknowledge the unity of the human race underlies its separation into rich and poor: at the beginning of the 21st century, the combined wealth of the 225 richest people exceeds the combined annual income of the poorest 2.5 billion, who live on less than US$2 a day (Homer-Dixon, *Ingenuity Gap*). One consequence of this is that 826 million people are chronically undernourished. An 'unshakeable consciousness of the oneness of mankind' (Universal House of Justice, *Promise* para. 39) is the definitive solution to this disparity since it responds to the underlying moral basis of complacency. Bahá'u'lláh stated that all human beings were created 'from the same dust' so that 'no one should exalt himself over the other . . . Since We have created you all from one same substance', he continued, 'it is incumbent on you to be even as one soul, to walk with the same feet, eat with the same mouth and dwell in the same land . . .' (Bahá'u'lláh, *Hidden Words*, Arabic no. 68). If we believed that humankind should 'eat with the same mouth', would we abandon our fellow beings to widespread, chronic hunger and grinding poverty?

Another symptom of disunity and a direct cause of poverty and hunger is conflict and war. It is no coincidence that 16 of the world's 20 poorest countries have suffered from a major conflict in the past 15 years or that in sub-Saharan Africa, the poorest region of the world, conflicts have directly or indirectly affected one in five people. Meanwhile, exorbitant military spending – perhaps the grossest symptom of disunity – robs resources from development. Annual world military expenditures (US$812 billion) are 14 times greater than spending on development assistance. Bahá'u'lláh counselled world leaders to 'Compose your differences, and reduce your armaments' (Bahá'u'lláh, *Gleanings* 250) so that the burden of expenditure on the people can be lightened.

The world community has recognized, in theory, that the right to food is a basic human right (FAO 'Fostering' no. 30). Translating theory into practice requires a realignment of international relations and economic systems guided by the principle of human unity. For this to happen, 'It [oneness of humankind] should . . . be universally proclaimed, taught in schools, and constantly asserted in every nation as preparation for the organic change in the structure of society which it implies' (Universal House of Justice, *Promise* para. 40).

Justice and Equity: The Twin Guardians

Unity is served by – and impossible without – the application of the principles of justice and equity. 'Justice and equity', said Bahá'u'lláh, 'are twin Guardians that watch over men. From them are revealed such blessed and perspicuous words as are the cause of the well-being of the world and the protection of the nations' (Bahá'u'lláh, *Epistle* 13). In the Bahá'í teachings these principles are found to apply directly to the resolution of critical inadequacies of the world food system. Bahá'u'lláh said, for example, that the implementation of justice is the key to satisfying material needs:

> The light of men is Justice. Quench it not with the contrary winds of oppression and tyranny. The purpose of justice is the appearance of unity among men . . . Were mankind to be adorned with this raiment, they would behold the day-star of the utterance, 'On that day God will satisfy everyone out of His abundance' [cf. Qur'án 4:129], shining resplendent above the horizon of the world. Appreciate ye the value of this utterance . . . (Bahá'u'lláh, *Tablets* 66–7).

> There can be no doubt whatever that if the day star of justice, which the clouds of tyranny have obscured, were to shed its light upon men, the face of the earth would be completely transformed (Bahá'u'lláh, *Gleanings* 219).

'Abdu'l-Bahá identifies tyranny – which might be defined here as the inequitable allocation of power, land and other food-producing resources in order to benefit a minority (individual, state or corporation) at the expense of the majority – as responsible for extreme hunger: 'When we see poverty allowed to reach a condition of starvation,' 'Abdu'l-Bahá says, 'it is a sure sign that somewhere we shall find tyranny' ('Abdu'l-Bahá, quoted in Esslemont, *New Era* 134). Scarcity of food from underproduction, inadequate resources, overpopulation, the passivity of the poor or a lack of technology (as is usually assumed) are not the causes of hunger but symptoms of an oppressive order. This observation precisely matches the research of economist and Nobel Laureate Amartya Sen, who found that there has never been a famine in a democratic country.

'Until [justice and right] are realized on the plane of existence,' continues 'Abdu'l-Bahá, 'all things shall be in disorder and remain imperfect' ('Abdu'l-Bahá,

Selections 304). 'We ask God to endow human souls with justice so that they may be fair, and may strive to provide for the comfort of all, that each member of humanity may pass his life in the utmost comfort and welfare. Then this material world will become the very paradise of the Kingdom . . .' ('Abdu'l-Bahá, *Foundations* 43).

As these passages suggest, justice is also a key to environmental protection and sustainability. Human beings can be unjust to other creatures and to the earth itself when, for example, we allow species to be destroyed or land and water to be eroded and polluted; Bahá'u'lláh calls on us to be 'the embodiments of justice and fairness amidst all creation' (Bahá'u'lláh, *Kitáb-i-Aqdas*, para. 187). Justice calls for a realignment of the relationship between man and nature, and 'Abdu'l-Bahá states that justice will transform the earth: 'No power on earth can prevail against the armies of justice, and every citadel must fall before them; for men willingly go down under the triumphant strokes of this decisive blade, and desolate places bloom and flourish under the tramplings of this host' ('Abdu'l-Bahá, *Secret* 70).

Parallel to justice is equity, 'the most fundamental among human virtues'. According to Bahá'u'lláh, 'The evaluation of all things must needs depend upon it' (Bahá'u'lláh, in *Bahá'í World Faith* 131). Equity as applied to agriculture might be defined as a fair allocation of production and of food-producing resources. Since a lack of food supplies and land is not the cause of hunger, the objective of agricultural policies designed with equity in mind would be to increase the inclusiveness of access to food and to the means of productivity, more so than to increase production. Since the worst forms of poverty are found in rural areas in developing nations and hunger is predominantly an experience of the rural poor, equity must be applied particularly to the needs of this segment of society.

Trustworthiness: The Purpose Underlying Creation

Trustworthiness is among the most important virtues in the estimation of Bahá'u'lláh. In addition to its spiritual value, its practice can transform material relationships and increase social order and well-being, affecting the food and agriculture system. '. . . trustworthiness is the chief means of attracting confirmation and prosperity', according to Bahá'u'lláh, who uses an agricultural metaphor in recommending its practice. 'We entreat God to make of it a radiant and mercifully showering rain-cloud that shall bring success and blessings to thy affairs' (Bahá'u'lláh, in *Trustworthiness* no. 34).

Bahá'u'lláh further describes trustworthiness as the 'goodliest vesture', the 'greatest of adornments', the 'first, the fundamental purpose underlying creation' (ibid. nos. 1, 7); 'the supreme instrument for the prosperity of the world, and the horizon of assurance unto all beings' (Bahá'u'lláh, *Tablets* 122); and 'the greatest portal leading unto the tranquillity and security of the people. In truth the stability of every affair hath depended and doth depend upon it. All the domains of power, of grandeur and of wealth are illumined by its light' (Bahá'u'lláh, *Tablets* 37). By the same token, through honesty 'man is exalted, and the door of security is unlocked before the face of all creation' (Bahá'u'lláh, *Epistle 23*).

How does this apply to the food and agriculture system? Wherever hunger and/ or environmental devastation are evident, one is sure to find corruption, nepotism, cronyism, greed, self-interest and similar breaches of public trust as underlying causes. 'Like ignorance and environmental degradation, corruption is a great enemy of development,' comments a senior advisor to the World Bank.

> Corruption weakens the State and its ability to promote development and social justice. It is regressive in the sense that its costs and negative economic impact tend to fall more heavily on small enterprises and on individuals in a weak economic position. Corruption is double jeopardy for the poor and unprotected. They pay a high share of monopoly rents and bribes, while they are often deprived of essential government services. Corruption undermines the State's legitimacy and, in extreme cases, may render a country ungovernable and lead to political instability or even war (Bottelier 1).

Corruption is difficult to eliminate through laws alone; fostering the value of trust-worthiness is the ultimate remedy.

Service: The Greatest Conceivable Blessing

Gandhi once stated that one cannot create a system that is so good that people do not have to be good. In other words, it is impossible to create a system that is ethically strong without the people involved in it acting from moral principles. This applies to the food and agricultural system and the organizations, governments, corporations and individuals that shape it, from the local moneylender to the international food trader.

Legal and legislative measures help to avoid injustice, inequity or breaches of public trust but by its very nature unethical behaviour tends to escape scrutiny, so that lacking an ethos of public interest beating in the heart of individuals responsible for ensuring the public good, there is no way to guarantee their ethics. The desire for at least a measure of public service must be discovered by each person and instilled into people through their culture and education. Once this is achieved, public service becomes a reward and animating value in and of itself. 'Abdu'l-Bahá discusses the honour of public service in his treatise on socioeconomic development, *The Secret of Divine Civilization*:

> . . . is there any deed in the world that would be nobler than service to the common good? Is there any greater blessing conceivable for a man, than that he should become the cause of the education, the development, the prosperity, the honour of his fellow-creatures? No, by the Lord God! The highest righteousness of all is for the blessed souls to take hold of the hands of the helpless and deliver them out of their ignorance and abasement and poverty, and with pure motives, and only for the sake of God, to arise and energetically devote themselves to the service of the masses, forgetting their own worldly advantage and working only to serve the general good

('Abdu'l-Bahá, *Secret* 103).

Is any larger bounty conceivable than this, that an individual, looking within himself, should find that by the confirming grace of God he has become the cause of peace and well-being, of happiness and advantage to his fellow men? No, by the one true God, there is no greater bliss, no more complete delight (ibid. 3).

Processes of Rural Development

While stressing the role of spiritual qualities in development, 'Abdu'l-Bahá nonetheless recommends that every effort be exerted 'in the fields of development and of civilization, in the acquisition of knowledge, the increase of trade, the improvement of agriculture and the promotion of modern discoveries' (*Agriculture and Rural* no. 1). Several passages in the Bahá'í texts apply specifically to agricultural and rural development in a Bahá'í context.

'Abdu'l-Bahá stresses the importance of rural development, stating that the solution to underdevelopment 'begins with the village, and when the village is reconstructed, then the cities will be also' ('Abdu'l-Bahá, in *Bahá'í World*, vol. 4, 450).

In the area of social and economic development, 'agriculture and the preservation of the ecological balance of the world' are of fundamental interest (Universal House of Justice, in *Conservation* 18).

Rural development projects pursued by the Bahá'ís should be built on a 'substructure of existing, sufficiently strong local Bahá'í communities . . . [and] the long-term conduct of the project should aim at self-sufficiency and not be dependent upon continuing financial support from outside (Universal House of Justice, *Agriculture and Rural* no. 13).

The local spiritual assembly, the local Bahá'í community's administrative institution, has the responsibility 'to lend their support to agricultural and industrial development, to consolidate the foundations of mutual assistance and co-operation . . .' (Shoghi Effendi, *Trustworthiness* no. 69).

In villages where a large number of Bahá'ís reside, 'The Local Spiritual Assemblies . . . must gradually widen the scope of their activities, not only to develop every aspect of the spiritual life of the believers within their jurisdiction, but also, through Bahá'í consultation, and through such Bahá'í principles as harmony between science and religion, the importance of education, and work as a form of worship, to promote the standards of agriculture and other skills in the life of the people' (Universal House of Justice, *Agriculture and Rural* no. 11).

Grassroots initiatives are favoured. 'Progress in the development field will largely depend on natural stirrings at the grassroots, and it should receive its driving force from those sources rather than from an imposition of plans and programmes from the top.' The types of initiatives that have been widely pursued include 'tutorial and other schools, and promotion of literacy, the launching of rural development programmes, the inception of educational radio stations, and the operation of agricultural and medical projects' (Universal House of Justice, letter 1983).

The model of Bahá'í development may be seen in the institution of the House of Worship (Ma<u>sh</u>riqu'l-A<u>dh</u>kár) and its dependencies. While the plan of the Bahá'í Faith does not call for their construction at the local level at this stage, Bahá'u'lláh has stated that Houses of Worship should be built in every community as places of worship for people of all faiths. These will form 'the spiritual centre of every Bahá'í community round which must flourish dependencies dedicated to the social, humanitarian, educational and scientific advancement of mankind' (ibid.).

> The first part to be built is the central edifice which is the spiritual heart of the community. Then, gradually, as the outward expression of this spiritual heart, the various dependencies, those 'institutions of social service as shall afford relief to the suffering, sustenance to the poor . . . and education to the ignorant' are erected and function. This process begins in an embryonic way long before a Bahá'í community reaches the stage of building its own Ma<u>sh</u>riqu'l-A<u>dh</u>kár, for even the first local centre that a Bahá'í community erects can begin to serve not only as the spiritual and administrative centre and gathering place of the community, but also as the site of a tutorial school and the heart of other aspects of community life (Universal House of Justice, letter 1984).

Feasts and holidays are seen as opportunities to initiate projects.

> During such blessed days institutions should be founded that may be of permanent benefit and value to the people . . . Therefore, the intelligent must . . . investigate reality to find out what important affair, what philanthropic institutions are most needed and what foundations should be laid for the community . . . If, however, the community is in need of widening the circle of commerce or industry or agriculture they should start the means so that the desired aim may be attained ('Abdu'l-Bahá, in *Lights* no. 1030).

People of capacity are important agents of development:

> Basically, 'people of capacity' are those individuals, no matter in what walk of life they are found, and no matter what their level of education, who demonstrate capacity in various ways. For example, among any group of people there are those who are outstanding because they show a capacity for understanding, for work, for efficient action, for leadership, for drawing other people together, for self-sacrificing and devoted service – for any number of qualities which enable them to respond actively to the needs of their environment and make a difference to it (Universal House of Justice, in *Agriculture and Rural* 4).

Consultation is seen as an essential element of the development process. In fact, Bahá'u'lláh has stated that 'No welfare and no well-being can be attained except through consultation' (Bahá'u'lláh, in *Consultation* 1). '. . . should the people of a village consult one another about their affairs,' 'Abdu'l-Bahá said, 'the right solution will certainly be revealed. In like manner, the members of each profession, such as in industry, should consult . . .' (*Consultation* 6).

Agriculture and Economics: A Divine Economy

In a letter found in *The World Order of Bahá'u'lláh*, Shoghi Effendi wrote that '[Bahá'u'lláh] as well as 'Abdu'l-Bahá after Him, has, unlike the Dispensations of the past, clearly and specifically laid down a set of Laws, established definite institutions, and provided for the essentials of a Divine Economy' (Shoghi Effendi, *World Order* 19). These do not take the form of detailed teachings on technical economics; instead, principles are provided to guide the Universal House of Justice and future economists. These principles apply at the international, national and local levels, and in each case, the food and agricultural system is acknowledged as fundamental. 'Abdu'l-Bahá asserted, 'commerce, industry, agriculture and the general affairs of the country are all intimately linked together. If one of these suffers an abuse, the detriment affects the mass' ('Abdu'l-Bahá, *Answered Questions* 276).

Bahá'u'lláh was highly critical of systems and practices during his time which were seen to be contrary to the principles of a 'divine economy'. '. . . the prevailing order', he said, 'Appeareth to be lamentably defective' (Bahá'u'lláh, *Tablets* 171). Despite the disorder into which the world has fallen, most people, including most experts and leaders of thought, seem glibly unaware of the depth of its social, economic and ecological predicament: 'So blind hath become the human heart that neither the disruption of the city, nor the reduction of the mountain in dust, nor even the cleaving of the earth, can shake off its torpor...' (Bahá'u'lláh, *Gleanings* 39).

However, the fallacies in current theories are evident in widespread poverty and in the growing crisis in environmental conditions undermining agricultural productivity. In *The Prosperity of Humankind*, the Bahá'í International Community notes

> The fallacies in theories based on the belief that there is no limit to nature's capacity to fulfil any demand made on it by human beings have now been coldly exposed. A culture which attaches absolute value to expansion, to acquisition, and to the satisfaction of people's wants is being compelled to recognize that such goals are not, by themselves, realistic guides to policy (Bahá'í International Community, *Prosperity* 24).

The Bahá'í teachings propose principles for a just and sustainable economic system; following are a number that apply to the restructuring of the food and agriculture system at the international and local levels.

POVERTY, PROSPERITY AND THE REDISTRIBUTION OF WEALTH

'Wealth is most commendable,' said 'Abdu'l-Bahá, 'provided the entire population is wealthy' ('Abdu'l-Bahá, *Secret* 24). The principle of oneness implies that a minimum standard of well-being is an inalienable human right.

'Every human being has the right to live; they have a right to rest, and to a certain amount of well-being' ('Abdu'l-Bahá, *Paris Talks* 131–2). 'The arrangements of the circumstances of the people must be such that poverty shall disappear and that everyone, as far as possible, according to his position and rank, shall be comfortable. Whilst the nobles and others in high rank are in easy circumstances, the poor also should be able to get their daily food and not be brought to the extremities of hunger' (*'Abdu'l-Bahá in London* 29).

Establishing equitable and effective means to redistribute wealth is a necessary element in the redesign of the food and agriculture system. The Bahá'í teachings offer a number of spiritual principles and practical measures in this regard.

Moderation and generosity are conducive to spiritual attainment:

> [The true seeker] should be content with little, and be freed from all inordinate desire . . . He should succour the dispossessed, and never withhold his favour from the destitute (Bahá'u'lláh, *Kitáb-i-Íqán* 193–4).

Wealth is praiseworthy under certain conditions:

> Wealth is praiseworthy in the highest degree, if it is acquired by an individual's own efforts and the grace of God, in commerce, agriculture, art and industry, and if it be expended for philanthropic purposes. Above all, if a judicious and resourceful individual should initiate measures which would universally enrich the masses of the people, there could be no undertaking greater than this, and it would rank in the sight of God as the supreme achievement, for such a benefactor would supply the needs and insure the comfort and well-being of a great multitude ('Abdu'l-Bahá, *Secret* 24).

Leaders of government are responsible to ensure the honesty of their governments, to prevent corruption and to minister to the poor. In a Tablet to the sultan of Turkey, Bahá'u'lláh stated:

> Beware lest thou aggrandize thy ministers at the expense of thy subjects. Fear the sighs of the poor and of the upright in heart who, at every break of day, bewail their plight, and be unto them a benignant sovereign. They, verily, are thy treasures on earth. It behoveth thee, therefore, to safeguard thy treasures from the assaults of them who wish to rob thee. Inquire into their affairs, and ascertain, every year, nay every month, their condition, and be not of them that are careless of their duty (Bahá'u'lláh, *Gleanings* 236).

Laws, such as a progressive income tax, are required to regulate economic status:

> . . . rules and laws should be established to regulate the excessive fortunes of certain private individuals and meet the needs of millions of the poor masses; thus a certain

moderation would be obtained. However, absolute equality is just as impossible, for absolute equality in fortunes, honours, commerce, agriculture, industry would end in disorderliness, in chaos, in disorganization of the means of existence, and in universal disappointment: the order of the community would be quite destroyed ('Abdu'l-Bahá, *Answered Questions* 274).

The degrees of society must be preserved. The farmer will continue to till the soil, the artist to pursue his art, the banker to finance the nations . . . But in this Bahá'í plan there is no class hatred. Each is to be protected and each individual member of the body politic is to live in the greatest comfort and happiness. Work is to be provided for all and there will be no needy ones seen in the streets ('Abdu'l-Bahá, in *Economics* no. 15).

One of the chief means of redistributing wealth is the Ḥuqúqu'lláh or Right of God. Bahá'u'lláh said that 19 per cent of a person's net wealth belongs to God and should be paid by the Bahá'ís to the House of Justice for various purposes, including the 'relief of the poor' ('Abdu'l-Bahá, in *Ḥuqúqu'lláh* no. 75). Although this amount is 'owed to God', it is not permissible to solicit payment; it must be given willingly. While the Bahá'í community remains small, the funds available from this source for development are relatively modest but as the size of the community grows it will become a massive resource for uplifting the status of the poor. Bahá'u'lláh said, 'This ordinance is binding upon everyone, and by observing it one will be raised to honour inasmuch as it will serve to purify one's possessions and will impart blessing, and added prosperity' (Bahá'u'lláh, in *Ḥuqúqu'lláh* no. 42). So significant is this law that 'If the offering be but a single grain it is regarded as the crowning glory of all the harvests of the world' (Bahá'u'lláh, in *Ḥuqúqu'lláh* no. 5).

While legal measures are needed to ensure equity, voluntary sharing is an important spiritual principle:

Man reacheth perfection through good deeds, voluntarily performed, not through good deeds the doing of which was forced upon him. And sharing is a personally chosen righteous act: that is, the rich should extend assistance to the poor, they should expend their substance for the poor, but of their own free will, and not because the poor have gained this end by force' ('Abdu'l-Bahá, *Selections* 115).

Contributions to the Cause of God will be compensated through divine bestowals:

O Friends of God! Be ye assured that in place of these contributions, your agriculture, your industry, and your commerce will be blessed by manifold increases, with goodly gifts and bestowals. He who cometh with one goodly deed will receive a tenfold reward. There is no doubt that the living Lord will abundantly confirm those who expend their wealth in His path ('Abdu'l-Bahá, *Bahá'í Prayers* 84).

One means of wealth distribution is by guarantee of fair wages to workers and their sharing in the profits of the enterprise:

> . . . the owners of properties, mines and factories should share their incomes with their employees and give a fairly certain percentage of their products to their workingmen in order that the employees may receive, beside their wages, some of the general income of the factory so that the employee may strive with his soul in the work ('Abdu'l-Bahá, *Foundations* 43).

Presumably, this applies to agricultural properties and enterprises.

Monopolistic enterprises designed to eliminate competition are not permitted according to Bahá'í principles:

> No more trusts will remain in the future. The question of the trusts will be wiped away entirely ('Abdu'l-Bahá, *Foundations* 43).

How this principle would apply to current or future world conditions is not clear but its spirit would seem to favour small and medium-sized enterprises over those larger enterprises which result in the gradual control of agricultural resources in the hands of a few. Similarly, arrangements that favour the accumulation of wealth in the richest and most advantaged industrial nations would be contrary to Bahá'í principle.

Inheritance is to be widely distributed:

Every Bahá'í is required to make a will. While each person is free to allocate his or her property as desired, Bahá'u'lláh gives extensive instructions regarding the settling of estates. If these instructions are taken as a model for the division of properties, it is apparent that property is to be widely dispersed rather than concentrated.

Property, Interest, Employment

Land tenure and property ownership is a central concern for farmers. On this subject, the Bahá'í writings are clear in their endorsement of the right of ownership. According to Shoghi Effendi, 'the Cause neither accepts the theories of the Capitalistic economics in full, nor can it agree with the Marxists and Communists in their repudiation of the principle of private ownership and of this vital sacred right of the individual' (Shoghi Effendi, in *Economics* no. 28). However, while the writings explicitly uphold the institution of private ownership, they also stress the necessity of introducing fundamental changes in its methods and features (Shoghi Effendi, *Directives* 19–20). An example of these changes would be profit sharing, which could be applied to agricultural workers on large estates and plantations or corporate farms.

Support for the right of private ownership should not be taken to mean that other forms of ownership or tenure such as cooperative enterprises or the communal ownership found in many developing countries and indigenous communities are not acceptable. It may also be that novel forms of tenure, such as land trusts administered by voluntary boards, will be devised or adopted according to local requirements. Shoghi Effendi states that the Bahá'í principles are meant to apply under widely different conditions; he said, for example, 'where the countries are rarely industrial and mostly agricultural, we should have to apply different laws from the West . . .' (Shoghi Effendi, in *Economics* no. 21).

Intellectual property is an important issue in agriculture today, whether in enterprises involving biotechnology or for rural and indigenous people with a unique knowledge of their local flora. A statement relevant to this topic is found in the letters of Shoghi Effendi: 'Those whose brains have contributed to the creation and improvement of the means of production must be fairly rewarded, though these means may be owned and controlled by others' (Shoghi Effendi, in *Economics* no. 26). Further to this issue, the principle that the benefits of civilization should be shared equitably will be important in determining the benefits that derive from discoveries through genetic technologies or ethnobotany.

Lending and interest as other key issues for farmers. Bahá'u'lláh abrogated the Islamic law against charging interest but recommended that a moderate rate of interest be maintained: 'this is a matter that should be practised with moderation and fairness . . . We exhort the loved ones of God to observe justice and fairness, and to do that which would prompt the friends of God to evince tender mercy and compassion towards each other' (Bahá'u'lláh, *Tablets* 134). He further stated 'the conduct of these affairs hath been entrusted to the men of the House of Justice that they may enforce them according to the exigencies of the time and the dictates of wisdom' (Bahá'u'lláh, *Tablets* 134).

REVITALIZING THE LOCAL AGRICULTURAL ECONOMY: START WITH THE FARMER

'Abdu'l-Bahá asserted that the transformation of economic systems as envisaged by the Bahá'í teachings 'must commence with the farmer and then be extended to the other classes inasmuch as the number of farmers is far greater than all other classes. Therefore, it is fitting to begin with the farmer in matters relating to economics for the farmer is the first active agent in human society' ('Abdu'l-Bahá, in *Economics* no. 9). He further stated that the solution to the economic problem 'begins with the village, and when the village is reconstructed, then the cities will be also' ('Abdu'l-Bahá, in *Bahá'í World*, vol. 4, 450). While demographics have shifted since 'Abdu'l-Bahá's time, approximately 60 per cent of people in the developing world are rural. India's labour force, for instance, is 67 per cent agricultural.

'Abdu'l-Bahá wrote and spoke extensively about the revitalization of village life. Modernization is clearly necessary given the economic and social stagnation into which village life has fallen and the lack of opportunities it provides. In *On History*, Eric Hobsbawm points to the anomaly that 'on the whole, the countries with the highest percentage of agricultural population are the ones which have difficulties in feeding themselves, or at any rate their rapidly growing non-farm populations, while the world's food surpluses come, on the whole, from a relatively tiny population in a few advanced countries'. Hobsbaum notes that advocates of economic growth are constantly surprised that they cannot replace the more inefficient farming systems of developing nations with the industrial model but they fail to recognize that success usually comes from 'reform adapted to the specific conditions of regional farming' (Hobsbaum, *On History* 157).

'Abdu'l-Bahá provides a model for village development, commonly called 'the village storehouse' or the 'house of finance'. The model is site specific; driven by the community itself; involves a general plan for development, including education, health care and social welfare; serves to ameliorate vagaries of climate which can lead to economic instability; provides measures for obtaining credit and for income stabilization; and seeks to broaden the bases of development by exploiting non-agricultural as well as agricultural opportunities. Several of the salient points of this model are taken from the writings of 'Abdu'l-Bahá.

The village storehouse is an institution created to administer the economic activities of the village:

It serves as a community development 'bank' which takes in, manages and redistributes revenues. 'In every village there must be established a general storehouse, which will have a number of revenues' ('Abdu'l-Bahá, *Foundations* 39). Details of this institution and its functions 'are to be fixed by the Universal House of Justice' ('Abdu'l-Bahá, in *Economics* no. 10).

The village storehouse is to be administered by a board elected or chosen from the notables:

> In every village a storehouse and an officer in charge are to be provided, while the notables of the village gather and form a board and to this board and officer the direction of the affairs of the village are entrusted. They take charge of all questions pertaining to the village, and the revenues of the storehouse such as tithes, tax on animals and other revenues are gathered in it and are given out for necessary expenditures ('Abdu'l-Bahá, in *Economics* no. 10).

> Certain trustees will be elected by the people in a given village to look after these transactions ('Abdu'l-Bahá, *Foundations* 40).

The storehouse is financed by various revenues:

A percentage of the harvest:

At the time of the harvest, under the direction of that board, a certain percentage of the entire harvest should be appropriated for the storehouse ('Abdu'l-Bahá, in *Economics* no. 9).

Various revenue sources are specified:

The storehouse has seven revenues: Tithes, taxes on animals, property without an heir, all lost objects whose owners cannot be traced, one third of all treasure-trove, one third of the produce of all mines, and voluntary contributions ('Abdu'l-Bahá, in *Economics* no. 9).

As to the revenues of the storehouse, the House of Justice must strive by every means possible to increase that amount, i.e. by every just means ('Abdu'l-Bahá, in *Economics* no. 10).

Progressive taxation:

Each person in the community whose income is equal to his individual producing capacity shall be exempt from taxation. But if his income is greater than his needs he must pay a tax until an adjustment is effected. That is to say, a man's capacity for production and his needs will be equalized and reconciled through taxation ('Abdu'l-Bahá, *Foundations* 37).

As to the first, the tenths or tithes: we will consider a farmer, one of the peasants. We will look into his income. We will find out, for instance, what is his annual revenue and also what are his expenditures. Now, if his income be equal to his expenditures, from such a farmer nothing whatever will be taken . . . Another farmer may have expenses running up to one thousand dollars we will say, and his income is two thousand dollars. From such an one a tenth will be required . . . But if his expenses be ten thousand and his income two hundred thousand then he must give an even half . . . Such a scale as this will determine allotment of taxes. All the income from such revenues will go to this general storehouse (ibid. 40).

Details to be determined by the House of Justice:

. . . the division and the fixing of everyone's share are to be arranged in accordance with the time and place by the House of Justice ('Abdu'l-Bahá, in *Economics* no. 10).

Revenues are redistributed in several ways:

This storehouse also has seven expenditures: 1) General running expenses of the storehouse, such as the salary of the secretary and the administration of public health. 2) Tithes to the government. 3) Taxes on animals to the government. 4) Costs of running an orphanage. 5) Costs of running a home for the incapacitated. 6) Costs of running a school. 7) Payment of subsidies to provide needed support of the poor ('Abdu'l-Bahá, in *Economics* no. 9).

'Negative income tax' will be applied to those in need:

[If a village member's] necessities exceed his production he shall receive an amount sufficient to equalize or adjust. Therefore taxation will be proportionate to capacity and production and there will be no poor in the community ('Abdu'l-Bahá, *Foundations* 37).

Income stabilization:

. . . there must be considered such emergencies as follows: a certain farmer whose expenses run up to ten thousand dollars and whose income is only five thousand, he will receive necessary expenses from the storehouse ('Abdu'l-Bahá, *Foundations* 40).

Service provision:

The storehouse will be responsible for social services in the village:

The poor in the village – their necessary expenses will be defrayed. And other members who for valid reasons are incapacitated – the blind, the old, the deaf – their comfort must be looked after. In the village no one will remain in need or in want ('Abdu'l-Bahá, *Foundations* 40).

Community development:

. . . if anything is deemed necessary for the village such as the providing of hygienic measures, the House of Justice must also make all the necessary provisions ('Abdu'l-Bahá, in *Economics* no. 10).

A certain amount must be provided . . . for the village's system of education [and] . . . a certain amount must be set aside for the administration of public health ('Abdu'l-Bahá, in *Economics* no. 9).

Excess funds go to the national treasury:

The farmers will be taken care of and if after all these expenses are defrayed any surplus is found in the storehouse it must be transferred to the national treasury ('Abdu'l-Bahá, *Foundations* 40).

'Abdu'l-Bahá's said that his ideas were intended as a model rather than a prescription:

What hath been stated is only an example and this doth not mean that it should be enforced exactly in this manner . . . These are only the preliminary principles; the House of Justice will arrange and widen them in accordance with time and place ('Abdu'l-Bahá, in *Economics* no. 10).

The concept of the village storehouse has roots deep in the cultures and religions of the past. Archaeologist Jacques Cauvin notes that one of the early Neolithic cultures of the Levant built 'the first rectangular constructions known in the Near East, or in the world'; these have been identified as granaries, marking the first time 'the storing of foodstuffs was organized outside the domestic quarters' (Cauvin, *Birth* 41). Basic as it was, this village storehouse might have been the first collective economic institution of the Neolithic period. It allowed early agricultural communities to assure a regular supply of food throughout the seasons (ibid. 2).

In 'The Bahá'í Village Granary' Calkins and Girard describe the evolution of this institution in various cultures: '. . . as early as the fourth century BC, the Chinese philosopher Mencius proposed the essentially practical concept of the "well-field" to promote food security at the sub-village level' (Calkins and Girard, 'Bahá'í Village Granary' 5). Using the Chinese character for 'well' (which is similar in shape to the symbol #) as his model, he

suggested that each of eight households could farm an individual peripheral field and leave the ninth, central field for cooperative production, tax payment and storage. If one of the households had a bad harvest, its members could survive the year by drawing from the common granary. This is one of the first examples of what modern economists call 'food security' strategies' (ibid. 6).

The authors go on to briefly trace the history and development of the storehouse idea through Judaism, Christianity and Islam.

Wright in *Non-Zero, The Logic of Human Destiny* cites another interesting example. Indigenous Hawaiians developed a storehouse as a religious and socioeconomic institution. In-kind taxes of food and crafts were stored and used for social insurance against food shortages, for 'redistributive feasts' and to feed labourers working on capital projects such as irrigation systems and fish ponds (Wright, *Non-Zero* 82–5).

AGRICULTURE, GLOBALIZATION AND INTERNATIONAL TRADE

Whatever one's opinion of the process of globalization, no one can deny that it is relentless. Today, said 'Abdu'l-Bahá,

. . . all the members of the human family, whether peoples or governments, cities or villages, have become increasingly interdependent. For none is self-sufficiency any longer possible, inasmuch as political ties unite all peoples and nations, and the bonds of trade and industry, of agriculture and education, are being strengthened every day ('Abdu'l-Bahá, *Selections* 31–2).

Rather than fearing this process, 'Abdu'l-Bahá, understands that it means, for the first time in history, that 'the unity of all mankind can . . . be achieved' (ibid.).

The world order envisioned by Bahá'u'lláh is designed to ameliorate international market forces, which tend to shortchange developing nations and ignore negative impacts on the rural poor. The Organization for Economic Cooperation and Development (OECD) reports, for example, that tariffs imposed by developed nations cost developing countries US$43.1 billion a year (in 1998); ironically, this is three-quarters of the value of international development assistance. The Bahá'í model eliminates such barriers and recommends trade instruments designed to foster genuine human progress.

Many of the spiritual and practical principles previously cited in this article – such as provisions for wealth redistribution – apply at the international level. The Bahá'í writings also call for democratic, global institutions to govern the flow of capital, goods and services between nations in a manner that is beneficial to each and all. Truly international institutions, acting on behalf of humanity as a whole, would counterbalance the power of any particular nation or bloc. These would include a world legislature, a world executive, an international police force and a world tribunal to adjudicate disputes (Shoghi Effendi, *World Order* 203–4). Bahá'u'lláh's global vision, however, 'repudiates excessive centralization . . . and disclaims all attempts at uniformity . . . Its watchword is unity in diversity . . .' (ibid. 42).

Conservation and the Sustainability of Agriculture

According to Bahá'u'lláh, 'All men have been created to carry forward an ever-advancing civilization' (Bahá'u'lláh, *Gleanings* 215). The world 'ever-advancing' implies that the process of human development must progress from one generation to the next. Consequently, to fulfil the purpose of our creation, the processes of civilization must be sustainable and our ability to control nature must be informed by the fact that civilization ultimately depends on the viability of natural systems. Bahá'u'lláh's statement raises the sustainable development of civilization to the status of a spiritual principle that is central to the purpose of our existence.

The Bahá'í International Community elaborated on this point in a concept paper on development:

> Bahá'í scriptures describe nature as a reflection of the sacred. They teach that nature should be valued and respected, but not worshipped; rather, it should serve humanity's efforts to carry forward an ever-advancing civilization. However, in light of the interdependence of all parts of nature, and the importance of evolution and diversity 'to the beauty, efficiency and perfection of the whole', every effort should be made to preserve as much as possible the earth's bio-diversity and natural order.

As trustees, or stewards, of the planet's vast resources and biological diversity, humanity must learn to make use of the earth's natural resources, both renewable and non-renewable, in a manner that ensures sustainability and equity into the distant reaches of time. This attitude of stewardship will require full consideration of the potential environmental consequences of all development activities. It will compel humanity to temper its actions with moderation and humility, realizing that the true value of nature cannot be expressed in economic terms. It will also require a deep understanding of the natural world and its role in humanity's collective development – both material and spiritual. Therefore, sustainable environmental management must come to be seen not as a discretionary commitment mankind can weigh against other competing interests, but rather as a fundamental responsibility that must be shouldered – a pre-requisite for spiritual development as well as the individual's physical survival (Bahá'í International Community, *Valuing Spirituality* 21–2).

Since agriculture is fundamental to civilization, a sustainable food and agriculture system is intrinsic to the world order prescribed by Bahá'u'lláh. The following points outline many of the ideas underlying a Bahá'í perspective on the sustainability of agriculture. Together, these ideas give substance to a new environmental ethos appropriate to a world civilization.

CIVILIZATION, SCIENCE AND TECHNOLOGY

The Bahá'í teachings emphatically encourage the processes of building civilization, including the development of sciences and technologies, which 'uplift the world of being, and are conducive to its exaltation' (Bahá'u'lláh, *Epistle* 26). In fact, the capacity for science and technical innovation in a sense defines what it means to be human and our scientific ability is seen as a means to reveal the hidden qualities of nature, fulfilling its God-given potential ('Abdu'l-Bahá, in *Bahá'í World Faith* 242). This same capacity is, however, potentially dangerous:

The civilization, so often vaunted by the learned exponents of arts and sciences, will, if allowed to overleap the bounds of moderation, bring great evil upon men (Bahá'u'lláh, *Gleanings* 342).

If a thing is carried to excess, it will prove a source of evil. Consider the civilization of the West, how it hath agitated and alarmed the peoples of the world . . . Strange and astonishing things exist in the earth . . . These things are capable of changing the whole atmosphere of the earth and their contamination would prove lethal (Bahá'u'lláh, *Tablets* 69).

To ensure that science and technology are beneficial, the Bahá'í teachings prescribe various measures. Civilization must be kept within the 'restraints of moderation'

(Bahá'u'lláh, *Gleanings* 343). Only those sciences 'As can profit the peoples of the earth' should be pursued (Bahá'u'lláh, *Tablets* 52). The teachings of Bahá'u'lláh are meant to restrain, moderate and balance science and technology, and thereby protect society and preserve nature. In fact, Bahá'u'lláh said, 'Each one of the ordinances We have revealed is a mighty stronghold for the preservation of the world of being. Verily, this Wronged One desireth naught but your security and elevation' (Bahá'u'lláh, *Tablets* 69). Religion is meant to moderate science by ensuring that its motivation is pure and that its goal is beneficial. 'Abdu'l-Bahá remarked that 'Every kind of knowledge, every science, is as a tree: if the fruit of it be the love of God, then is it a blessed tree . . .' However, he warned that if the love of God is not intrinsic to the pursuit of science, 'that tree is but dried-up wood, and shall only feed the fire' ('Abdu'l-Bahá, *Selections* 181).

Sustainable Agricultural Development and Religion

In innumerable passages in the Bahá'í texts, both human progress *and* world regeneration are advanced as goals of God's revelation (italics are added for emphasis in the following passages).

> That which is conducive to the *regeneration of the world* and the *salvation of the peoples* and kindreds of the earth hath been sent down from the heaven of the utterance of Him Who is the Desire of the world (Bahá'u'lláh, *Tablets* 223).

> . . . the counsels which the Pen of the Wronged One hath revealed constitute the supreme animating power for the *advancement of the world* and the *exaltation of its peoples*. Arise, O people, and, by the power of God's might, resolve to gain the victory over your own selves, that haply the *whole earth* might be freed and sanctified from its servitude to the gods of its idle fancies . . . (Bahá'u'lláh, *Tablets* 86).

> The Call of God, when raised, breathed a new life into the *body of mankind*, and infused a new spirit into *the whole creation*. It is for this reason that the world hath been moved to its depths, and the *hearts and consciences of men* been quickened. Erelong the evidences of this regeneration will be revealed, and the fast asleep will be awakened ('Abdu'l-Bahá, in Shoghi Effendi, *World Order* 169).

> Great is the station of man. Great must also be his endeavours for the *rehabilitation of the world* and the *well-being of nations* (Bahá'u'lláh, *Tablets* 174).

The Natural World

Agroecosystems are derived from and remain dependent on natural systems.

The Bahá'í discourse contains many significant ideas about nature, its functions, purpose and value that will influence our understanding and practice of agriculture. A number of these points follow.

Nature is an expression of the divine:

> Nature is sacred in the sense that it is an expression of the divine (Bahá'u'lláh, *Tablets* 142).

Nature is sustained through the Will of God:

> There can be no doubt whatever that if for one moment the tide of His mercy and grace were to be withheld from the world, it would completely perish (Bahá'u'lláh *Gleanings* 68).

Nature's hidden capacities and potentials are educed by God's revelation:

> . . . the moment the word expressing My attribute 'the Omniscient' issueth forth from My mouth, every created thing will, according to its capacity and limitations, be invested with the power to unfold the knowledge of the most marvellous sciences, and will be empowered to manifest them in the course of time . . . (Bahá'u'lláh, *Gleanings* 142).

> Consider, for instance, the revelation of the light of the Name of God, the Educator. Behold, how in all things the evidences of such a revelation are manifest, how the betterment of all beings dependeth upon it . . . Its influence pervadeth all things and sustaineth them. It is for this reason that God hath assumed the title, 'Lord of all worlds' (Bahá'u'lláh, *Gleanings* 189–90).

Nature is a recipient of and responds to divine revelation:

> The whole creation hath been made the recipient of the revelation of the All-Merciful . . . (Bahá'u'lláh, in Shoghi Effendi, *World Order* 169).

> Every Prophet hath announced the coming of this Day, and every Messenger hath groaned in His yearning for this Revelation – a revelation which, no sooner had it been revealed than all created things cried out saying, 'The earth is God's, the Most Exalted, the Most Great' (Bahá'u'lláh, in Shoghi Effendi, *Advent* 77–8).

Physical space is made sacred through worship:

> Blessed is the spot, and the house, and the place, and the city, and the heart, and the mountain, and the refuge, and the cave, and the valley, and the land, and the sea, and the island, and the meadow where mention of God hath been made, and His

praise glorified (Bahá'u'lláh, in *Bahá'í Prayers* frontispiece).

Nature is a 'Book' of revelation:

> The Book of Creation is in accord with the written Book . . . the Book of creation is the command of God and the repository of divine mysteries. In it there are great signs, universal images, perfect words, exalted symbols and secrets of all things, whether of the past or of the future . . . when thou gazest at the Book of creation thou wilt observe the signs, symbols, realities and reflections of the hidden mysteries of the bounties of His Holiness the Incomparable One ('Abdu'l-Bahá, in Nakhjavani, *Response* 13).

That nature is the source of human prosperity should humble humanity:

> Every man of discernment, while walking upon the earth, feeleth indeed abashed, inasmuch as he is fully aware that the thing which is the source of his prosperity, his wealth, his might, his exaltation, his advancement and power is, as ordained by God, the very earth which is trodden beneath the feet of all men (Bahá'u'lláh, *Epistle* 44).

Nature reveals God but is not in itself divine:

> He is really a believer in the Unity of God who recognizeth in each and every created thing the sign of the revelation of Him Who is the Eternal Truth, and not he who maintaineth that the creature is indistinguishable from the Creator (Bahá'u'lláh, *Gleanings* 189).

Nature is not to be worshipped:

> What ignorance and stupidity it is to worship and adore nature, when God in His goodness has made us masters thereof ('Abdu'l-Bahá, *Paris Talks* 123).

In relationship to God and to the spiritual realities, the physical world is insignificant:

> O My servants! Were ye to discover the hidden, the shoreless oceans of My incorruptible wealth, ye would, of a certainty, esteem as nothing the world, nay, the entire creation (Bahá'u'lláh, *Gleanings* 323).

> Disencumber yourselves of all attachment to this world and the vanities thereof (ibid. 276).

Nature is imperfect and in need of development in order to facilitate civilization:

> Nature is the material world. When we look upon it, we see that it is dark and

imperfect . . . that is to say, we must illumine the dark world of nature ('Abdu'l-Bahá, *Promulgation* 308–9).

If the earth is not cultivated, it becomes a jungle where useless weeds grow; but if a cultivator comes and tills the ground, it produces crops which nourish living creatures. It is evident, therefore, that the soil needs the cultivation of the farmer ('Abdu'l-Bahá, *Answered Questions* 7).

APPRECIATION FOR NATURAL DIVERSITY AND ECOLOGICAL RELATIONSHIPS

The Bahá'í writings contain many passages that demonstrate a profound appreciation and understanding of ecology and provide insights into the operation of agroecosystems.

The unity of nature is derived from its diversity. 'Abdu'l-Bahá said,

Were one to observe with an eye that discovereth the realities of all things, it would become clear that the greatest relationship that bindeth the world of being together lieth in the range of created things themselves . . . ('Abdu'l-Bahá, in *Compilation,* vol. 1, 71).

He further said that an indwelling spirit of cooperation is a fundamental property of nature:

. . . all beings are connected together like a chain; and reciprocal help, assistance and influence belonging to the properties of things are the causes of the existence, development and growth of created beings ('Abdu'l-Bahá, *Answered Questions* 178–9).

An example of the cooperative nature of relationships is the complementary functions of plants and animals: 'Each of these two maketh use of certain elements in the air on which its own life dependeth, while each increaseth the quantity of such elements as are essential for the life of the other.' 'Abdu'l-Bahá then extends this idea to all relationships: 'Of like kind are the relationships that exist among all created things. Hence it was stated that co-operation and reciprocity are essential properties which are inherent in the unified system of the world of existence, and without which the entire creation would be reduced to nothingness' ('Abdu'l-Bahá, in *Ḥuqúqu'lláh* no. 61).

HUMANITY AND NATURE

In considering the underlying principles involved in the development of a sustainable agriculture, it is important to understand the concept of the relationship of humanity to nature described in the Bahá'í writings. This understanding will form the basis for reshaping attitudes towards nature and, consequently, agricultural practices.

Among the countless species, humankind has a unique function: 'But for man, who, on My earth, would remember Me,' says Bahá'u'lláh, 'and how could My attributes and My names be revealed?' (Bahá'u'lláh, *Epistle* 49). The appearance of the capacity to know and love the Creator is the reason for creation and only the human being has been given a capacity for faith. Bahá'u'lláh states that,

> Having created the world and all that liveth and moveth therein, He, through the direct operation of His unconstrained and sovereign Will, chose to confer upon man the unique distinction and capacity to know Him and to love Him – a capacity that must needs be regarded as the generating impulse and the primary purpose underlying the whole of creation . . . Upon the inmost reality of each and every created thing He hath shed the light of one of His names, and made it a recipient of the glory of one of His attributes. Upon the reality of man, however, He hath focused the radiance of all of His names and attributes, and made it a mirror of His own Self. Alone of all created things man hath been singled out for so great a favour, so enduring a bounty (Bahá'u'lláh, *Gleanings 65*).

'Abdu'l-Bahá describes nature and humanity in the following way, an eloquent statement of the principles of ecology:

> As preordained by the Fountainhead of Creation, the temple of the world hath been fashioned after the image and likeness of the human body. In fact each mirroreth forth the image of the other, wert thou but to observe with discerning eyes. By this is meant that even as the human body in this world which is outwardly composed of different limbs and organs, is in reality a closely integrated coherent entity, similarly the structure of the physical world is like unto a single being whose limbs and members are inseparably linked together ('Abdu'l-Bahá, in *Ḥuqúqu'lláh* no. 61).

'Reflect', says 'Abdu'l-Bahá, 'upon the inner realities of the universe, the secret wisdoms involved, the enigmas, the inter-relationships, the rules that govern all. For every part of the universe is connected with every other part by ties that are very powerful and admit of no imbalance, nor any slackening whatever . . . ('Abdu'l-Bahá, in *Conservation* 4). 'Regard ye the world', states Bahá'u'lláh, 'as a man's body, which is afflicted with divers ailments, and the recovery of which dependeth upon the harmonizing of all of its component elements' (Bahá'u'lláh, *Epistle* 55).

This 'ecological' view of natural unity conceives of the earth as a whole system, a living organism, of which the human species (to the extent that we are physical beings) is a part. However, it is only the physical element of humanity that is 'part' of nature. We are told in the Bahá'í writings that the human reality is also a spiritual reality that *encompasses* the physical world. 'Should anyone suppose', says 'Abdu'l-Bahá, 'that man is but a part of the world of nature, and he being endowed with these perfections, these being but manifestations of the world of nature, and thus nature is the originator of these perfections and is not deprived therefrom, to him we make reply and say: the part dependeth upon the whole; the part cannot possess perfections whereof the whole is deprived' ('Abdu'l-Bahá, *Tablet to August Forel* 12). Humanity cannot be merely 'part' of the physical whole when it has qualities and capacities that the whole does not possess. As humanity has the abilities of the rational soul, the ability of creative thought, the ability to master nature through science and so on, it must be of a different and higher order than nature, which is deprived of these qualities and capacities.

The Bahá'í writings conceive of the human being as a reality that encompasses the physical world and as a microcosm of the world. The world of creation is described as the 'Book of Creation', one of two forms of the revelation of God, and 'Man is said to be the greatest representative of God, and he is the Book of Creation . . .' ('Abdu'l-Bahá, *Answered Questions* 236).

Rather than the human reality evolving from the physical world and adapting to its physical environment, the 'temple of the world', says 'Abdu'l-Bahá, has been 'fashioned after the image and likeness of the human body' ('Abdu'l-Bahá, in *Conservation* 4). In describing this concept of the human being, Bahá'u'lláh restates an Islamic tradition:

> Dost thou reckon thyself only a puny form
> When within thee the universe is folded?
> (Quoted in Bahá'u'lláh, *Seven Valleys* 34).

Writing of the relationship of humanity and nature in his book *The Covenant of Bahá'u'lláh*, Taherzadeh states, 'One of the principles of nature is that higher forms of life revolve around, and depend upon, the lowest' (11). 'There is a delicate relationship between all levels of creation in which the lower kingdom serves the higher while the higher kingdom lives in harmony with the lower. Indeed, the world of nature is placed at man's disposal to enrich the quality of his life while on this earth, while man is duty bound to respect and preserve his environment' (3).

In fact, the exalted station of the human being would seem to be conditional.

> When man allows the spirit, through his soul, to enlighten his understanding, then does he contain all creation; because man, being the culmination of all that went before and thus superior to all previous evolutions, contains the lower world within himself. Illumined by the spirit through the instrumentality of the soul, man's radiant intelligence makes him the crowning-point of creation.

> But on the other hand, when man does not open his mind and heart to the blessing of the spirit, but turns his soul toward the material side, towards the bodily part of his nature, then is he fallen from his high place and he becomes inferior to the inhabitants of the lower animal kingdom . . . Men such as this, plan to work evil, to hurt and to destroy; they are entirely without the spirit of divine compassion, for the celestial quality of the soul has been dominated by that of the material ('Abdu'l-Bahá, *Paris Talks* 12–13).

Just as the unique position and capacity of humanity results in its mastery over nature, and often in its destructive impact on the ecosphere, the capacities of the human soul have also the potential to generate a profound comprehension of reality, as when sensing the universe within, the human being develops a sympathetic and caring attitude to nature.

A unique responsibility accompanies human powers and capacities: 'the proper exercise of this responsibility is the key to whether . . . inventive genius produces beneficial results, or creates havoc in the material world,' states the Universal House of Justice (*Conservation* 2). It is when humanity comes into harmony with the purpose of creation by embracing the covenant of God that it comes into harmony with the material world of which its physical aspect is a part.

> Know thou that he is truly learned who hath acknowledged My Revelation, and drunk from the Ocean of My knowledge, and soared in the atmosphere of My love, and cast away all besides Me, and taken firm hold on that which hath been sent down from the Kingdom of My wondrous utterance. He, verily, is even as an eye unto mankind, and as the spirit of life unto the body of all creation (Bahá'u'lláh, *Epistle* 83).

It is in this context that we understand the limitations of nature; for humanity to live in nature, ignorant of the spiritual reality, mocks the very purpose of nature's existence. Nature, without the presence of humanity, is without purpose. 'Abdu'l-Bahá states that 'If there were no man, the perfections of the spirit would not appear, and the light of the mind would not be resplendent in this world. This world would be like a body without a soul' ('Abdu'l-Bahá, *Answered Questions* 201).

The human being, however, can educe the purpose and capacities of nature. By itself, 'the world of nature is incomplete, imperfect until awakened and illumined by the light and stimulus of education' ('Abdu'l-Bahá, *Promulgation* 309). 'Lofty is the station of man,' writes Bahá'u'lláh in the Book of the Covenant, 'were he to hold fast to righteousness and truth and to remain firm and steadfast in the Cause . . . His is the loftiest station, and his influence educateth the world of being' (Bahá'u'lláh, *Tablets* 220).

Without human presence and human influence, nature is imperfect. 'In these days there are new schools of philosophy blindly claiming that the world of nature is perfect,' writes 'Abdu'l-Bahá. '. . . If the world of nature were perfect and complete in itself, there would be no need of . . . training and cultivation in the human world . . .' ('Abdu'l-Bahá, *Promulgation* 309–10). Humanity must be educated to free itself from the limitations of the physical, to attain the spiritual qualities that are greater than the physical. The 'natural' state must be overcome in order for a person to be fully human. 'The mission of the Prophets of God has been to train the souls of humanity and free them from the thraldom of natural instincts and physical tendencies' (ibid. 310).

Limiting ourselves to the boundaries of the physical undermines the purpose of nature, which is to provide a place for faith to become manifest. Sole identification with the physical, with nature, is dangerous to humankind and ultimately makes our presence dangerous to the physical realm itself. We are told to, 'Walk thou high above the world of being through the power of the Most Great Name, that thou mayest become aware of the immemorial mysteries and be acquainted with that wherewith no one is acquainted' (Bahá'u'lláh *Tablets* 142–3). At the same time, we understand that the human being, detached from nature, becomes a source of education and of life to the natural world. In the same passage, Bahá'u'lláh continues, 'Be thou as a throbbing artery, pulsating in the body of the entire creation, that through the heat generated by this motion there may appear that which will quicken the hearts of those who hesitate' (ibid. 143).

The Bahá'í teachings give human beings the responsibility to conserve the ecological balance of nature. 'Great is the station of man,' says Bahá'u'lláh. 'Great must also be his endeavours for the rehabilitation of the world and the well-being of nations' (Bahá'u'lláh, *Tablets* 174). 'Truly, We desire to behold you as manifestations of paradise on earth . . .' (Bahá'u'lláh, *Kitáb-i-Aqdas* para. 106). Consequently, 'Abdu'l-Bahá said, 'Let your ambition be the achievement on earth of a Heavenly civilization! I ask for you the supreme blessing, that you may be so filled with the vitality of the Heavenly Spirit that you may be the cause of life to the world' ('Abdu'l-Bahá, *Paris Talks* 99).

Future agricultural systems will benefit from this profound understanding of the responsibilities of our species for the sustainability and development of nature.

Animals, Nature and Agriculture

The Bahá'í teachings contain a number of references relevant to animal agriculture, including the ways in which animals are treated and used for human purposes and the manner in which the food and agricultural system is organized. A summary follows.

Animals are perfect in the sense that they are true to their inherent nature:

> In its natural condition and plane of limitation the animal is perfect ('Abdu'l-Bahá, *Promulgation* 311).

Animal sensibilities are restricted to physical sensations:

> The animal . . . is utterly lacking spiritual susceptibilities . . . The animal possesses no power of ideation or conscious intelligence; it is a captive of the senses and deprived of that which lies beyond them ('Abdu'l-Bahá, *Promulgation* 177).

> The animal can neither recognize nor apprehend the spiritual power of man and makes no distinction between man and itself ('Abdu'l-Bahá, *Promulgation*, 311).

Kindness to animals is a virtue. Cruelty is prohibited:

> Burden not an animal with more than it can bear. We, truly, have prohibited such

treatment through a most binding interdiction in the Book. Be ye the embodiments of justice and fairness amidst all creation (Bahá'u'lláh, *Kitáb-i-Aqdas* 87).

... to the blessed animals the utmost kindness must be shown, the more the better. Tenderness and loving-kindness are basic principles of God's heavenly Kingdom. Ye should most carefully bear this matter in mind ('Abdu'l-Bahá, *Selections* 160).

'Abdu'l-Bahá offered the following poem on this topic (ibid. 256):

Unless ye must,
Bruise not the serpent in the dust,
How much less wound a man.
And if ye can,
No ant should ye alarm,
Much less a brother harm.

Animals have feelings similar to human beings and therefore must be treated with compassion:

Briefly, it is not only their fellow human beings that the beloved of God must treat with mercy and compassion, rather must they show forth the utmost loving-kindness to every living creature. For in all physical respects, and where the animal spirit is concerned, the selfsame feelings are shared by animal and man. Man hath not grasped this truth, however, and he believeth that physical sensations are confined to human beings, wherefore is he unjust to the animals, and cruel.

And yet in truth, what difference is there when it cometh to physical sensations? The feelings are one and the same, whether ye inflict pain on man or on beast. There is no difference here whatever. And indeed ye do worse to harm an animal, for man hath a language, he can lodge a complaint, he can cry out and moan; if injured he can have recourse to the authorities and these will protect him from his aggressor. But the hapless beast is mute, able neither to express its hurt nor take its case to the authorities. If a man inflict a thousand ills upon a beast, it can neither ward him off with speech nor hale him into court. Therefore is it essential that ye show forth the utmost consideration to the animal, and that ye be even kinder to him than to your fellow man (ibid. 158–9).

Children should be trained to love animals:

Train your children from their earliest days to be infinitely tender and loving to animals. If an animal be sick, let the children try to heal it, if it be hungry, let them feed it, if thirsty, let them quench its thirst, if weary, let them see that it rests (ibid. 159).

Dangerous animals should be controlled:

> Most human beings are sinners, but the beasts are innocent. Surely those without sin
> should receive the most kindness and love – all except animals which are harmful,
> such as bloodthirsty wolves, such as poisonous snakes, and similar pernicious
> creatures, the reason being that kindness to these is an injustice to human beings
> and other animals as well (ibid.).

Hunting is permitted but not to excess:

> . . . hunt not to excess. Tread ye the path of justice and equity in all things
> (Bahá'u'lláh, *Kitáb-i-Aqdas* para. 60).

> The Universal House of Justice will, in due course, have to consider what constitutes
> an excess in hunting (ibid. p. 203).

The eating of meat is both natural and lawful:

> I have read thy letter, wherein thou didst express astonishment at some of the laws
> of God, such as that concerning the hunting of innocent animals, creatures who are
> guilty of no wrong.
>   Be thou not surprised at this . . . In the physical realm of creation, all things
> are eaters and eaten: the plant drinketh in the mineral, the animal doth crop
> and swallow down the plant, man doth feed upon the animal, and the mineral
> devoureth the body of man . . .
>   Whensoever thou does examine, through a microscope, the water man
> drinketh, the air he doth breathe, thou wilt see that with every breath of air, man
> taketh in an abundance of animal life, and with every draught of water, he also
> swalloweth down a great variety of animals. How could it ever be possible to put
> a stop to this process? For all creatures are eaters and eaten, and the very fabric of
> life is reared upon this fact. Were it not so, the ties that interlace all created things
> within the universe would be unravelled.
>   And further, whensoever a thing is destroyed, and decayeth, and is cut off
> from life, it is promoted into a world that is greater than the world it knew before.
> It leaveth for example, the life of the mineral and goeth forward into the life of
> the plant; then it departeth out of the vegetable life and ascendeth into that of
> the animal, following which it forsaketh the life of the animal and riseth into the
> realm of human life, and this is out of the grace of thy Lord, the Merciful, the
> Compassionate ('Abdu'l-Bahá, *Selections* 157–8).

A vegetarian diet is best:

> As humanity progresses, meat will be used less and less, for the teeth of man are
> not carnivorous . . . When mankind is more fully developed, the eating of meat will

gradually cease ('Abdu'l-Bahá, *Promulgation* 170–1).

. . . the food of man is cereals and fruit . . . he is not in need of meat, nor is he obliged to eat it. Even without eating meat he would live with the utmost vigour and energy . . . Truly, the killing of animals and the eating of their meat is somewhat contrary to pity and compassion, and if one can content oneself with cereals, fruit, oil and nuts, such as pistachios, almonds and so on, it would undoubtedly be better and more pleasing ('Abdu'l-Bahá, in *Compilation*, vol. 1, 462).

. . . eating meat is not forbidden or unlawful, nay, the point is this, that it is possible for man to live without eating meat and still be strong. Meat is nourishing and containeth the elements of herbs, seeds and fruits; therefore sometimes it is essential for the sick and for the rehabilitation of health. There is no objection in the Law of God to the eating of meat if it is required. So if thy constitution is rather weak and thou findest meat useful, thou mayest eat it (ibid. 463).

In regard to the question as to whether people ought to kill animals for food or not, there is no explicit statement in the Bahá'í Sacred Scriptures (as far as I know) in favour or against it. It is certain, however, that if man can live on a purely vegetarian diet and thus avoid killing animals, it would be much preferable (Shoghi Effendi, in ibid. 476).

Animal experimentation is permissible but must be carried out humanely:

Once we change human hearts, there will be no more cruelty to animals, and medical research will be carried out in a way which will eliminate as much suffering in experiments as possible (Shoghi Effendi, in *Lights* no. 994).

The Universal House of Justice has received your letter . . . enquiring the Bahá'í point of view on the vivisection of animals. The beloved Guardian was asked a similar question to which his secretary replied on his behalf . . . : 'As there is no definite and conclusive statement on Vivisection in the Bahá'í Teachings, this is a matter which the International House of Justice will have to pass upon in the future.'
    The House of Justice does not wish to legislate upon this matter at the present time. It is left to the consciences of the individual friends, who should make their decisions in light of the teachings concerning animals and their treatment.
    In this connection the House of Justice instructs us to say that in a Tablet in which He stresses the need for kindness to animals, 'Abdu'l-Bahá states that it would be permissible to perform an operation on a living animal for the purposes of research even if the animal were killed thereby, but that the animal must be well anaesthetized and that the utmost care must be exercised that it does not suffer (ibid. no. 995).

Exhortations and Prohibitions

In the Bahá'í teachings there are a number of laws prohibiting various aspects of human behaviour, personal and social, as well as many exhortations that encourage or discourage certain behaviours. A discussion of several relevant to a study of agriculture, food and rural life follows.

Drinking of alcohol and the use of opium, cocaine and marijuana are prohibited (Bahá'u'lláh, *Kitáb-i-Aqdas* 226–7; 238–9):

Currently, some 75 million tonnes of beer and wine are produced worldwide every year, in addition to other forms of alcoholic beverages. Marijuana is considered the most lucrative cash crop grown in the agricultural state of California, the opium poppy is a major crop in several parts of the world, including Burma and Afghanistan, and coca is a major crop in Columbia, Peru and several other nations. Among the benefits of eliminating these socially destructive products would be the release of considerable labour, land and other resources for useful forms of agriculture production.

Although not prohibited, the use of tobacco is discouraged ('Abdu'l-Bahá, *Selections* 147):

Tobacco is another major crop and discontinuing its production would release significant resources for beneficial crops. It is estimated, for example, that 33 million farmers and agricultural workers are involved in tobacco production. In addition to the negative health impacts resulting from tobacco use, importing tobacco results in significant foreign exchange losses for many developing nations. Two-thirds of countries import more tobacco than they export and, of these, ten lost more than US$100 million in foreign exchange. Of the 62 countries that have a positive balance of trade in tobacco, half earned less than US$20 million from exports, whereas three of the most highly developed nations earned more than US$1 billion.

The use of anything unclean and impure is discouraged:

> . . . the Scriptures forbid the eating or the use of any unclean thing. Some of these prohibitions were absolute, and binding upon all . . . But there are other forbidden things which do not cause immediate harm, and the injurious effects of which are only gradually produced: such acts are also repugnant to the Lord, and blameworthy in His sight, and repellent. The absolute unlawfulness of these, however, hath not been expressly set forth in the Text, but their avoidance is necessary to purity, cleanliness, the preservation of health, and freedom from addiction ('Abdu'l-Bahá, *Selections* 147).

While there are no specific texts on this topic, it would seem reasonable to assume that the use of substances such as pesticides would fit into this category if harmful residues were to be left on food. Also relevant to this topic are writings that encourage '. . . in every aspect of life, purity and holiness, cleanliness and refinement . . . Even in the physical realm, cleanliness will after conduce to spirituality . . . ('Abdu'l-Bahá, *Selections* 146–7).

Simple, 'natural' diets are recommended:

There are few if any laws in the Bahá'í Faith about diet. In general, however, there appears to be encouragement for a relatively simple diet ('Abdu'l-Bahá, *Selections* 152–6).

Birth control is permitted for family planning:

Reason indicates that at some point limiting the expansion of the human population will be a necessity, given it is generally recognized that there are limits to both the availability of various resources – including agricultural resources – to support human population and the capacity of the planet to absorb wastes. While there is nothing explicit in the Bahá'í scriptures on this topic, Shoghi Effendi and the Universal House of Justice have made several pertinent comments (see *Lights* nos. 1160–70). The Bahá'í teachings definitely oppose forms of birth control that preclude a couple from bearing any children at all, such as sterilization, since raising children is the primary purpose of marriage. However, it is entirely up to a couple to decide how many children to have. This would suggest that compliance with the goal of zero population growth, which is slightly more than two children per couple on average, would not contravene Bahá'í principles.

The Right of God does not apply to agricultural equipment:

> Ḥuqúq is not payable on agricultural tools and equipment, and on animals used in ploughing the land, to the extent that these are necessary ('Abdu'l-Bahá, in *Ḥuqúqu'lláh* no. 68).

The provisions for dowries is revised:

In much of the rural world, dowries are a common feature of the institution of marriage, although paid in various ways. Sometimes the payments are quite considerable and in some cases can deepen the poverty of rural families. The provisions of the Kitáb-i-Aqdas (207–9) remove all variants: dowries are paid to the bride and their size is not onerous; they are also smaller for rural areas than cities.

Transformation

Bahá'í discourse is ultimately concerned with the processes of transformation.

These processes are of particular significance to our theme given both the intractable nature of the problems inherent in the food and agriculture system and the seeming inability of most governments to make substantive progress in dealing with them. This is particularly frustrating since there is near universal agreement, through the World Food Summit's consultative process, on the measures necessary to solve these problems. The inability to muster the will to change has been identified by the FAO as the key factor inhibiting substantive progress in achieving food security (FAO 'New Challenges' no. 58).

But how can the will to change be mustered? How will the volition required to enact the necessary measures be formed? And how will we initiate and sustain action to implement the profound changes required to create a just, equitable and sustainable food system?

According to the FAO Committee on World Food Security, looking at food and agricultural issues 'from an ethical and human rights standpoint may contribute to the development of a consensus on how they can be better addressed in the common interest of humanity . . .' (FAO 'New Challenges' no. 58). In other words, consultation on these issues must be raised to the level of moral and spiritual principle. On this topic, the Universal House of Justice states: 'The essential merit of spiritual principle is that it not only presents a perspective which harmonizes with that which is immanent in human nature, it also induces an attitude, a dynamic, a will, an aspiration, which facilitate the discovery and implementation of practical measures' (Universal House of Justice, *Promise* no. 37). From a religious viewpoint, spiritual principles are God-given truths and adherence to them attracts the power of divine assistance.

It is impossible to separate the Bahá'í perspective on social transformation from the mystical aspects of faith. 'The Bahá'í Faith, like all other Divine Religions,' said Shoghi Effendi, 'is . . . fundamentally mystic in character. Its chief goal is the development of the individual and society, through the acquisition of spiritual virtues and powers' (Shoghi Effendi, *Directives* 86). These virtues and powers are channelled through the ancient covenant between God and humankind.

The centrality of the covenant and its power to transform the world is forcefully stated in the Bahá'í writings. The term 'covenant' refers to a binding agreement between God and humanity, whereby God provides certain blessings in return for certain behaviours. God provides all the physical requirements for life and – through the educators of humankind, the prophets and founders of religion – the impetus for our material and spiritual development. The obligations of humanity in this covenant are twofold: to recognize the divine educator and to follow his laws and ordinances. Following these obligations releases an immense transformative power to the world, the only power capable of bringing about a global transformation.

History attests to the transforming power of religion. The philosopher Karl Jaspers points, for example, to the 'Axial age' in the middle of the first millennium BCE, when the appearance of Buddha, Zoroaster, the Hebrew prophets, the Greek philosophers and the Chinese sages resulted in the worldwide emergence of moral conscience. An even more dramatic social transformation occurred during and immediately following the life of Muhammad (Fromkin, *Way* 45–64).

This transformative power is evident in the world today, according to 'Abdu'l-Bahá:

> Know this for a certainty that today, the penetrative power in the arteries of the world of humanity is the power of the Covenant. The body of the world will not be moved through any power except through the power of the Covenant. There is no other power like unto this. This Spirit of the Covenant is the real Centre of love and is reflecting its rays to all parts of the globe, which are resuscitating and regenerating man and illuminating the path to the Divine Kingdom ('Abdu'l-Bahá, in *Power* 1).

Notice that 'Abdu'l-Bahá identifies the influence of the covenant on both humanity and the world as a whole. In another passage, he states:

> Today the pulsating power in the arteries of the body of the world is the spirit of the Covenant – the spirit which is the cause of life. Whosoever is vivified with this spirit, the freshness and beauty of life become manifest in him, he is baptized with the Holy Spirit, he is born again, is freed from oppression and tyranny, from heedlessness and harshness which deaden the spirit, and attains to everlasting life ('Abdu'l-Bahá, in *Compilation*, vol. 1, 127).

The covenant is the one force capable of organizing human society for the regeneration of the world. '. . . the pivot of the oneness of mankind is nothing else but the power of the Covenant,' says 'Abdu'l-Bahá. '. . . The power of the Covenant is as the heat of the sun which quickeneth and promoteth the development of all created things on earth. The light of the Covenant, in like manner, is the educator of the minds, the spirits, the hearts and souls of men' (ibid. 128). The covenant will unify humanity in its endeavours to carry forward an ever-advancing civilization: 'No power can eliminate misunderstandings except that of the Covenant. The power of the Covenant is all-embracing, and resolveth all difficulties . . .' (ibid.).

The covenant is articulated progressively by the prophets and founders of religions through their sacred scriptures; the Revelation of Bahá'u'lláh is its most recent expression, Bahá'u'lláh is its current agent and his articulation of its provisions are specifically tailored to the requirements of our time.

Practically speaking, how can the covenant of Bahá'u'lláh transform the world and achieve the goal of a just, equitable and sustainable food system? As the above quotations attest, the power of the covenant is operating in the world today through the Revelation of Bahá'u'lláh, tearing down the moribund customs and institutions of an old order and preparing the way for a new one. The evidence of transformation is clear, according to the Universal House of Justice:

> Indeed, no domain of life remains unaffected. In the burgeoning energy, the magnified

perspectives, the heightened global consciousness; in the social and political turbulence, the fall of kingdoms, the emancipation of nations, the intermixture of cultures, the clamour for development; in the agitation over the extremes of wealth and poverty, the acute concern over the abuse of the environment, the leap of consciousness regarding the rights of women; in the growing tendency towards ecumenism, the increasing call for a new world order; in the astounding advances in the realms of science, technology, literature and the arts – in all this tumult, with its paradoxical manifestations of chaos and order, integration and disintegration, are the signs of His power as World Reformer, the proof of His claim as Divine Physician, the truth of His Word as the All-Knowing Counsellor (Tribute by the Universal House of Justice to Bahá'u'lláh on the Centenary of His Passing, May 1992 Commemoration at Bahjí of the Ascension of Bahá'u'lláh).

By recognizing Bahá'u'lláh as the source of the transformation occurring in the world and the centre of the ancient covenant of God in this age and committing itself wholeheartedly to the laws and ordinances he has provided, humanity will attract the power of divine assistance, the power that created, sustains and educates all things. Once recognized, the covenant serves to 'direct and canalize' the forces released by the Revelation of Bahá'u'lláh (Shoghi Effendi, *God Passes By* 237). It is not merely a spiritual concept; the laws, ordinances and institutions it inaugurates are destined to be 'a pattern for future society, a supreme instrument for the establishment of the Most Great Peace, and the one agency for the unification of the world, and the proclamation of the reign of righteousness and justice upon the earth' (Shoghi Effendi, *World Order* 19).

Conclusion

In summary, agricultural development is a 'fundamental principle' for the advancement of humankind. For this reason we are instructed to give 'special regard' to agricultural development, more specifically to a form of development shaped by and serving the cause of justice, equity and sustainability. The task of building a new social and economic order is associated with the redesign of agriculture to ensure economic viability for producers and the equitable development of nations.

We are asked to elevate our agricultural work to a form of worship and to conduct our lives individually and collectively in such fashion as to ensure a sustainable society by balancing technical and spiritual development. We are given a vision of our relatedness to the earth but called to an inspired station where we are empowered to take full responsibility in carrying forward an ever-advancing civilization. In this view, agriculture is elevated from mere commerce to a spiritual practice.

The task of agricultural development cannot be carried out in isolation from the process of spiritual development recognizing, as 'Abdu'l-Bahá said, that 'When the love of God is established, everything else will be realized' ('Abdu'l-Bahá, *Promulgation* 239).

Great disparities entrench hunger and poverty, rural communities are stagnant and destabilized and the agricultural environment is threatened but the transformative power of the divine covenant is available to help humanity transform the world. In this regard, 'Abdu'l-Bahá offered these words of hope:

> . . . thanks to the unfailing grace of God, the loving-kindness of His favoured ones, the unrivalled endeavours of wise and capable souls, and the thoughts and ideas of the peerless leaders of this age, nothing whatsoever can be regarded as unattainable ('Abdu'l-Bahá, *Secret* 66).

Works Cited

'Abdu'l-Bahá. *Foundations of World Unity*. Wilmette, IL: Bahá'í Publishing Trust, 1945.
— *Paris Talks*. London: Bahá'í Publishing Trust, 1967.
— *The Promulgation of Universal Peace*. Wilmette, IL: Bahá'í Publishing Trust, 1982.
— *The Secret of Divine Civilization*. Wilmette, IL: Bahá'í Publishing Trust, 1990.
— *Selections from the Writings of 'Abdu'l-Bahá*. Haifa: Bahá'í World Centre, 1978.
— *Some Answered Questions*. Wilmette, IL: Bahá'í Publishing Trust, 1981.
— *Tablet to August Forel*. Wilmette: Bahá'í Publishing Trust, 1978.
'Abdu'l-Bahá in London. London: Bahá'í Publishing Trust, 1987.
Agriculture and Rural Life: Additional Extracts. Comp. The Research Department of the Universal House of Justice, 1 May 1997.
Bahá'í Education. Compilation of the Research Department of the Universal House of Justice. Haifa: Bahá'í World Centre. Revised July 1990.
Bahá'í International Community. *The Prosperity of Humankind*. London: Bahá'í Publishing Trust, 1995.
— *Valuing Spirituality in Development: Initial Considerations Regarding the Creation of Spiritually Based Indicators for Development*. London: Bahá'í Publishing Trust, 1998. A concept paper presented to the 'World Faiths and Development Dialogue' hosted by the President of the World Bank and the Archbishop of Canterbury at Lambeth Palace, London, 18–19 February 1998.
Bahá'í Prayers: A Selection of Prayers revealed by Bahá'u'lláh, the Báb and 'Abdu'l-Bahá. Wilmette, IL: Bahá'í Publishing Trust, 2002.
The Bahá'í World, vols. 1–12, 1925–54. rpt. Wilmette, IL: Bahá'í Publishing Trust, 1980.
Bahá'í World Faith. Wilmette, IL: Bahá'í Publishing Trust, 2nd edn. 1976.
Bahá'u'lláh. *Epistle to the Son of the Wolf*. Wilmette, IL: Bahá'í Publishing Trust, 1988.
— *Gleanings from the Writings of Bahá'u'lláh*. Wilmette, IL: Bahá'í Publishing Trust, 1983.
— *The Hidden Words*. Wilmette, IL: Bahá'í Publishing Trust, 1990.
— *The Kitáb-i-Aqdas*. Haifa: Bahá'í World Centre, 1992.
— *Kitáb-i-Íqán*. Wilmette, IL: Bahá'í Publishing Trust, 1989.

— *The Seven Valleys and the Four Valleys.* Wilmette, IL: Bahá'í Publishing Trust, 1991.

— *Tablets of Bahá'u'lláh.* Wilmette, IL: Bahá'í Publishing Trust, 1988.

Balyuzi, H. M. *'Abdu'l-Bahá: The Centre of the Covenant of Bahá'u'lláh.* Oxford: George Ronald, 2nd edn. with minor corr. 1987.

Bottelier, Pieter. 'Corruption and Development: Remarks for the International Symposium on the Prevention and Control of Financial Fraud.' The World Bank, Beijing, 19 October 1998.

Calkins, Peter and Benoit Girard. 'The Bahá'í Village Granary: Spiritual Underpinnings and Applications to North America'. *Journal of Bahá'í Studies,* vol. 8, no. 3 (1998), pp. 1–17.

Cauvin, Jacques. *The Birth of the Gods and the Origins of Agriculture.* Trans. Trevor Watkins. Cambridge: Cambridge University Press, 2000.

The Compilation of Compilations. Prepared by the Universal House of Justice 1963– 1990. 2 vols. [Mona Vale NSW]: Bahá'í Publications Australia, 1991.

Conservation of the Earth's Resources. Compilation of the Research Department of the Universal House of Justice. London: Bahá'í Publishing Trust, 1990.

Consultation: A Compilation of Extracts from the Bahá'í Writings. Compiled by the Research Department of the Universal House of Justice. London: Bahá'í Publishing Trust, rev. edn. 1990.

Directives from the Guardian. Compiled by Gertrude Garrida. New Delhi: Bahá'í Publishing Trust, 1973.

Duncan, Colin A. M. *The Centrality of Agriculture, Between Humankind and the Rest of Nature.* Montreal: McGill-Queen's University Press, 1996.

Economics, Agriculture and Related Subjects. Compilation of the Research Department of the Universal House of Justice, 1 May 1997.

Eliade, Mircea (ed.). 'Agriculture'. *The Encyclopedia of Religion,* vol. 1. New York: Macmillan Publishing Co., 1987.

Esslemont, J.E. *Bahá'u'lláh and the New Era.* London: Bahá'í Publishing Trust, 1974.

Extracts from the Bahá'í Writings on the Subject of Agriculture and Related Subjects. Compilation of the Research Department of the Universal House of Justice, rev. edn. 12 November 2001.

FAO (Food and Agriculture Organization of the United Nations). 'Fostering the Political Will to Fight Hunger'. Committee on World Food Security, Twenty-seventh Session, Rome, 28 May –1 June 2001.

— 'New Challenges to the Achievements of the World Food Summit Goals'. Committee on World Food Security, Twenty-seventh Session, Rome, 28 May –1 June 2001.

Fromkin, David. *The Way of the World, From the Dawn of Civilizations to the Eve of the Twenty-first Century.* New York: Alfred A. Knopf, 1999.

Fukuoka, Masanobu. *One Straw Revolution.* Emmaus, PA: Rodale Press, 1978.

Hobsbawm, Eric. *On History.* London: Abacus, 1998.

Homer-Dixon, Thomas. *The Ingenuity Gap.* Toronto: Knopf Canada, 2000.

Ḥuqúqu'lláh. Compiled by the Research Department of the Universal House of Justice. Oakham: Bahá'í Publishing Trust, rev. edn. 1989.

Lights of Guidance: A Bahá'í Reference File. Compiled by Helen Hornby. New Delhi:

Bahá'í Publishing Trust, 2nd edn. 1988.

Nakhjavani, Bahíyyih. *Response*. Oxford: George Ronald, 1981.

The Power of the Covenant. Thornhill, ON: National Spiritual Assembly of the Bahá'ís of Canada, Part 1, 'Bahá'u'lláh's Covenant with Mankind', 1976.

Shoghi Effendi. *The Advent of Divine Justice*. Wilmette, IL: Bahá'í Publishing Trust, 1990.

— *God Passes By*. Wilmette, IL: Bahá'í Publishing Trust, rev. edn. 1995.

— Letter written on behalf of Shoghi Effendi to an individual, 20 September 1929, in a memorandum from the Research Department to the Universal House of Justice entitled 'Science and Religion', 13 August 1997.

— *The World Order of Bahá'u'lláh*. Wilmette, IL: Bahá'í Publishing Trust, 1991.

Taherzadeh, Adib. *The Covenant of Bahá'u'lláh*. Oxford: George Ronald, 1992.

Thomas, Hugh. *An Unfinished History of the World*. London: Papermac, 1995.

Trustworthiness. A Compilation of Extracts from the Bahá'í Writings. Compiled by the Research Department of the Universal House of Justice. London: Bahá'í Publishing Trust, 1987.

Universal House of Justice. Letter to the Bahá'ís of the World, 20 October 1983.

— Letter written on behalf of the Universal House of Justice, 8 May 1984.

— *The Promise of World Peace*. London: Bahá'í Publishing Trust, 1985.

— Tribute by the Universal House of Justice to Bahá'u'lláh on the Centenary of His Passing, May 1992.

Wood, Stanley, et. al. *Pilot Analysis of Global Ecosystems: Agroecosystems*. Washington DC: World Resources Institute, 2000.

Wright, Robin. *Non-Zero, The Logic of Human Destiny*. New York: Pantheon Books, 2000.

Paul Hanley is a writer by profession, with a special interest in religion, science, agriculture and environment. His previous book Earthcare: Ecological Agriculture in Saskatchewan *was published in 1980. He has been a newspaper columnist since 1988 and has published more than a thousand articles as a freelance writer. Hanley became a Bahá'í in 1975. A virtual commuter, he lives on a smallholding in rural Saskatchewan where he pursues an interest in lifestyles with a low environmental impact.*

The Involvement of the Central Figures of the Bahá'í Faith in Agriculture

Iraj Poostchi

One of the unique features of the Bahá'í Faith is the keen interest shown by and the involvement of its Central Figures in the life and fortunes of rural people in 19th-century Persia and the Ottoman-controlled territories of the Near East. The interest of the Central Figures – the Báb, Bahá'u'lláh and 'Abdu'l-Bahá – in farming and agriculture, which is well documented in many of their writings, was translated into the actual operation and implementation of routine farm activities and cultural practices. A short survey of the appalling conditions imposed on the peasantry of Persia and the Ottoman Empire reveals some of the misfortunes the food producers of the time endured. Fully aware of and even enduring some of these hardships, the Central Figures of the Bahá'í Faith assigned a deservedly significant station to farmers and food producers. Indeed, farmers are destined to play a significant role in the world order outlined by Bahá'u'lláh.

Introduction

The central role that agriculture and farming play in human history is only too obvious. However, despite tremendous technological advances in the science of crop and animal production, current approaches to agriculture and farming are neither sustainable nor ecologically sound. In the past three decades many research findings have shown that studying agriculture as an isolated entity, ignoring its holistic nature, results in environmentally hazardous, ecologically damaging and economically unsustainable practices (Poostchi, *Rural Development*).

Agriculture is the central preoccupation, driving force and lifeline of village and rural communities all over the world, whether in the so-called developed or undeveloped parts of the globe. Where agriculture and farming are studied and practised in isolation, without involving other sectors of rural life, such as its social, economic, cultural and religious aspects or its customs and traditions, the farming community begins a gradual process of disintegration. Unfortunately, this process is often both gradual and hardly visible.

Sadly, this has been the main approach in the past 50 years and today we are facing its dire consequences. In the rich and industrial nations of the world these consequences are frequently ameliorated by the payment each year of enormous farm subsidies which, in one form or another, amount to some US$250 billion (Poostchi, *Food Security, Agriculture*). In the less economically fortunate parts of the world, the disintegration of farming communities, slow or sometimes rapid, is followed by often irreversible environmental damage (Poostchi, *Agriculture*).

Agriculture, farming and rural development are inseparable parts of a great entity which should not be subject to fragmentation. This idea is a hallmark of an enlightened approach to improving the life of millions of subsistence farmers, landless poor and the rural destitute. Ironically, it also applies in developed countries.

It is in this context that the personal involvement and special roles played by the Central Figures of the Bahá'í Faith, in designating a unique position for the farmer in society and laying down the foundation for a sound agricultural system for the future, will be considered.

Rural Conditions in 19th-century Persia

The Village

One cannot adequately appreciate the strong support of the Central Figures for agriculture, farmers and rural people without reviewing the conditions of peasants and serfs in 19th-century Persia and the Ottoman Empire, the time and places in which they lived (see Poostchi, *Agriculture*).

Agricultural and farming conditions in Persia, where both the Báb and Bahá'u'lláh undertook their ministries, had remained much the same for centuries (Vali, *Character*). Throughout the short life of the Báb and the longer life of Bahá'u'lláh they were in constant contact with farmers, peasants, serfs, sharecroppers, landlords and owners of large estates, as well as with the tribesmen, tribal chiefs and communities that provided the bulk of the meat and dairy products for the nation.

For almost three thousand years the village had been the base unit and backbone for the social, political, cultural, religious and economic life into which the farming community and rural population of Persia was organized. Even today, at the threshold of the 21st century, the village in Iran has maintained its critical role in the organizational structure of the farm, artisan, trade and business sectors of the nation.

The socioeconomic structure of the village centred on the land-owning nobility whose large estates were supported almost entirely by the rents and profits from the farmland on which the peasants and sharecroppers were the most important agents of production and wealth creation. Indeed, the nobility, officialdom and the army of the time could not have survived had it not been for the strenuous work of the Persian peasantry (ibid.).

Agricultural production involved both crops and animal products. These met the increasing demand for food in urban areas. Crop production was the mainstay of large estates and land holdings operated by a system of bailiffs *(mobashire)* appointed by an (often) absentee landlord to administer and supervise his holdings. But the vital task of growing crops, such as ploughing, preparing the seedbed, sowing, care and management of the crops, irrigation, cleaning of the irrigation ditches and harvest was left squarely on the shoulders of peasants, serfs, sharecroppers and smallholders (peasants with small parcels of land). Of these, peasants and sharecroppers did the most and received the least in return (Denman, *King's Vista*; Lambton, *Landlords and Peasants*; Nyrop, *Iran*).

Living Conditions of the Rural Poor

The smallholder- or peasant-owned properties were for the most part small plots, perhaps a half to one hectare (almost one to 2.5 acres), owned and operated by farmers and their families, who often employed landless villagers and relatives during the periods of peak farm activity, such as planting and harvest times. Most of these owner-operated holdings were on isolated patches of land in mountain valleys and foothills (Denman, *King's Vista*; Lambton, *Landlords and Peasants*; Nyrop, *Iran*).

When it came to reaping the fruits of their labour, the peasants and sharecroppers did not fare well. The harvested crops were divided according to the number and type of inputs contributed by the landlord and the peasant. These inputs were seed, land, water, the labour of the peasants or sharecroppers, and the draught animals used to plough the land and thresh the small grains. Each of these inputs would receive 20 per cent of the harvested crop. The extent to which the sharecroppers supplied seed, draught animals and labour varied in different parts of the country.

Under this system of production, a peasant's share, on average, ranged from about one-fifth to as high as one half and even three-fifths. But too often they were short-changed. For example, before the division of the harvest and the allocation of each party's share, the landlord excluded the seed required for the next sowing. Even worse, if the landlord had provided the seed beforehand he would charge an interest of 50 per cent on his loan (Curzon, *Persia* vol. 1).

Peasants seldom had a written lease or contract or, for that matter, any security of tenure. The landlord, his agent or lessee could discharge them at will. However, tradition and custom often worked against such decisions or practices. Furthermore, peasants were also responsible for the unpaid general maintenance of the estate, including clearing and cleaning main irrigation ditches or *qanats* (underground aquifers), building and road repairs, and work in the landlord's private orchard or garden.

Several additional factors contributed to low incomes. Sharecroppers were often forced, through absolute necessity, to sell a part of their share of the crop at the time of the harvest, when prices were generally low. Thus they were constantly plagued by debt. It was hard for them to get loans or advances in the open market. If the landlord ever gave a loan or advance, it was given against the security of the next crop. If there was a severe drought and a poor harvest, the peasants were literally ruined. Some landlords could even force peasants to sell their shares at arbitrary fixed prices on the threat of withholding water or other necessities during the ensuing season.

Their financial misfortunes did not stop at these payments. A substantial portion of the peasants' share of the harvest was taken away immediately after the harvest to pay for past debts and the interest they carried, resulting in their perpetual indebtedness. Meanwhile, the interest charged on the already heavy and accumulated debt became progressively larger until the peasant or sharecropper was hopelessly ruined (Vali, *Character*).

Often, when an advance was provided by the landlord, it was given as a consumption loan in-kind during the winter months when grain prices were high, whereas the repayment was demanded at harvest either in cash or in equivalent grain, when prices were low. Consequently, the amount of grain required to pay off the debt was far greater than the amount originally received. In reality, once forced through sheer poverty to take an advance, a peasant was likely to be left in a permanent state of poverty (ibid.).

Though slightly better off, smallholders, peasant owner-operators and small farmers did little better. Often, the land they cultivated consisted of small lots of infertile soils, both shallow and stony. Consequently their crops yielded poorly.

The landless village inhabitants and farm labourers who owned no land and had no right whatsoever to use land as the sharecroppers or peasants did, had no other means of livelihood than their labour. They could be dismissed at will no matter how menial their job. They could only survive by working for the relatively better off peasants or the landlord as seasonal agricultural workers, weeding, threshing wheat and barley, grazing sheep, goats and cattle, planting rice seedlings, picking cotton, or digging ditches (ibid.).

Accounts of Rural Life

The peasant's status was so low that a classical Persian text, *The Confessions of Ghazan Khan, The Mongul*, stated, 'the earth and the very dust of the ground mean more to the lords than did the cultivators who toiled upon it . . . the surface of the truckways, says the Confessions, does not receive such beatings as do the serfs' (quoted in Lambton, *Landlords and Peasants*).

In another account the misfortunes of the 19th-century Persian peasantry are clearly described:

> One sees that the Persian peasant is poor, illiterate, impassive and stolid, but in appearance he is robust in strength, well built; he is like an ox. He usually has some cloth on his back, but seldom a beggar. With no help and knowledge, yet with the grossest ignorance, he combines a rude skill and strenuous work in turning into account the scanty resources of nature. Indeed, he is patient and persevering. The most miserable time for him is when the water supply breaks down, or, when following a long drought famine sets in, then hungry, starved, unfed and uncared for, the Persian peasantry die off like flies (Curzon, *Persia* vol. 1).

During the 19th century Persia was stricken by plague and devastated by famines. An account narrates that

> Plagues . . . fell upon them with a fury that none could escape. That scourge scattered devastation wherever it spread. Prince and peasant alike felt its sting and bowed to its yoke. It held the populace in its grip, and refused to relax its hold upon them. As malignant as the fever which decimated the province of Gílán, these sudden afflictions continued to lay waste the land (Shoghi Effendi, *God Passes By* 85).

The fever was probably a widespread outbreak of malaria. The peasants were constantly beset by this disease, or by tuberculosis, as well as by others commonly caused by poor nutrition (Frye, *Iran*).

In another account it is noted that 'Famine added its horrors to the stupendous weight of afflictions under which people were groaning. The gaunt spectacle of starvation stalked abroad amidst them, and the prospect of a slow and painful death haunted their vision . . .' (Shoghi Effendi, *God Passes By* 85).

A historically significant and severe famine during the time of Bahá'u'lláh swept Persia after the martyrdom of Badí'. It is related that Mullá 'Alí-Akbar begged Bahá'u'lláh for the famine to come to an end (Taherzadeh, *Revelation*, vol. 3, 200–1).

The Burden of Taxes and Rents

Whereas the rich enjoyed all privileges while living on the back of the peasants, these stricken subjects of the monarchy also had a number of taxes imposed upon them by both the central government and provincial rulers. These included a poll tax, livestock taxes, taxes on weaving, land taxes and charges for the use of irrigation water.

Peasants and sharecroppers also had to pay fixed rents. These could be paid in-kind, in money or both. The level of rent was relatively high, usually amounting to half if not two-thirds of the total produce (Vali, *Character*). Rent almost entirely absorbed the peasant's or sharecropper's surplus, over and above the necessary toil and the costs of production. As a consequence they were often underfed and undernourished, along with their families and draught animals. They had to cope with this gradual worsening of the condition of their health simply to maintain their rights to the use of land (ibid.). Leavened wheat bread constituted their staple food (English, *Village*).

Conditions in the Arab States

The Central Figures of the Faith also resided in the Arab states of the Ottoman Empire – Iraq, Jordan, Syria and Palestine. The agricultural systems of this region were not greatly different from that of neighbouring Persia, as far as peasants and sharecroppers were concerned. Agriculture and farming were the main occupation of a large majority of the population of both Turkey and the Arab states and both were in a state of stagnation.

The problems besetting the peasantry were somewhat different here. For example, the absence of adequately designed, maintained and operated drainage systems made the rural people victims of alternate floods and droughts. Many peasants and sharecroppers could not dispose of their meagre surplus because markets were often inaccessible. Therefore production of crops and animal products was limited to the needs of the family (Earle, *Great Powers* 12).

Large estates existing side by side with a sharecropper peasantry formed the backbone of the agricultural and food production systems. In common with their counterparts in Persia, the Arab peasantry was badly exposed to rapacious, profiteering landlords. It is also important to remember that during this period the basic freehold ownership of agricultural land was vested in the sultan. But the right or privilege to cultivate the land was leased to cultivator units called *ciflik*. This was defined as the amount or the area of land that could be ploughed by a pair (*cift*) of oxen, normally averaging about 60 to 150 *donums* (one *donum* is about 940 square metres or almost one-quarter of an acre) (Shaw, *History* 150; Yapp, *Near East*).

Sharecropping was the system used as the mainstay of agricultural production. As in Persia, the harvest was divided between the landlord and the tenant/sharecropper/peasant in proportion to each party's contribution of inputs.

In a large part of the Ottoman Empire the village community was the basic economic unit and the village lands were held in common usage and periodically redistributed among peasants.

Much like their overtly exploited Persian counterparts, the smallholders and peasants under Ottoman rule had also to pay taxes on their crops and animals. The right of collecting taxes was considered to be one of the most basic attributes of sovereignty. Indeed, the ruling class of the empire was created and maintained by the sultan for the exercise of this attribute (Shaw, *History* 150). The right to collect the state's tax share of the produce was sold to the highest bidder. The only way the peasants could avoid paying the tax was to serve in the Imperial Army for at least five years.

Taxes included the tithe (one-tenth), which had its origin and authorization in Islamic law (Shari'ih), and those decreed by the sultan on the basis of his sovereign right to legislate on secular matters (Shaw, *History* 150). Whatever the amount of food, fibre, fruits and vegetables produced, ten per cent had to be set aside for the tithe. There were also taxes on farm animals that varied between 1.5 and 10 per cent (ibid. 99). In addition, a basic household tax was imposed on villages and rural towns in return for the right to cultivate the land or *cift*. In areas where this tax was not imposed, a pasture tax was collected from the Christian cultivators (ibid. 150). In addition, a compulsory tax was collected throughout the region (Yapp, *Near East*).

The Central Figures

The Bahá'í Faith is unique among the world's great religions in that it has given unprecedented importance to farmers. Its Central Figures understood the grinding poverty of rural people. They had a keen interest in and a heartfelt appreciation for the toils of the men, women and children who, in the unrelenting heat of summer and the paralyzing cold of winter, tilled the land and produced crops and animal products to feed others (Poostchi, *Agriculture*).

It is of great historic significance for the Bahá'í Faith that in the early days of the Bábí dispensation a number of agricultural villages and towns played such prominent and distinguished roles in its development. Hundreds of peasants, farmers and orchard-men laid down their lives for the establishment and consolidation of the Báb's nascent Faith. In later years the Bahá'í Faith expanded greatly among peasants, farmers and rural communities. In some villages the majority of the population accepted the Faith.

From 1844 onwards, many farms, fields, orchards, woodlands and tree plantations were destroyed and levelled by mobs incited against the Bábís and Bahá'ís. Their livestock was herded away, personal properties looted, and harvests and grain stores pillaged or burnt to ashes. Even today, in the cradle of the Faith, many Bahá'í farms have been looted and the families forced to abandon their land for fear of their lives. Their heroic deeds and sacrifices bear witness to the involvement of the Central Figures in their lives.

The Báb

Living in Iran all his life, until his martyrdom in 1850, the Báb was fully aware of the plight of the peasants and the landless of his time. During his travels in the southern province of Fars, he met many rural people both before and after he declared his prophetic mission as the founder of the Bábí dispensation and forerunner of Bahá'u'lláh. Later, in his journeys from the city of Shiraz to the fortress of Mákú in the northwest province of Ádhirbáyján, he spent many days and nights in villages and rural towns, meeting people from the agricultural classes who came from far and near to hear his message of a new day and also to be blessed by him. In his meetings with these people he was made aware of their wretched conditions, of the crop failures and the constant anxiety, uncertainty, hunger and disease.

The Báb's family and close relatives owned estates both around his birthplace Shiraz and in the environs of the city of Yazd, a town located on the margins of the central desert of Iran. Some years before proclaiming his divine mission, the Báb spent many hours of his youth in the fields situated on the northern fringes of his birthplace.

In his writings he strongly recommends that the major elements of agricultural production, such as irrigation water, land, energy, etc., should be freely put at the disposal of food producers, cultivators and the public. To qualify this statement he added that if labour were involved in supplying these elements of production, then only a fair 'carriage', 'porterage' or compensation was to be charged, such as could be easily paid (Merchant, *Bahá'í Faith*).

Bahá'u'lláh
IN PERSIA

Bahá'u'lláh, the founder of the Bahá'í Faith, spent some 36 years in Persia, sometimes actively engaged in the administration, management and even routine operation of his father's estates on the outskirts of Tehran and in the village of Tákúr in the district of Núr, in the province of Mázindarán. This province, located on the Caspian Sea, has a subtropical climate.

Bahá'u'lláh grew up amidst beautiful scenery and land unmatched in its agricultural potential, as testified by his son, 'Abdu'l-Bahá: 'Persia, herself, moreover, from the standpoint of her temperate climate and natural beauties, her geographical advantages and her rich soil, is blessed to a supreme degree' ('Abdu'l-Bahá, *Secret* 9–10).

Bahá'u'lláh was much enamoured by the beauty of nature, the lush farmland of the Caspian's slopes and the magnificent wooded mountains surrounding his family's country estate. In his youth he spent much of the spring and summer in the open country.

In the early years of his life Bahá'u'lláh had firsthand experience of the various factors involved in farming systems and the agrarian structures of the time, the routine farm operations, the extremely demanding physical work and the living conditions of the villagers.

Before his exile to Iraq Bahá'u'lláh spent many summers at Tákur and in the neighbouring villages. Growing rice and raising cattle and sheep were, and still are, important agricultural activities in Núr. In the southern part of the district the foothills rise above the Caspian lowlands into the mountain villages where the weather is cool and fine. Here, nomads and villagers are primarily dependent on livestock, as they were in Bahá'u'lláh's time. The animals are driven up to the mountain pastures in summer (Curzon, *Persia* vols. 1 and 2).

Bahá'u'lláh visited the district of Núr in 1844, the year 1260 AH, a year of specific interest to Islamic theologians (Nabíl, *Dawn-Breakers* 112). During his visit 'peasants . . . flocked to the residence of Bahá'u'lláh' (ibid. 116). During this trip he went to the village of Sa'ádat-Ábád, not far from his own land (ibid. 116–17). He would often talk to peasants and sharecroppers in the course of his riding excursions into the country.

While Bahá'u'lláh was still a youth in his mid-twenties, his father, Mírzá Buzurg, the Vazír-i-Núrí, had acquired two-thirds of the village of Qúch-Ḥiṣár in the vicinity of Tehran. The village was renowned for its charm, beauty and abundance of water. Bahá'u'lláh spent many days there in administering and actively operating its cropping and food production programmes. This was fulltime work and also part of his life and ministry among rural people.

Mírzá Buzurg had a large family to support and soon ran into financial difficulties. In the management of the estate, Bahá'u'lláh witnessed his father's farming problems and relentless battle against impoverishment. In the late 1830s this village proved an invaluable security against borrowing money for day to day expenses and it was mortgaged several times (Balyuzi, *Eminent* 339–40; Poostchi, *Agriculture*).

In 1839 Mírzá Buzurg passed away under great financial strain and from the weight of his predicament. The management and operation of Qúch-Ḥiṣár then fell to Bahá'u'lláh, who had to negotiate loans, arrange for new mortgages and pay his father's debts (ibid. 342).

Equally significant was Bahá'u'lláh's work in administering and operating his family's estate in the village of Tákur, including the allocation of land and irrigation water to peasants and sharecroppers, as well as animal husbandry. Unfortunately, a natural disaster struck this village. Indeed, 'the first loss he suffered was occasioned by a great flood which, running in the mountains of Mázindarán, swept with great violence over the village of Tákur, and utterly destroyed half the mansion of the

Vazír, situated above the fortress of that village' (Nabíl, *Dawn-Breakers* 109).

A number of relevant facts about the life of Bahá'u'lláh were recorded in interviews with his family by Lady Blomfield and published in her book *The Chosen Highway*. We learn, for example, that although Bahá'u'lláh came from a wealthy and prominent family that owned large estates, he did not exploit the peasants under his care as was common at the time. 'Even in the early years of their married life,' reports Bahá'u'lláh's daughter, Bahíyyih Khánum,

> they, my father and mother, took part as little as possible in State functions, social ceremonies, and the luxurious habits of ordinary highly-placed and wealthy families in the land of Persia; she, and her noble-hearted husband, counted these worldly pleasures meaningless, and preferred rather to occupy themselves in caring for the poor, and for all who were unhappy, or in trouble.
>
> From our doors nobody was ever turned away; the hospitable board was spread for all comers.
>
> . . . the people called my father 'The Father of the Poor', and they spoke of my mother as 'The Mother of Consolation' . . .

Bahíyyih Khánum recounts that in the village of Níavirán, which was Bahá'u'lláh's property, the villagers 'were all and individually cared for by him' (Blomfield, *Chosen Highway* 40)

After his espousal of the cause of the Báb, Bahá'u'lláh was stripped of all his properties and possessions and cast into prison. The family then experienced privation, illness and hunger. Through periods of exile, they were reduced to extreme poverty.

> Ásíyih Khanum, my dear mother, was in delicate health, her strength was diminished by the hardships she had undergone, but she always worked beyond her force.
>
> Sometimes my father himself helped in the cooking, as that hard work was too much for the dainty, refined, gentle lady . . . He gave this help before his sojourn in the wilderness of Sulaymáníyyih, and after his return (ibid. 47).

> The food [of Bahá'u'lláh when in Sulaymáníyyih] was easy to describe – coarse bread, a little cheese was the usual diet . . . (ibid. 54).

THE PERIOD OF EXILE

Bahá'u'lláh's interest in farming and contact with rural people continued after his exile from Persia and the start of his prophetic mission. The remaining 39 years of his life were spent in Iraq, Turkey and the Ottoman Arab states.

Bahá'u'lláh's keen interest in promoting agriculture was so great that even while exiled in Iraq (1853–63) he instructed his followers to cultivate the land, even if they only had one day in which to do it. Thus when the community faced exile from Iraq, even as they were making arrangements for their journey, they continued to cultivate the land and when they finally set out, Bahá'u'lláh instructed them to distribute the produce among the friends.

During his period in Iraq Bahá'u'lláh spent some two years (1854–6) in the mountain of Sar-Galú near the town of Sulaymáníyyih in Kurdistan, on the Persian–Iraqi border. During his seclusion in a most inhospitable mountain terrain, with its freezing cold winters, he came to know the local animal herders, tribesmen, migrating tribal people and peasants (Taherzadeh, *Revelation* vol. 1, 60–1).

Bahá'u'lláh's innate interest in village life and farm work was at a later date shared by his close family. Bahá'u'lláh's faithful half-brother Mírzá Muḥammad-Qulí and his family occupied fertile farmlands in the Jordan Valley near the Sea of Galilee (Lake Kinneret/Tiberias), south of a hamlet called Nuqayb (Balyuzi, *'Abdu'l-Bahá* 418–19). Other relatives farmed lands near a small settlement called Samras (or Samrih) (Ruhe, *Door* 208).

On one occasion Persian pilgrims came to visit Bahá'u'lláh in 'Akká, then in Palestine. They were served a lunch of meat and vegetables, which also contained potatoes. These pilgrims had never seen or tasted potatoes before. Bahá'u'lláh advised them to take potato tubers to their village of Seysan in the northwest province of Ádhirbáyján in Persia. He told them that potatoes are nutritious and would serve as a good substitute for other staple foods such as wheat or rice in times of poor harvests and famine. Before they left 'Akká, Bahá'u'lláh asked 'Abdu'l-Bahá to fill a cloth sack with potatoes for them to take back. This was both a gift and a symbolic gesture; the potato plant has white flowers and the pilgrims had brought Bahá'u'lláh white, strongly aromatic flowering narcissus plants all the way from the village of Seysan. Today Seysan is a major potato producing area. The farmers, Bahá'ís and non-Bahá'ís alike, produce a 'syrup' from potato starch which is used extensively in making a confectionery.

In *An Early Pilgrimage*, May Maxwell recounts a charming story told by the gardener Abul-Qásim which shows the concern that Bahá'u'lláh showed for nature. He said

> that during one hot summer there had been a pest of locusts and they had consumed most of the foliage in the surrounding country. One day Abul-Qásim saw a thick cloud coming swiftly towards the garden, and in a moment thousands of locusts were covering the tall trees beneath which Bahá'u'lláh so often sat. Abul-Qásim hastened to the house at the end of the garden and coming before his Lord besought Him, saying: 'My Lord, the locusts have come, and are eating away the shade from above Thy blessed head. I beg of Thee to cause them to depart.' The Manifestation smiled, and said: '*The locusts must be fed; let them be.*' Much chagrined, Abul-Qásim returned to the garden and for some time watched the destructive work in silence; but presently, unable to bear it, he ventured to return again to Bahá'u'lláh and humbly entreat Him to send away the locusts. The Blessed Perfection arose and went into the garden and stood beneath the trees covered with the insects. Then He said: '*Abul-Qásim does not want you; God protect you.*' And lifting up the hem of His robe He shook it, and

immediately all the locusts arose in a body and flew away (Maxwell, *Pilgrimage* 33–4).

'Abdu'l-Bahá

Although 'Abdu'l-Bahá was born into a life of wealth and luxury, at an early age 'all the former luxury of the family was at an end . . . Homeless, utterly impoverished, engulfed in trouble, sorrow, and misery, suffering from sheer want and extraordinary privations – such were the conditions under which his childhood's life was spent' (Blomfield, *Chosen Highway* 80–1).

When only eight years of age he accompanied Bahá'u'lláh and the rest of his family into exile in Iraq. However, over the years, he developed a deep-rooted interest in and a wide knowledge of the agrarian structure of the 19th-century Middle East. His contribution of detailed procedures for the development of agriculture and of rural areas is original, unique and immense.

'Abdu'l-Bahá enjoyed farms and liked country folk. In the Holy Land, for example, he often invited a passing Bedouin or a shepherd to come and sit beside him and share his meal (Balyuzi, *'Abdu'l-Bahá* 239). He strongly felt and shared the misfortunes of the farmers, expressing his concern with the finest of sentiments. For example, when a group of Bahá'í farmers from Persia experienced a continued drought, pest attacks and other problems, he supplicated divine assistance as he wrote them, stating: 'O God! Grant Thy favour, and bestow Thy blessing. Vouchsafe Thy grace, and give a portion of Thy bounty. Enable these men to witness during this year the fulfillment of their hopes. Send down Thy heavenly rain, and provide Thy plenteousness and abundance. Thou art the Powerful, the Mighty' ('Abdu'l-Bahá, in *Economics* no. 3).

'Abdu'l-Bahá had access to properties and agricultural land in the Jordan Valley and beyond it at Samrih and 'Adasíyyih, as well as on the shores of the Sea of Galilee, and some of these were cultivated and produced crops.

'Abdu'l-Bahá would stay in the vicinity of Tiberias from time to time and invariably visited the Bahá'í farmers in the area. In summer the heat in Tiberias and the lands that lie below it is intense and onerous. Because of the tense political circumstances of the time and until the return to normal conditions, 'Abdu'l-Bahá had to spend days and weeks in this area. It was during these travels that he collected and purchased wheat from local farmers and shipped it to Haifa. The wheat was for the Bahá'í community. In one his letters to the friends he states 'that much more wheat will be dispatched when camels are available' (Balyuzi, *'Abdu'l-Bahá* 419). These events demonstrate the degree to which 'Abdu'l-Bahá was involved in both the production and distribution of wheat to those badly in need of this commodity. In this connection we see another account of his concerns for securing food supplies:

> . . . soon the task of raising and providing food for the Bahá'í community [in Haifa and 'Akká] and many others in need faced Him. The mismanagement and impositions of the Ottoman overlord were gradually leading to a state of near

famine (ibid. 415).

'Abdu'l-Bahá's foresight in instructing Bahá'í farmers to grow grain during the First World War allowed for the storage of considerable emergency supplies. This enabled him to feed the population of 'Akká during the deprivation of the war years and even to aid the British army in meeting its needs in 1918 (Ruhe, *Door* 209). He received a knighthood from the British government for this service.

Bordering Israel (Palestine) and Syria at the southern base of the Golan Heights is the Jordanian village of 'Adasíyyih, 'its fields stretching westward into the fertile alluvium of the valley, its grazing lands extending eastward up the hill-slopes. Here settled nearly thirty Bahá'í families, originally on land owned by 'Abdu'l-Bahá' (ibid. 208). Indeed, 'Abdu'l-Bahá had given these Bahá'í farmers specific guidance in farming operations and often advised them on their agricultural practices.

Descendants of these Bahá'ís narrate that, for example, 'Abdu'l-Bahá advised their parents who were working on the land to allocate a particular site for planting a specific type of fruit tree. Furthermore, he told them to allow a certain distance (interspace) between trees in all directions.

'Abdu'l-Bahá 'walked the spiritual path with practical feet'. He was closely involved in the care of the Bahá'í and non-Bahá'í community of 'Akká and Haifa in the war years, down to details of diet and farming methods. The prescribed diet was often simple:

> lentils, dried beans, delicious olives and their oil, and sometimes milk, eggs, and even some goat's meat . . .
>
> The strictest economy was the rule, from necessity, there being so many mouths to feed, some of whom, being in terrible distress, had to be cared for and saved from sheer starvation.
>
> 'Abdu'l-Bahá had taught the friends to grow nourishing vegetables, which, with the corn from His village of 'Adasíyyih – where there were marvellous crops – kept many from perishing of hunger (Blomfield, *Chosen Highway* 190).

He was also a cook. For example, at one Naw-Rúz feast at Bahjí, all the friends were invited and 'Abdu'l-Bahá cooked the meal himself (ibid. 193)

During 'Abdu'l-Bahá's historic travels in America, he often spoke about agricultural development. His ongoing interest in this issue was demonstrated in his special visit to an agricultural fair in Salt Lake City, Utah. He toured the fair accompanied by its president and was offered samples of vegetables, fruits and flowers. A number of the fruits and flowers caught his attention and he instructed that seeds be purchased for the holy shrines in Haifa. He took note of farm implements and irrigation equipment and obtained information on methods of use and costs, and praised the progress of agriculture in the United States.

For 'Abdu'l-Bahá, agriculture and the natural world supplied many of the metaphors he used to illustrate the teachings of Bahá'u'lláh. At the fair in Salt Lake City, for example, he told one of the reporters who had come to hear him that 'as I arrived in town I found great bustling and activity. I asked what was the event. I was told the Agricultural Fair was on.' 'Abdu'l-Bahá then said that

> Bahá'u'lláh had also organized an Agricultural Fair in Persia. The difference is that your Agricultural Fair is worldly, but Bahá'u'lláh's Fair is divine. In this Agricultural Fair many dignified persons are gathered and thus their affection is earthly, but in Bahá'u'lláh's Fair are gathered holy souls who irrigate the lands of hearts with eternal life-giving water, and their affection is celestial. This Agricultural Fair is illumined with earthly lights, that Agricultural Fair's illuminations are heavenly . . . As I compared these two Agricultural Fairs I became very happy and prayed that God provide abundant harvests for your cultivation and grant potential for eternal life and spiritual disposition (quoted in Poostchi, *Agriculture* 133).

In a Tablet from 'Abdu'l-Bahá to Mrs Agnes Parsons in Dublin, New Hampshire, he gives an outline and a pattern for a village community. He took the village as his starting point, because, in his own words 'the farmer is the primary factor in the body politic' (Balyuzi, *'Abdu'l-Bahá* 239).

'Abdu'l-Bahá placed great stress on the problems of socioeconomic development and encouraged the Bahá'ís to become active in efforts conducive to prosperity, beginning at the village level. He recommended that the Bahá'ís of Persia establish joint ventures in trade and business, in raising the levels of industrial production and also the expansion and development of agriculture ('Abdu'l-Bahá, *Makátíb* 235). As early as 1890 Bahá'í rural traders, businessmen, orchard owners, farmers and traders tried to set up partnerships, ventures and organizations to implement a number of Bahá'í approaches to agriculture. Thus a series of cooperatives, agribusinesses and agricultural commodity trading companies were formed in some small rural towns and large villages during the lifetime of 'Abdu'l-Bahá which continued to function as late as the mid-1980s. While these were formed to emulate the Bahá'í ideals of agriculture, most of the commodity trading companies had to be dissolved or were discontinued owing to administrative difficulties arising when a new wave of persecution swept the Bahá'í community.

It was understood that prosperity was only acceptable, however, when it conformed to moral precepts. One instance of the application of this principle occurred in the 1880s when the Persian believers and Bahá'í farmers received Tablets from Bahá'u'lláh, and later from 'Abdu'l-Bahá, forbidding them from growing poppy plants for the production of the opium and cannabis (hemp) for hashish. In a letter to a number of believers and Bahá'í farmers of Sarvestan in Fars province, 'Abdu'l-Bahá stated the planting of poppies and production of opium was not allowed except for medicinal purposes (Ishráq Khávarí, *Ganjínih* 435). Because of their high quality, poppies were an extremely good cash crop for the growers and traders in small towns who would sell the opium for use in larger cities and for export to European and North American pharmaceutical companies. The Bahá'í farmers in Iran stopped growing poppy plants and cannabis. Only 40 years later did the government of Iran put a ban on the production of these crops. Similarly, most Bahá'í farmers in the areas where tobacco production was predominant gradually gave up tobacco production in favour of other crops despite the high commercial value of tobacco and the promotional incentives from the state monopoly at the time.

In many of his writings 'Abdu'l-Bahá expressed his concern for the planet's ecological balance. May Maxwell recounts a conversation over dinner in which 'Abdu'l-Bahá said 'we should always be kind and merciful to every creature; that cruelty was sin and that the human race should never injure any of God's creatures, but ought to be always careful to do nothing to diminish or exterminate any order of living thing . . .' (Maxwell, *Pilgrimage* 29).

His appreciation of natural order and beauty is perhaps best exemplified by the efforts he made to restore the eroded slopes of Mount Carmel and to establish extensive gardens at the Bahá'í shrines in Haifa and 'Akká, including the lovely Riḍván garden he planted for his father. 'Abdu'l-Bahá took a direct interest in this work, obtaining land, flowers and other plants for the gardens and even carrying soil in his cloak to add to the gardens. His dedication to these projects was taken up by Shoghi Effendi, his grandson and Guardian of the Bahá'í Faith, who personally designed the extensive gardens in Haifa and around 'Akká and managed their development. Like Bahá'u'lláh and 'Abdu'l-Bahá, Shoghi Effendi also encouraged the agricultural pursuits and conservation efforts of the Bahá'ís around the world.

By 2001 the landscaping initiated by 'Abdu'l-Bahá on Mount Carmel had been brought to fruition by the Universal House of Justice and had become, in the opinion of many, one of the wonders of the world. In a letter dated 4 January 1994, the Universal House of Justice commented that 'The beauty and magnificence of the Gardens and the Terraces now under development are symbolic of the nature of the transformation which is destined to occur both within the hearts of the world's peoples and in the physical environment of the planet.'

Works Cited

'Abdu'l-Bahá. *Makátíb-i-'Abdu'l-Bahá*, vol. 3. Tehran: Mu'assissih-yi Millí-yi Maṭbú'át Amrí (translated from the Persian).

— *The Promulgation of Universal Peace*. Wilmette, IL: Bahá'í Publishing Trust, 1982.

Balyuzi, H. M. *'Abdu'l-Bahá: The Centre of the Covenant of Bahá'u'lláh*. Oxford: George Ronald, 2nd edn. with minor corr. 1987.

— *Eminent Bahá'ís in the Time of Bahá'u'lláh: with some Historical Background*. Oxford: George Ronald, 1985.

Blomfield, Lady [Sara Louise]. *The Chosen Highway*. Wilmette, IL: Bahá'í Publishing Trust, 1967.

Curzon, G.N. *Persia and the Persian Question,* vols. 1 and 2. London: Frank Cass and Co., 1966.

Denman, D.R. *The King's Vista*. Berkhamstead: Geographical Publications, 1973.

Earle, E. M. *Turkey, The Great Powers, and the Baghdad Railway: A Study in Imperialism*. New York: Russell and Russell, 1966.

Economics, Agriculture and Related Subjects. Compilation of the Research Department of the Universal House of Justice, 1 May 1997.

English, P.W. *Village and Settlement in Iran. Settlement and Economy in Kirman Basin*. Madison, WI: The University of Wisconsin Press, 1966.

Frye, R. *Iran: An Economic Profile*. Washington DC: The Middle East Institute, 1962.

Ishráq Khávarí, 'Abdu'l-Ḥamíd. *Ganjínih-yi Ḥudúd va Aḥkám*. New Delhi: Bahá'í Publishing Trust, 1971 (translated from the Persian).

Lambton, A.K.S. *Landlords and Peasants in Persia*. London: Clarendon Press, 1953.

Maxwell, May. *An Early Pilgrimage*. Oxford: George Ronald, 1976.

Merchant, K.K. *Bahá'í Faith Means World Unity*. Calcutta.

Nabíl-i-Aʹẓam. *The Dawn-Breakers: Nabíl's Narrative of the Early Days of the Bahá'í Revelation*. Wilmette, IL: Bahá'í Publishing Trust, 1970.

Nyrop, R.F. *Iran, A Country Study*. Washington DC: The American University, 3rd edn. 1978.

Poostchi, Iraj. *Agriculture Beyond 2000: A Bahá'í Perspective*. Henley-on-Thames: Poostchi Publishing, 1992.

— *Food Security, The Other Side of the Coin*. Worldscape, vol. 1, no. 1. University of Guelph, ON: Center for International Programs, 1987.

— *Rural Development and the Developing Countries: An Introductory Interdisciplinary Approach*. Oshawa: Alger Press, 1986.

Ruhe, David S. *Door of Hope: A Century of the Bahá'í Faith in the Holy Land*. Oxford: George Ronald, 1983.

Shaw, Stanford J. *History of Ottoman Empire and Modern Turkey*, vol. 1. Cambridge: Cambridge University Press, 1976.

Shaw, S. J. and Ezal Kural Shaw. *History of Ottoman Empire and Modern Turkey*, vol. 2. Cambridge: Cambridge University Press, 1977.

Shoghi Effendi. *God Passes By*. Wilmette, IL: Bahá'í Publishing Trust, rev. edn. 1974.

Taherzadeh, Adib. *The Revelation of Bahá'u'lláh*, vol. 1. Oxford: George Ronald, rev. edn. 1975.

— *The Revelation of Bahá'u'lláh*, vol. 3. Oxford: George Ronald, 1983.

— *The Revelation of Bahá'u'lláh*, vol. 4. Oxford: George Ronald, 1987.

The Universal House of Justice. Letter of 4 January 1994.

Vali, A. *The Character of the Organization of Production in Iranian Agriculture 1891–1925*. Bielfield Studies on Sociology of Development, vol. 9. Saff Brucken/Fort Lauderdale: Verlag Breitenbac Publishers, 1980.

Yapp, M.E. *The Making of the Modern Near East*. London: Longman, 1987.

Iraj Poostchi was a professor of agronomy with over 40 years experience in teaching, research and extension in agriculture and rural development in both the developed and developing world. He was the founder and first head of the Department of National (Rural) Development at Shiraz University, director of its Rural Training Centre and the founder and first director of its Agricultural Experimental Station. He is the founder of the International Society for Agriculture and Rural Development (ISARD) and has implemented more than 800 projects, programmes, experiments and field trials in 25 countries. While in Iran, he operated his own farm.

Section 2

Rethinking Food, Agriculture and Rural Development

A Perspective on Food in the Bahá'í Faith

Paul Fieldhouse

All people need food to live but, for a variety of reasons, not any old food will do. Throughout history human groups have invested food and food practices with social and spiritual significance. More than simply a means of survival, food is a vehicle for expressing meanings and values concerning the place of humans in the world, the association between nature and culture, and the relationship between the human and the divine.

This chapter sets out to accomplish three things: firstly to briefly establish the plural nature of food as a biological, cultural and spiritual substance; secondly to illustrate how food plays a part in the thought and practice of major world religions; and thirdly to explore some aspects of food within the Bahá'í teachings, specifically the two themes of food, health and the body and commensality. How does the Bahá'í Faith understand the material and cultural role of food? As a new, world religion, does it attribute to food similar meanings and functions as those found in ancient religions or does it present a quite different case? Thinking about food in this way draws attention to the significance of 'culture' in 'agriculture'.

Food, Biology and (Agri)culture

The imperative of providing sufficient food to meet physiological needs has provided more or less of a challenge to human groups throughout history and it seems that almost anything can or has served as human food. Self-evidently people can only choose from what food is available, which is a complex product of geography, economics, science and politics mediated in many instances through the food industry and advertising. However, no human group eats everything that is on offer; not all possible choices are regarded as being acceptable. Right from the start, children learn what is considered culturally appropriate both in terms of food/non-food and in terms of specific eating contexts. This happens through socialization processes whereby children become acquainted with the norms, values, expectations and customs of the culture they live in – the boundaries of expected or accepted behaviour. Food is often a marker of such cultural boundaries – whether these are regional, national, religious or other. Collective identities are created around food and used to define self and 'other'. 'I am a Hindu – the cow is sacred'; 'I am a Jew; I do not eat pork'; 'They eat dogs; they are not like us'. Food readily lends itself to nationalism, regionalism, ethnocentrism and all sorts of other isms; the 'other' is defined by what s/he does or does not eat and this is invariably judged to be inferior to one's own practice. Food behaviour is thus a guide to both social relationships and to social structure. Social anthropologists have demonstrated the existence of structural rules and patterns that underlie food choice and have presented food as a sort of language – a system of communication, a body of images, a protocol of usages, situations and behaviours (Levi-Strauss, *Raw*), (Douglas, 'Deciphering'), (Barthes, 'Psycho-Sociology'). Patterns of food preparation, distribution and consumption are expressions of status and social distance, of political power and of family bonds. Food choice both reflects and creates social distinctions as seekers after social status emulate the food habits and manners of the admired group in an attempt to accumulate 'cultural capital' (Bourdieu, *Distinction*). Food is extensively used in social intercourse as a means of expressing friendship and respect. The quality and quantity of food offered or shared reflects a common understanding of the closeness of various types of social relationships. Food is also used as a manipulative tool to purchase favours or to bring about desired behaviours and as a weapon with which to humiliate rivals. It confers status through ownership or usage and is commonly a part of ritual proceedings. Food is a central element in the festivals and celebrations which provide temporal structure to our lives.

As individuals we make food choices within a socio-cultural framework of food meanings. However we also bring to bear own our particular tastes – preferences and dislikes that arise from sensory and emotive responses to food. We seem to prefer certain tastes such as sweetness and saltiness, which some have seen as evidence of evolutionary adaptation. Other tastes are intrinsically distasteful, yet we learn to like them – and indeed invest them with great cultural status. Differences in food preferences have been linked to personality traits such as introversion/ extroversion and to mental states such as anxiety and depression. Certainly many people have experienced for themselves how mood affects food choice. There is also a burgeoning postmodernist interest in the role of food in creating subjectivity and embodying personal as well as cultural identity. Much like fashionable clothes that make a statement about the wearer, food becomes a designer commodity used in a quest to construct subjectivity, to distinguish oneself from the rest, to invest mass consumption with personal meaning (Lupton, *Food*).

Thus people make choices from the foodstuffs available to them which reflect a constellation of social, economic, political and cultural influences as well as personal preferences. Religion is one such influence and religious adherents around the world are more or less circumscribed in their food choices by the teachings of their chosen faith.

Religion and Food

Religious teachings about food include both dietary laws and guidance about what may be termed customary practice. Through unquestioned obedience to dietary laws adherents can demonstrate their acceptance of religious authority. No rational explanation of the laws is required; it is enough that they are the Word of God. On the other hand deliberate flouting of dietary laws may signal personal rebellion or a challenge to orthodoxy. Modern followers of ancient faiths sometimes claim that ritual prescriptions that once made sense are no longer meaningful or are impracticable in contemporary situations, so once strict food practices become attenuated or lapse altogether. Observing dietary laws can provide a public as well as personal

Figure 1: Comparative examples of religious dietary guidance

Religion	Food Restrictions
Judaism	Permit only animals with cloven hooves and that chew the cud Permit only fish with scales and fins No blood
Islam	No blood No pork No intoxicating liquor
Sikhism	No beef
Hinduism	Must not kill or eat any animal

	Days of the Year
Christianity	No meat on Fridays during Lent (Catholics) Fast on Wednesday and Friday (Greek Orthodox)
Judaism	Passover Seder plate

	Time of Day
Islam	Abstain from food and drink between sunrise and sunset during Ramadan
Buddhism	Monks do not eat after midday

	Preparation of Food
Judaism	Ritual slaughtering of animals No food preparation on Sabbath Separate utensils for meat and dairy products
Islam	Ritual animal slaughter
Hinduism	Ritual bathing and donning of clean clothes by Brahmins before eating

	Fasts
Christian	40-day Great Lent fast before Easter; 40-day Advent fast (Greek Orthodox)
Islam	Month of Ramadan 13th, 14th, 15th of each month
Bahá'í	19-day Fast

Reproduced with the permission of Nelson Thornes Ltd from *Food and Nutrition Customs and Culture*, 2nd edition (Paul Fieldhouse) ISBN 0 7487 3723 5, first published in 1996.

affirmation of faith, for example through symbolic remembrance of historic events commemorated with feasting or fasting. In obeying dietary laws one is continually reminded that one is a member of the faith. Food acts as a mark of group identity, strengthens feelings of belonging and becomes a material reflection of the spiritual bonds that link co-religionists. Conversely, dietary rules may serve to demonstrate separateness by clearly demarcating cultural boundaries between religions.

Fasting is a practice common to many religions, though its intent and meaning vary. Often it is associated with self-denial, a way of showing that one is more interested in spiritual than in worldly values. Extreme fasting has been seen as a way of attaining holiness. It may also be a form of penance, remembrance or supplication. Food is used as a means of communicating with God or other supernatural forces, through sacrifices or sacrificial rituals. Offerings may be made to give thanks, to placate the deity and so forestall disaster or to seek favours and good fortune. The ancient practice of human sacrifice has given way to animal and plant offerings or to purely symbolic acts such as the giving up of certain foods during holy days. Frequently, food offered to God during rituals is subsequently consumed by those present or is distributed to the poor and needy. This is an example of how food simultaneously fulfils a spiritual and material role and in so doing strengthens both religious and secular bonds. The gods themselves may be the meal and there are parallels between ancient sacrifices and the Christian Eucharist. Finally, religious practices may serve, incidentally or purposefully, to encourage ecological sustainability through conservation and judicious use of scarce resources. For example, the Hindu sanction against harming cows helps to ensure that farmers do not slaughter this valuable resource even during times of hardship.

Religious codes often dictate exclusion of whole categories of foods from consumption. What must not be eaten may be determined by characteristics of individuals such as age, gender, social or physiological status, or by external constraints such as time of day or time of year (figure 1). Prescriptive rules of what must be eaten, when and how are the counterpart of prohibitions. Religious food practices often require the use of specific foods in specific situations, especially during special celebrations such as feasts or fasts, where particular foods often have important symbolic values.

Religious food customs originate in three main ways. Some are required by God and are described in scriptures; others are decreed by religious or political leaders; still others arise through adaptation of existing local customary food practices and are subject to continuous adaptation and reinterpretation. Changes may occur as a result of religious reform or revisionism, acculturation and cultural exchange, as well as through individual, family or community adaptations.

Food in the Bahá'í Faith

At first glance it appears that food does not figure prominently in Bahá'í teachings. There are certainly no dietary codes setting out what may or may not be eaten, when and with whom. 'Abdu'l-Bahá describes food laws as non-essential and temporary; when first introduced they are adapted to the needs of mankind but as conditions change, they lose their relevance. As an example he points out that the flesh and milk of camels were acceptable foods during Abraham's time but became unlawful because of a vow made by Jacob ('Abdu'l-Bahá, *Promulgation* 404).

As noted earlier, food has commonly been used as a cultural marker – a sign both of inclusion and exclusion. In Hindu society, for example, there are strict rules governing food transactions between castes, that is, who may eat with whom and who may give or receive food to and from whom. In the 15th century Guru Nanak, founder of the Sikh faith, attempted to transcend religious and social barriers by enjoining Muslims and Hindus of all castes to eat together in communal langars. Speaking of the situation in Persia at the time of Bahá'u'lláh's appearance, 'Abdul-Bahá says that people and tribes were separated by hatred and violent strife so that they would not come together for any purpose other than war: 'they would not partake of the same food, or drink of the same water; association and intercourse were impossible' ('Abdu'l-Baha, *Promulgation* 129). He continues: 'Bahá'u'lláh founded the oneness of humanity among these people and bound their hearts together with such ties of love that they were completely united.' The Bahá'í Faith, in eschewing food rules, would also appear to be removing an important cultural boundary marker, dismantling an apparatus for distinguishing between 'us' and 'them'.

Rather than setting out rules, Bahá'í teachings provide guidance and emphasize the responsibility of individual believers to live a virtuous life. The idea that diet and food practices are constitutive of a virtuous life is an old one, though the practical expression of such ideals has varied historically (Foucault, *Sexuality*). In ancient Greece, moderation and self-mastery in diet were indications of rationality and capacity to conduct oneself successfully in political life. For the Romans, more detailed dietary regimens guided everyday conduct; individuals had a moral responsibility for self-care and preservation of health. In early Christianity food and appetite became linked with lust and worldly pleasure; ascetic practices were required as acts of denial aimed at suppressing desire. Diet and self-regulation became for many centuries part of a religious discipline which aimed to control the soul (Turner, *Body*). Religious conviction also inspired the efforts of 18th and 19th century dietary reformers in the West and melded with scientific rationalism in 20th century founders of modern nutritional science like Wilbur Atwater. The secular followers of modern dietary advice in avoiding 'bad' high-fat foods and maintaining 'healthy weights' are still practising virtue. The Baha'i Faith, with its emphasis on the harmony of science and religion, presents a singular food discourse that invokes themes of naturalness, simplicity, moderation, compassion and justice and which upholds both the material and spiritual value of food.

Food, Health and the Body

'The bounty of good health is the greatest of all gifts' ('Abdu'l-Bahá, *Selections* 151).

Health and healing are addressed in numerous writings of Bahá'u'lláh, 'Abdu'l-Bahá, Shoghi Effendi and the Universal of Justice. Bahá'ís are charged with the responsibility of looking after their own health, for the preservation of bodily health and well-being is necessary in order to pursue a life of service and devotion. The body is regarded as the temple of the human spirit and consequently should be treated as a willing, obedient and efficient servant. Shoghi Effendi describes the body as being like a horse that must be cared for so that it can do its work (Shoghi Effendi, in *Lights* no. 1013). Contemporary secular definitions have also moved away from conceptualizing health as an ideal state of well-being or an end in itself, to seeing it as a capacity – a resource for everyday living (World Health Organization). This requirement for self-care rejects both ascetic and hedonistic practices. For while asceticism symbolizes disengagement with everyday life – contrary to Baha'i commitment to community involvement and service – hedonism shows an undue concern with selfish desires.

> If the health and well-being of the body be expended in the path of the Kingdom, this is very acceptable and praiseworthy; and if it is expended to the benefit of the human world in general – even though it be to their material benefit and be a means of doing good – that is also acceptable. But if the health and welfare of man be spent in sensual desires, in a life on the animal plane, and in devilish pursuits – then disease is better than such health; nay death itself is preferable to such a life ('Abdu'l-Bahá, in *Bahá'í World Faith* 376).

Instead moderation is advised, which is directed towards producing a state of detachment. This moderation takes the form of a 'balanced natural diet', without excess and adapted to climate and the type of work in which the body is engaged – a formulation which differs little from contemporary nutritional science concepts. What does differ is the way in which this balance is to be achieved. Whereas nutritional science requires of people conscious choice of a 'balanced diet' based on knowledge of nutrient values and a sophisticated awareness of educational messages, 'Abdu'l-Bahá invokes a theory of natural selection of foods derived from inherent human capacities. 'Abdu'l-Bahá uses the idea that animals can 'naturally' discern what they need in their diet, for their constitution 'longs for' what it needs. He suggests that humans can also do this but that their ability to do so is obscured by foolish and unnatural modes of living, by which he means ignoring the principle of moderation and indulging the appetites. '. . . when the constitution is in a state of equilibrium, there is no doubt that whatever is relished will be beneficial to health' ('Abdu'l-Bahá, *Selections* 154). The idea that humans choose certain foods because they are programmed to know what is physiologically good for them has a perennial appeal. For early peoples food and disease became quickly linked through common experience and there would have been evolutionary advantages to being able to identify and avoid poisonous substances. Over time this practice may have come to seem natural. The selectivity theory insists that the body knows what is good for it and that given free choice humans would automatically select nutritionally adequate diets. At the beginning of the 20th century, just as the modern science of nutrition was emerging, Dr Woods Hutchinson in the United States claimed that instinct was far superior to reason, leading the average man naturally to 'three square meals a day, consisting of anything he can find in the market, and just as much of it as he can afford' (Hutchinson, *Diet*). To test this idea of natural food choices in conditions where cultural learning was minimal, early nutrition researchers experimented with allowing newly weaned infants to choose their own diets from a selection of offered foods (Davis, 'Self-Selection'). Definite preferences were shown which changed unpredictably from time to time; appetite was the guiding factor and the diets consumed were nutritionally adequate but probably only because the selection of nutritious foods offered made it difficult for this not to happen. More recent studies have shown that children seem to prefer high fat foods, which are both widely available and culturally valued (Agras et al., 'Relationships'). There are, of course, ethical problems with this type of study but it seems unlikely that, given a completely free choice of foods, infants, children or indeed adults would select a nutritionally adequate diet.

The idea of 'naturalness' also arises in Bahá'í writings in regard to food combinations.

> But man hath perversely continued to serve his lustful appetites, and he would not content himself with simple foods. Rather, he prepared for himself food that was compounded of many ingredients, of substances differing one from the other . . . and he abandoned the temperance and moderation of a natural way of life. The result was the engendering of diseases both violent and diverse ('Abdu'l-Bahá, *Selections* 152–3).

It is not clear whether this criticism of dietary practices refers to the use of food transformed through processing of some kind or to the combining of different foodstuffs in one meal. Both ideas certainly have a long history. The influential 10th century Arab physician Avicenna cautioned that specific food combinations could be either good or harmful. For example, milk was not to be eaten with sour foods or fish, and pulses were not to be eaten with cheese. The suggestion that it is inappropriate to combine foods persists today in popular nutrition writing that exhorts people to eat, for example, only carbohydrate food or only protein foods at any one meal under the assumption that this aids digestion and assimilation of nutrients. However, food combining is generally dismissed by the contemporary scientific establishment as an unfounded fad. On the other hand, the idea that as food is more removed from its natural state, that is when it is more artificial or 'compounded' it becomes less healthy and more likely to cause disease, has a certain resonance with contemporary scientific theory that lays substantial blame for chronic disease on diets rich in fat and sugar – which means, essentially, the products of food manufacturing and processing.

Food and Healing

The Universal House of Justice has pointed out that no specific school of nutrition or medicine is associated with Baha'i teachings but rather there are certain guidelines, indications and principles that may be useful. A statement issued on behalf of Shoghi Effendi cautioned that 'It is premature, to try and elaborate on the few general references to health and medicine made in our Holy Scriptures' (Universal House of Justice, in *Compilation*, vol. 1, 486). It is nevertheless clear that Baha'i teachings give food a pre-eminent role not only in maintaining health but also as the preferred means for treatment of disease. 'Treat disease through diet, by preference, refraining from the use of drugs; and if you find what is required in a single herb, do not resort to a compounded medicament' (Bahá'u'lláh, Tablet to Physician, in ibid. 460). As with normal food selection, animal behaviour is again offered as an analogy for human needs. Animals are not cured by drugs but rather use their powers of taste and smell to discern what foods are needed for healing. For example, if its body needs more sugar, the sensory perceptions of the animal will alter in such a way as to lead it to desire and locate sweet herbs.

Disease Results from a Disturbance of Balance in the Body

> But the principal causes of disease are physical; for the human body is composed of numerous elements, but in the measure of an especial equilibrium. As long as this equilibrium is maintained, man is preserved from disease; but if this essential balance, which is the pivot of the constitution, is disturbed, the constitution is disordered, and disease will supervene ('Abdu'l-Bahá, *Answered Questions* 257).

Such a concept of balance is familiar in ancient medical systems such as the Greek humoural theory, the Indian ayurvedic system and the Chinese yin-yang continuum. It persists in Indo-Mediterranean and Latin American concepts of hot and cold bodily states and as part of popular medical wisdom in the West.

Greek humoural theory held that there were four bodily elements each of which had particular characteristics: blood – hot and wet; phlegm – cold and wet; black bile – cold and dry; yellow bile – hot and dry. Medical practice consisted of understanding the normal mixture of humours or complexion of a person, the complexion of their illness and the method of restoring harmony in the body. Humoural theory and practice was spread widely by Christian, Jewish and Muslim physicians including Avicenna, who wrote treatises that formed the basis for centuries of medical practice. In Persia a unique blend of Quranic and Hippocratic medical principles and practices emerged that made room for both folk healers and professional physicians and that employed astrology, religion and magic as well as therapeutic principles (Ebrahimnejad, 'Persian Medicine'). Attempts to introduce 'modern medicine' continually came up against the self-interest of those who wanted to cling to older theories and the result was a syncretism rather than replacement of one system with the other. In using the language of allopathic medicine and also exhorting the virtues of consulting qualified physicians, Bahá'u'lláh and 'Abdul-Bahá were therefore employing terminology and concepts familiar to people of the day.

If disease is a consequence of bodily imbalance then treatment consists in restoring this balance.

> All the elements that are combined in man exist also in vegetables; therefore, if one of the constituents which compose the body of man diminishes, and he partakes of foods in which there is much of that diminished constituent, then the equilibrium will be established, and a cure will be obtained ('Abdu'l-Bahá, *Answered Questions* 258).

Changes in diet bear a complex relationship to internal homeostatic balance so that there are inherent difficulties in linking a specific dietary substance to a specific bodily condition. Ingested foods must be broken down into simpler chemical components, absorbed in the body and transported to cellular sites to be used or stored. Nevertheless the concept of 'balance' has remained central to nutrition teaching although it is expressed in different ways, drawing on both folk wisdom and rationalistic scientific research.

Whereas western health reformers have opposed the concepts of natural and scientific knowledge of food, 'Abdu'l-Bahá does not do so, rather endorsing both approaches. 'In matters of health, particularly regarding diet and nutrition, the House of Justice advises the friends to seek the help and advice of experts and doctors' (Universal House of Justice, in *Compilation*, vol. 1, 487).

The injunction to seek the best that medical science has to offer at any time implies that newer knowledge of the role and pathways of food in maintaining health and combatting disease should be accepted by Bahá'ís. While contemporary practitioners of popular nutrition continue to promote old ideas, Bahá'ís are specifically obliged to consult doctors 'well trained in the medical sciences' (ibid. 486). Ironically this newer medical knowledge, resting exclusively on rationalistic principles, has to a large extent undermined the messages of naturalness and simplicity contained in Bahá'í writings. Furthermore, modern scientific medical training pays scant attention to nutrition and the role of food in health and disease. Bahá'í teachings recognize this deficiency but nevertheless look forward to a time when all illness will be treated by food.

> The science of medicine is still in a condition of infancy: it has not reached maturity. But when it has reached this point, cures will be performed by things which are not repulsive to the smell and taste of man – that is to say by aliments, fruits and vegetables which are agreeable to the taste and have an agreeable smell ('Abdu'l-Bahá, *Answered Questions* 257).

While 'Abdu'l-Bahá looks to the future to establish the true value of food in treating illness, the idea of diet as a panacea has persisted through the centuries just as medicine and dietetics have been interwoven and largely interchangeable. In 18th-century Britain George Cheyne wrote in *An Essay on Regimen*: 'It is diet alone, proper and specific diet, in Quantity, Quality and Order, which is the sole universal remedy and the only Means known to [medical] Art' (Cheyne, *Essay*). Sylvester Graham and John Kellogg in the US were 19th-century apostles of 'the regimen' and the conviction that correct diet promises unlimited health benefits persists in the 'alternative' nutrition and health movements and literature of today. The scientific establishment is much more cautious in its approach and claims but it is interesting in light of 'Abdu'l-Bahá's words to note that right now we are seeing a tremendous explosion of scientific as well as commercial interest in 'functional foods' and 'nutraceuticals'. Functional foods are foods that are deemed to have specific effects on the body beyond their basic nutritional value. For example, fish contains omega-3 fatty acids, believed to have a role in preventing cardiovascular disease, while many fruits and vegetables contain phytochemicals that may reduce cancer risk. Nutraceuticals, sometimes known as 'medical foods', are biochemically active food components that can be isolated and used in a therapeutic way. It is ironic that these latest developments in food science provide a sort of endorsement for what older traditions and popular belief have maintained all along. Food is medicine.

Vegetarianism

The themes of simplicity and naturalness that inform Bahá'í teachings on food also underlie Bahá'í ideas about vegetarianism. Before considering those ideas in more detail, a brief overview of vegetarianism is presented.

Vegetarianism is not a unitary concept; there is a spectrum of behaviour amongst people who describe themselves as vegetarians. Vegans avoid eating any animal product whatsoever, whether or not it involves the killing of the animal. Others allow dairy products and eggs, while 'lax vegetarians' happily consume fish, chicken and other non-red meats. There is also a fundamental distinction between vegetarianism as a normative socio-cultural behaviour and vegetarianism as a conscious individual choice. Vegetarianism may be predicated on health, ecological or ethical beliefs, which are often intertwined.

Health arguments for vegetarianism usually focus on the relationship between diet and chronic disease, particularly degenerative conditions such as cardiovascular disease, diabetes and various intestinal disorders, as well as cancer of the colon and breast and dental caries. Diets that emphasise fruit, vegetables, whole cereals and pulses tend to be higher in bulk and lower in calories, sugars and fats than a typical meat-centred regime; thus it is not surprising that studies have shown vegetarians to be lighter on average than non-vegetarians, and to have lower blood cholesterol levels and lower blood pressures. The vegetarian health practices of Seventh Day Adventists have certainly conferred nutritional benefits on them. As a group they suffer fewer chronic diet-related disorders such as hypertension and cancer than do the general population (Phillips, *Role of Lifestyle*). Critics maintain that vegetarian diets tend to be low in essential nutrients and pose a threat to health through under-nutrition. Certainly this can happen with poorly planned vegetarian diets that do not take adequate account of the need to assure protein complementarity. The debate is longstanding. The Neo-Platonist philosopher Porphyry wrote a treatise entitled 'Abstinence from Animal Food' in which he refuted arguments that meat is essential for health and strength. Rather, he insisted, meat is associated with both physical disease and corrupts the soul (Wynne-Tyson, *Porphyry*). However, eating meat as a mainstay of the diet does not of necessity produce untoward health effects and is sometimes the only option. Traditional societies of hunters and trappers that have relied heavily on meat have exhibited high levels of health. Indeed modern degenerative diseases only became significant amongst Inuit and First Nations peoples of Canada with the destruction of traditional ways of life and the spread of southern refined foods and dietary patterns (Schaefer et al., 'Eskimo Populations'; Schaefer and Steckle, *Dietary Habits*).

Brought into public prominence by the publication of Francis Moore Lappe's *Diet for a Small Planet*, ecological perspectives on vegetarianism bring into question the sustainability of large-scale meat consumption and the inefficiencies of intensive livestock production (Lappe, *Diet*). Both arguments are frequently linked to ethical stances regarding world hunger and inequitable resource consumption. The rising world demand for meat, epitomized by the meat-centred diet of North Americans, encourages the use of energy-intensive methods of food production which places tremendous pressure on ecosystems and on resource usage and has led to claims that environmental responsibility demands the elimination of livestock (Rifkin, *Beyond Beef*). Others reject as impractical Rifkin's utopian vision of a return to a 'natural' world, while agreeing that current methods of animal rearing are wasteful and unsustainable and should be eliminated. Instead, they suggest animal rearing should be reintegrated into traditional pastoralist practices where animals are part of the natural ecosystem and are raised for food instead of primarily for profit (Gussow, 'Ecology'). This approach accommodates the reality that there are ecosystems (such as the Arctic) where dependence on plant food is simply not an option. Even in more temperate climates not all land is arable; some is more suited to animal rearing.

A third dimension of vegetarianism, that has both religious and secular aspects, invokes ethical arguments that appeal to compassion and respect for life. Religious views emerge from the idea that humans are an interdependent part of creation and do not have any special claims over animals. This reasoning reaches its apotheosis in the Jain concept of *ahimsa* or non-injury to living beings. Jain monks are fastidious in preserving life, for example by sweeping the floor in front of them to avoid treading on insects and filtering water to avoid inadvertently swallowing any small creatures. Beliefs in metempsychosis, the transmigration of souls, similarly motivate orthodox Buddhists and Hindus. One Hindu commentator proposed that vegetarianism contributes to the superior spiritual position of Hinduism and that it is necessary for proper worship and attainment of spiritual freedom (Bon, 'Hinduism'). Vegetarianism is thus an indicator of devotion to a moral life. In contrast, the Judaeo-Christian tradition after the Flood seems to explicitly give humans the right to exploit the earth's resources, including animals, for their own ends. Nevertheless, Christian vegetarians find plenty of support in the Bible for their beliefs and may see non-meat eating as a way to recover an Edenic existence. In Islam, despite the notable prohibition on pork and some other minor flesh prohibitions, food is seen generally as a gift from God that should be received gratefully. Muhammad recommended a meat stew as suitable for serving to guests. Nevertheless, some Sufi orders have praised vegetarianism as a more compassionate practice and have viewed animal consumption as conducive to animalistic behaviour.

Secular arguments focus more frequently on the idea of animal rights and condemn both the eating of creatures that have demonstrable interests and rights and the cruelty inherent in rearing animals under modern factory farm conditions (Singer, *Ethics*). These arguments are rejected outright in philosophical positions that deny that animals can have natural rights. Nevertheless, Nick Fiddes argues that there is a continuing decline in the popularity of meat in western countries (particularly in the UK) that he ascribes to a changing moral stance that is widening the sphere of human compassion to include animals. As evidence of this he cites an increased popularity of vegetarianism along with increases in anti-fur and other animal welfare activities as well as meat industry attempts to glamorize meat and dissociate the bought product from the actual animal. Fiddes suggests that this change is associated with a disillusionment with modernity and the Enlightenment goal of human domination over nature (Fiddes, 'Declining Meat').

Ethical arguments for vegetarianism also make appeals to justice. It is simply not possible for most of the world's population to obtain meat-centred diets resembling the North American pattern. North American consumption habits are only possible if others do not get enough, which is manifestly unjust. By reducing the demand for meat, land and resources that are used for intensive animal rearing are freed to produce larger quantities of plant crops. In this way vegetarianism allows for a more equitable sharing of the world's resources and contributes to reducing world hunger and malnutrition by 'co-ordinating food production with human needs' (Hershaft, 'Food Crisis'; Sabry, 'Food Production').

Vegetarianism has thus been presented through the ages as a strategy for achieving both spiritual and material goals and for advancing both individual health and collective well-being. Themes of health, economics, ecology and spirituality interconnect and draw strength from each other. All these themes appear in the Bahá'í teachings.

Vegetarianism in the Bahá'í writings

All that has been created is for man who is at the apex of creation and who must be thankful for the divine bestowals, so that through his gratitude he may learn to understand life as a divine benefit ('Abdu'l-Bahá, *Divine Philosophy* 134).

Eat ye, O people, of the good things which God hath allowed you, and deprive not yourselves from His wondrous bounties (Bahá'u'lláh, in Shoghi Effendi, *Advent* 33).

Animal food is not forbidden in the Bahá'í teachings. All foods are available for human consumption, though this permissiveness is mediated by health, ethical and ecological considerations that uphold the value and desirability of vegetarianism. Meat is acknowledged to be a nutritious and even sometimes essential food, for example for rehabilitation of the sick.

> Meat is nourishing and containeth the elements of herbs, seeds and fruits; therefore sometimes it is essential for the sick and for the rehabilitation of health. There is no objection in the Law of God to the eating of meat if it is required. So if thy constitution is rather weak and thou findest meat useful, thou mayest eat it ('Abdu'l-Bahá, in *Compilation*, vol. 1, 463).

Nevertheless it is undoubtedly possible to live without meat:

> The food of the future will be fruit and grains. The time will come when meat is no longer eaten. Medical science is yet only in its infancy, but it has shown that our natural diet is that which grows out of the ground. The people will gradually develop up to the condition of taking only this natural food ('Abdu'l-Bahá, in *Bahá'í Scriptures* no. 830).

There appears to be some ambiguity around the notion that meat is permissible. 'Abdu'l-Bahá states that God determined the food of every living being and to eat contrary to that determination is not approved. As evidence of the naturalness of vegetarianism he then discourses at length on the nature of animal and human teeth. Carnivorous animals have teeth, talons and claws that are specifically designed for meat-eating while grazing animals have teeth suitable for chewing on vegetable matter. Human teeth are designed to grind grain and cut fruit and vegetables, indicating that man's food is intended to be cereal and fruit and not meat ('Abdu'l-Bahá, *Promulgation* 103, 170–1). To demonstrate that health is not compromised by a vegetarian diet 'Abdu'l-Bahá cites the case of Indian Brahmins for whom non-meat eating does not diminish their 'strength, power, vigour, outward senses or intellectual virtues' ('Abdu'l-Bahá, in *Compilation* 462). Contemporary with 'Abdu'l-Bahá, Hereward Carrington in England produced a work entitled 'The Natural Food of Man, Being an Attempt to Prove from Comparative Anatomy, Physiology, Chemistry and Hygiene, that the Original, Best and Natural Diet of Man is Fruit and Nuts'. The idea that humans are naturally fruit-eaters is a physiological 'proof' long favoured by vegetarians. However, there are also cogent arguments that non-meat eating is primarily a consequence of want, not of choice, and that primates, including humans, increase their dietary meat when it is economically feasible to do so (Hamilton and Busse, 'Carnivory'). The term 'meat-hunger' has been used to describe a supposed craving for meat especially amongst people living at subsistence level. However, in many human societies meat consumption is associated with wealth, prestige and power, so that it is possible to make a social argument for explaining the desirability of meat without invoking the slippery concept of 'naturalness'.

'Wolves, lions, tigers are ferocious because it is their natural and necessary means for attaining food. Man has no need of such ferocity; his food is provided in other ways' ('Abdu'l-Bahá, *Promulgation* 119). Undoubtedly, both vegetarianism and meat-eating are compatible with human health but because meat is unnecessary and is an inefficient source of energy, the killing of animals has moral implications. 'Abdu'l-Bahá describes the killing of animals and the eating of their meat as contrary to pity and compassion and suggests that it would be more pleasing to content oneself with cereals, fruit, oil and nuts. Refraining from killing animals will enhance spiritual qualities. In a letter written to an individual believer Shoghi Effendi affirmed this position but also admitted that the topic was controversial:

> In regard to the question as to whether people ought to kill animals for food or not, there is no explicit statement in the Bahá'í Sacred Scriptures (as far as I know) in favour or against it. It is certain, however, that if man can live on a purely vegetarian diet and thus avoid killing animals, it would be much preferable. This is, however, a very controversial question and the Bahá'ís are free to express their views on it (Shoghi Effendi, in *Compilation* 476).

Vegetarianism may be linked to justice. Meat-centred diets make huge demands on world resources including available land and energy. To consume a meat-rich diet therefore means maintaining control over considerable resources, resources that are not shared with the majority of the world's population. The high prestige accorded to meat in many parts of the world reflects its symbolic value as a sign of wealth and power. Meat is preferentially given to men, the strongest hunter or the richest noble. Eating simply by adopting a vegetarian diet can be interpreted as a gesture of social justice and solidarity. 'It is more kingly to be satisfied with a crust of stale bread than to enjoy a sumptuous dinner of many courses, the money for which comes out of the pockets of others' ('Abdu'l-Bahá, *Bahai Scriptures* no. 829).

If vegetarianism has so many desirable traits, why then did Bahá'u'lláh permit the consumption of meat? One way of looking at it might be to go back to the idea of cultural boundaries. If you do not wish to create boundaries or barriers you do not set up food rules that might exclude or alienate potential followers. Because Bahá'u'lláh was presenting a discourse of unity he did not need distinct food laws to identify believers; conversely no one had to change his or her customary food habits in order to become a Bahá'í.

In Islamic law foods are classified into one of five categories: obligatory, recommended, neutral, disapproved or prohibited. It seems that in Bahá'í teachings meat is being treated as a disapproved or perhaps a neutral item: consumption is not prohibited but there is merit in abstaining. Islamic law also recognizes that necessity may legitimately override usual observance; for example, a fast should be broken if there is a threat to health. The Bahá'í suggestion that meat is of particular value for nourishing the sick appears to follow a similar line of reasoning. A permissive stance is also in line with Islamic belief that God does not want to make life unnecessarily difficult for his people.

There is also no inconsistency in permitting a practice while at the same time drawing attention to its moral shortcomings and advocating for its elimination over time. Other Bahá'í laws were only to be introduced gradually as people developed the capacity to respond to the requisite responsibilities and inconsistencies in practice are accepted. For example, the prohibition on smoking (which in Arabic reads as 'drinking smoke') during fasting is most consistently adhered to by Baha'is of Middle Eastern origin. Berman, from a Jewish perspective, similarly maintains that permitting meat consumption was a concession by God to man's imperfection and that humans are still not morally ready to forgo the eating of flesh (Berman, *Vegetarianism*). The presumption that there will be a time when humans do not eat meat suggests that changing eating habits are part and parcel of the pursuit of spiritual progression. The relinquishment of meat is an individual choice that takes on value as a symbol of this spiritual progression. There are interesting parallels here to Norbert Elias's concept of a 'curve of civilization' which views the gradual de-emphasis of meat in the diet as a marker of refinement and civilized behaviour (Elias, *Civilising Process*). In the Middle Ages, when the whole dead animal or substantial parts of it were brought to the table, carving was an indispensable accomplishment for the man of breeding. Gradually, this practice went out of fashion and meat-carving was relegated to behind the scenes where it was carried out by servants. Today, we usually avoid any reminders that the meat on our plate has anything to do with killing animals (though carving the roast on festive occasions remains as a high-prestige (male) prerogative). This gradual removal of meat from pride of place at the table may imply that vegetarianism is the logical next step on the civilizing curve, as the 'threshold of repugnance' advances.

Commensality

Food sharing is an almost universal medium for expressing fellowship; it embodies values of hospitality, duty, giving, sacrifice and compassion. The sharing of food has been a common theme in religious traditions and both the giving and receiving of food are often raised to the level of religious duties. Muhammad exalted the virtues of hospitality and commended believers to accept food that was offered, even if it meant breaking a fast, for to refuse such food was to refuse God's bounty and to neglect an opportunity to honour a noble act. In the Sufi tradition particularly, hospitality assumed tremendous importance and endures in the form of feeding stations in Sufi centres and at Moulid festivals. Following in this Middle Eastern tradition, Bahá'ís embraced the importance of hospitality as a means to creating unity and justice. '. . . offer thou salutary water to the athirst; bestow the bread of life upon the hungered' ('Abdu'l-Bahá, *Tablets* 126). 'Direct your whole effort toward the happiness of those who are despondent, bestow food upon the hungry . . .' ('Abdu'l-Bahá, *Promulgation* 469). However, Bahá'ís are cautioned by their administrative institutions 'not to presume on the hospitality' of others and not to let others 'take undue advantage' of their own hospitality (Walbridge, *Sacred Acts* 212), an injunction reminiscent of Muhammad's counsel that hospitality which extends beyond three days becomes charity.

Charitable giving – of money or of food – is an integral part of some religions. In some ways charity may be read as an extension of customary hospitality to strangers, characterized by the 'impersonal' nature of the transaction; the giver and the receiver do not necessarily know one another (though they may come to do so). While individual Bahá'ís may indeed support charities such as food banks and soup kitchens, collectively Bahá'ís have been active in supporting food security through social development projects rather than through feeding programmes *per se*.

While food may be provided to specific individuals as a gesture of hospitality or an act of charity, it is also commonly shared in fellowship in the communal context of a feast. The word 'feast' denotes a special occasion, commonly public, on which food is consumed of a different quality and quantity to that of everyday meals. In many places the feast is a community event with no exclusive guest list: everyone is welcome. In general, foods used for feasting are 1) scarce, 2) high quality, 3) often expensive and 4) difficult and time-consuming to prepare. That is, they have high status and are definitely different to everyday fare (Fieldhouse, *Food* 193). The Bahá'í 'feast', though, has a very particular meaning. It first appears in the Arabic Bayán as a command to entertain 19 people every 19 days even if one is only able to give them water. Bahá'u'lláh explains that its purpose is to 'bind hearts together' (Bahá'u'lláh, *Kitáb-i-Aqdas* para. 57) with material means. Early feasts emphasized hospitality and were purely social occasions. Gradually, though, the feast became a more formalized religious event, as Walbridge explains:

> Illustrative of this phase were the 'Nineteen Day Teas' for Bahá'í women, begun in Chicago in 1901 and soon observed in other cities. After 1905 a more formal feast, combining a meal and devotions, came into practice in America . . . [The first formal 19 Day Feast in Canada was held in Montreal in 1922.] The Bahá'ís at first precisely copied a feast hosted by 'Abdu'l-Bahá in 'Akká in 1905. On the basis of the passage in the Kitáb-i-Aqdas, the Bahá'ís understood the feast as a way of unifying the Bahá'í community. In America it supplemented the weekly worship meetings that most communities held. Not surprisingly, the American Bahá'ís associated the feast with the Lord's Supper, an analogy that 'Abdu'l-Bahá Himself made (Walbridge, *Sacred Acts* 208).

As the modern tripartite form of the 19 Day Feast emerged under the direction of Shoghi Effendi, it incorporated devotional, administrative and social components. The feast as it is now practised differs from religious gatherings in other faiths in being exclusive to members of the religion. However, non-Bahá'í visitors should be welcomed at the social portion of the feast, recalling the priority accorded to hospitality. The type and amount of food provided at a feast is not prescribed but is rather a function of local custom and resources, indicating that it is the symbolic rather than the material value of the food that is important.

Conclusion

While there is not space here to explore other food-related issues such as fasting and food symbolism, it does seem that there is a Bahá'í discourse on food that draws on both scientific knowledge and religious teaching and that gives rise to distinct practices and understandings of the role of food. Themes of sharing and hospitality, care of the body and vegetarianism exhibit both similarities and differences to those of other faith traditions, while the absence of prescriptive dietary codes may symbolize the removal of boundaries between races, cultures and religions, supporting the unique Bahá'í concept of the unity of humankind.

Works Cited

'Abdu'l-Bahá. *Foundations of World Unity*. Wilmette, IL: Bahá'í Publishing Trust, 1945.
— *The Promulgation of Universal Peace*. Wilmette, IL: Bahá'í Publishing Trust, 1982.
— *Selections from the Writings of 'Abdu'l-Bahá*. Haifa: Bahá'í World Centre, 1978.
— *Some Answered Questions*. Wilmette, IL: Bahá'í Publishing Trust, 1981.
— *Tablets of Abdul-Baha Abbas*. Chicago: Bahá'í Publishing Society, vol. 1, 1909.
Abdul Baha on Divine Philosophy. Boston: The Tudor Press, 1918.
Agras, S.W. , et al. 'Relationships between the Eating Behaviors of Parents and Their 18-Month-Old Children: A Laboratory Study'. *International Journal of Eating Disorders*, no. 7 (1988), pp. 461–8.
Bahai Scriptures. New York: Brentano's, 1923.
Bahá'u'lláh. 'Tablet to the Physician'. *Bahá'í Studies Bulletin*, nos. 6.4 to 7.2 (1992), pp. 18–65.
Barthes, R. 'Towards a Psycho-Sociology of Contemporary Food Consumption'. *Food and Drink in History*. R. Forster and O. Ranum (eds.). Baltimore: Johns Hopkins University Press, 1979.
Berman, L.A. *Vegetarianism and the Jewish Tradition*. New York: Ktav Publishers, 1982.
Bon, B.H. 'What Hinduism Can Offer is World Fellowship'. *Indian Philosophy and Culture*, vol. 11 (1966), pp. 1–7.
Bourdieu, P. *Distinction. A Social Critique of the Judgement of Taste*. London: Routledge, Kegan and Paul, 1984.
Carrington, H. *The Natural Food of Man, Being an Attempt to Prove from Comparative Anatomy, Physiology, Chemistry and Hygiene That the Original Best and Natural Diet of Man is Fruit and Nuts*. London: C.W. Daniels, 1912.
Cheyne, G. *An Essay on Regimen*. London: C. Rivington, 1740.
Davis, C.M. 'Self-Selection of Diets by Newly Weaned Infants: An Experimental Study'. *American Journal of Diseases of Childhood*, vol. 36 (1928), pp. 651–79.
Douglas, M. 'Deciphering a Meal'. *Daedelus*, vol. 101 (1972), pp. 61–81.
Ebrahimnejad, H. 'Theory and Practice in Nineteenth Century Persian Medicine:

Intellectual and Institutional Reforms'. *History of Science*, vol. 38, no. 2 (2000), pp. 171–8.

Elias, N. *The Civilising Process: The History of Manners*, vol. 1. Oxford: Blackwell, (1939) 1978.

Fiddes, N. 'Declining Meat'. *Food, Health and Identity*. P. Caplan (ed.). London: Routledge, 1997.

Fieldhouse, P. *Food and Nutrition: Customs and Culture*. London: Chapman & Hall, 2nd edn. 1995.

Foucault, M. *The History of Sexuality*, vol. 2: *The Uses of Pleasure*. New York: Vintage, 1990.

Grundy, Julia M. *Ten Days in the Light of 'Akká*. Wilmette, IL: Bahá'í Publishing Trust, 1979.

Gussow, J.D. 'Ecology and Vegetarian Considerations: Does Environmental Re-sponsibility Demand the Elimination of Livestock?' *American Journal of Clinical Nutrition*, vol. 59, Suppl. (1994), pp. 1110–6S.

Hamilton, W.J., and C.D. Busse. 'Primate Carnivory and Its Significance to Human Diets'. *Bioscience*, vol. 28, no. 12 (1975), pp. 761–6.

Hershaft, A. 'Solving the Population Food Crisis by "Eating for Life"'. *Vegetarian Times*. July –August 1978, p. 64.

Hutchinson, W. 'Some Diet Delusions'. *McClure's*, vol. 1906, p. 611.

Lappe, F.M. *Diet for a Small Planet*. Tenth Anniversary Edition. New York: Ballentine Books, 1982.

Levi-Strauss, C. *The Raw and the Cooked*. New York: Harper & Row, 1969.

Lupton, D. *Food, the Body and the Self*. London: Sage, 1996.

Phillips, R.L. 'Role of Lifestyle and Dietary Habits in Risk of Cancer among Seventh Day Adventists'. *Cancer Research*, vol. 35, no. 11 (1975), pp. 3513–22.

Rifkin, J. *Beyond Beef: The Rise and Fall of the Cattle Culture*. New York: Dutton, 1992.

Sabry, Z.I. 'Coordinating Food Production with Human Needs'. *Chemistry in Canada*, vol. 27, no. 2 (1975), pp. 16–19.

Schaefer, O., and J. Steckle. *Dietary Habits of Native Populations*. Science Advisory Board of the Northwest Territories, 1980.

Schaefer, O., et al. 'General and Nutritional Health in Two Eskimo Populations at Different Stages of Acculturation'. *Canadian Journal of Public Health*, vol. 71, no. 6 (1980), pp. 397–405.

Shoghi Effendi. *The Advent of Divine Justice*. Wilmette, IL: Bahá'í Publishing Trust, 1990.

Singer, P. *Practical Ethics*. London: Cambridge University Press, 1979.

Turner, B. S. *The Body & Society*. London: Sage, 2nd edn. 1996.

Walbridge, John. *Sacred Acts, Sacred Space, Sacred Time*. Oxford: George Ronald, 1996.

World Health Organization. *The Ottawa Charter for Health Promotion*. Geneva: WHO, 1996.

Wynne-Tyson, E. (ed.). *Porphyry on Abstinence from Animal Food*. London: Century Press, 1965.

Paul Fieldhouse obtained his undergraduate degree in Nutrition from the University of Surrey and his Master of Philosophy in Health and Human Behaviour through the Council for National Academic Awards at Leeds Polytechnic. Before immigrating to Canada in 1980 he was a Senior Lecturer in Nutrition and Dietetics at Leeds Polytechnic [now Leeds Metropolitan University]. In Canada, Paul took up a post as Assistant Professor of Foods and Nutrition at the University of Alberta, where he continued to teach and write about these subjects. In 1989 Paul joined the Manitoba Ministry of Health. He is currently nutrition policy analyst for the department and an Adjunct Professor in the Faculty of Nursing at the University of Manitoba. Paul has written several textbooks on community nutrition and on food and culture, as well as publishing in academic journals and contributing encyclopaedia articles on food and religion. He recently completed an interdisciplinary PhD at the University of Manitoba on the topic of 'Food, Justice, and the Bahá'í Faith'.

Rethinking the Management of Small Rural Businesses

Michel P. Zahrai

Introduction

Most third world countries remain agrarian societies; indeed the urban development of the last 30 years is a new phenomenon and urban settlements, however big, reproduce social behaviours and allegiances inherited from their rural connection. This is why changes and disruption in rural areas have consequences for a country as a whole. The proletariatization of rural areas and the creation of an ever-increasing army of landless labourers as a result of the introduction of capitalism and the destruction of the traditional social fabric is one of the most fundamental agents of change in the rural and urban landscape of most third world countries. The speedy rise of slums, favelas and other sprawling urban shanty towns is directly linked to this poverty dynamic in the countryside. It is estimated that between 1950 and 1970 migration from rural areas accounted for 45 to 55 per cent of urban population growth in the world. The present trend of industrialization in the third world indicates that urban areas will not be able to absorb the continuous flow of migrants from the countryside where social and economic relationships have broken down. This conclusion implies that the agricultural sector will have to generate productive employment for increasing numbers of people for many years to come.

However, a renewed focus on the rural sector should not be advocated solely as a temporary relief for the urban areas; on the contrary, restoring dynamism and pride in rural life should be seen as a prerequisite to harmonious global development. Indeed, as one early 20th-century thinker put it, 'the solution begins with the village, and when the village is reconstructed, then the cities will be also' (`Abdu'l-Bahá, in *Bahá'í World* 450). Restoring stability and enthusiasm in the countryside is an arduous task which requires a simultaneous focus on both social and economic issues. However, the first prerequisite for social and economic well-being is the provision of productive employment opportunities that will provide rural dwellers with the means and confidence to 'reconstruct the village' as a place of peace and progress.

Two main sectors have a great influence on the carrying capacity of the rural areas: the small farm sector and the informal small business sector.

If the present trend in agriculture towards increased productivity of labour through mechanization and new cultivation techniques continues, the labour absorption capacity of the small farm sector will remain limited in the future. On the other hand, the informal sector, which is made up of rural non-farm activity, will play an increasing role in rural employment. Indeed, at the beginning of the 1980s, off-farm employment made up 43 per cent of the labour force in Colombia, 28 per cent in Kenya and 37 per cent in Malaysia. This trend has accelerated in subsequent years.

Characteristics of Small Rural Businesses

Despite the variety and size of small rural businesses – which range from craftsmen and small workshops to micro-agroindustrial businesses milling grain or making cheese – they have common characteristics:

- Small scale: They are usually family owned and operated; start up costs are covered mostly through family savings and rely only rarely and marginally on a loan component.

- Labour intensive: Production and service activities often rely on labour; equipment is simple and a great deal of ingenuity goes into the respective processes.

- Minimal capital input: Owing to a scarcity of capital and a lack of access to cheap sources of credit, investment in equipment and working capital is very small.

- Local market orientation: Most microenterprises find both their customers and suppliers within a very localized area. Rarely does the scope of the activity extend beyond the village and its environs.

- Resilience/flexibility: The preceding characteristics suggest that small business activity is very resilient to change, whether for good or bad. In addition, it is well adapted to the specific context and efficiently organizes the existing factors of production.

Role of Small Rural Businesses
Dynamization of Rural Areas

The most visible and far-reaching contribution of the establishment of small businesses in a given region is the integrative forces that it sets in motion. Indeed, small businesses have linkage potential that brings together, on a local basis, demand and supply. In addition, small businesses have a multiplier effect which stimulates the emergence of dynamic villages or rural towns which act like magnets for the surrounding countryside. This newly-found stability can reverse the process of depopulation and the disintegration of social and economic relations that plague rural areas.

Employment Potential

The development of employment opportunities through the emergence of small businesses will have three main consequences:

- stem and reverse the tide of rural-urban migration

- provide employment to the poorer sections of rural dwellers who have been displaced by the process of land concentration

- reduce this concentration pattern by providing off-farm opportunities to family members of the small farm sector thus reducing the need for distress land sales in times of agricultural hardship

Stimulation of Village Life

A stable and active village life will usually settle around the small cottage industries and agroindustrial businesses. The multiplier effect of the latter will not only create new business opportunities but will also inject new dynamism into the surrounding agricultural sector. The main consequence of this dual phenomenon will be the strengthening and growth of a bustling market. In addition, closer integration will stimulate more responsive patterns of social relations and a higher degree of cohesion and identification in the community. This reinforcement of social ties will stimulate the emergence of more representative and active local organizations and authorities.

Provision of Basic Services

The establishment of an active village life sustained by its own economic strength will provide the appropriate conditions for the implementation and strengthening of basic services. Indeed, the main prerequisites for the successful operation of basic services such as utilities, health and educational institutions is the stability of the environment and the potential of the settlement to act as a catalyst for the surrounding area.

Participation

One of the most promising potentials of small businesses is their capacity to stimulate new, broadly-based patterns of participation which transcend the established elitist relations of production prevalent in rural areas. A larger portion of the population can thus participate in the economic life of the area and contribute to the advancement of the community. The emergence of new social relations emphasizing participation and responsibility provides a fundamental landmark for sustainable development. The role of women is especially visible in this sector, giving them new sources of income but also a new position within the social framework of the community.

Stability of Income

One of the characteristic features of agriculture is the seasonal nature of income generation. Indeed, for most rural farming families, the bulk of yearly cash inflow occurs at harvest time and the quality/quantity of the harvest will determine to a large extent the well-being of the family for the year to come; this phenomenon is the same for the community as a whole. Small businesses have the capacity partially to offset this natural instability by providing both regular and alternate sources of income to both the individual and the community. In addition, the existence of new, less volatile sources of income will provide a further boost to fiscal revenue which can then be reinvested for social and infrastructure purposes.

Outcomes

As we have seen, there are many positive outcomes that a rural community can derive from the establishment of small enterprises. The most important is the contribution to the reconstruction of village life, both social and economic, based on more participative and responsible patterns of relationships. These new dynamic ties are the firm foundation on which rural areas can create the conditions for providing well-being and welfare to the rural population. However, besides this collective integration role, small businesses have the potential to cater for and nurture the development of the individual.

Developing the Individual

The person is both the object and actor of sustainable development, thus development is sensible only if it focuses on the individual; it must be a process aimed at liberating his physical, intellectual, social, emotional and spiritual potential in order to increase his capacity to contribute to the society to which he belongs: 'All men have been created to carry forward an ever-advancing civilization' (Bahá'u'lláh, *Gleanings* 215). Many factors contribute to the balanced development of the individual and prime among them is engagement in work. Indeed, work in a spirit of service 'has a value in itself, because it draws us nearer to God' (Shoghi Effendi, in *Lights* no. 2106). In addition, the development of the individual involves transformation, and transformation is reflected in one's behaviour and action. This process is achieved through 'fewness of words and abundance of deeds' (Bahá'u'lláh, *Tablets* 156). Since business organization in its multitude of forms, focuses and sizes is a means of action *par excellence*, it holds great promise for the development of the individual.

Small business organizations are an ideal instrument for the individual to crystallize his or her creativity, imagination and motivation. The combinations of skill, aspiration and motivation that lie at the heart of a business enterprise are as numerous and varied as the needs to be satisfied.

One of the individual's fundamental characteristics is the need continually to surpass his or her own self, to meet new challenges and new struggles. 'Life is after all a struggle. Progress is attained through struggle, and without such a struggle life ceases to have a meaning . . .' (Shoghi Effendi, in *Lights* no. 1870). Business is one of the most useful vehicles for this spirit of initiative and entrepreneurship.

Small business also has the great potential of enabling the individual to experience responsibility within the wider context of the local environment in which they both operate. Both the entrepreneur and the employer witness this sense of responsibility, albeit at different levels. In addition, small business provides an excellent framework for participation in decision-making through the process of consultation. Consultation provides an ideal forum for the expression of diversity and the practice of team work.

Because they are integrated into the surrounding environment, participants in the small business sector experience an acute sense of belonging and usefulness to their community. A strong identity and sense of purpose are two vital assets on the road to transformation and full development of human potential.

The combination of these four potentials can trigger a virtuous circle where transformation, improvement and service become primary objectives of the individual's existence; the context of the business organization offers him the means to express and manifest this newly-found purpose.

Conclusion

As we have seen, the emergence of a small business sector in rural areas can be very beneficial to both the collective and the individual. On the one hand, it contributes to the development of an active community life while, on the other, providing the individual with a space to grow and develop autonomously. The main challenge to the practitioners of development trying to implement a small business promotion scheme in any given rural area is how to transform this latent potential into reality. Although there are numerous possible answers to this challenge, it is the application of management practice within these small businesses that will determine whether or not this promising sector can live up to expectations.

Management Practice

In a broad sense, business organizations are instruments; they are the means through which an objective is achieved. As any other instrument, they are absolutely neutral. It is the human being through management that gives the business a direction and sets the guidelines to achieve the objective.

Definition of Management Practice

The role of management practice is to organize and set in motion available resources or factors of production in order to achieve/solve a given economic or social objective/problem. The factors of production include labour, land, raw materials, technology and capital, to mention only the most important ones. This definition implies that the two major focuses of management practice are the setting of operational objectives and the application of the technique to achieve them. The former is the 'where' while the latter is the 'how'. Any human action is made up of these two fundamental elements: an objective and the means to achieve it. Let us now review the features of desirable management practice.

Characteristics of Management Practice for Small Rural Businesses

In order to reap the full benefits of small rural business schemes, certain factors should be emphasized in the management practice set up and followed by the entrepreneur.

CONSULTATION

A forum for dialogue and participation in decision-making should be set up by the manager. This will enable him to improve significantly the reflection and input for the decision-making process while securing the motivation, responsibility and dedication of the employees.

CULTURAL SENSITIVITY

A successful management practice must integrate at its core the cultural specificities of the local circumstances. In this sense, management models which may have been very successful in other contexts may prove incapable of catering for important aspects of life in a specific environment.

INTEGRATION WITH THE LOCAL ECONOMY

The most potent agent of development in a given context is a business organization whose backward and forward linkages are rooted in the local/regional economy. Indeed, this integrative character will concentrate the multiplier effect on the surrounding area, thereby consolidating social and economic ties within the community. A management practice which emphasizes this process should be encouraged.

SOCIAL INTEGRATION

Because of its novelty as a rural mode of production, the small business sector of the rural economy does not suffer, unlike agriculture, from the constraints of a traditional/antiquated system of social relations of production. On the contrary, the small business sector has the opportunity to enlarge the spectrum of participation and integration to rural groups that were more or less marginalized from the dominant social and economic relationships. Thus management practice should encourage the recruitment of employees based on competence rather than gender, social or economic considerations; in this sense, discriminatory practices regarding the employment of women should be fought vigorously.

Vision Statement

The formulation of a vision for the business is one of the most fundamental components of management practice. This vision must incorporate not only objectives internal to the business itself but also provide an explicit sense of purpose for the business within the community. This latter aspect requires the formulation of a vision at the collective level by all social and economic agents of the community, which implies understanding and accepting that the collective vision overrides the individual business's internal objectives. The commitment of each member of this small business sector to participate in the construction of this vision and conform to its content is a core component of desirable management practice. A strong and representative community-based authority is mandatory in order to serve as a catalyst and enforcer of this collective vision.

The Search for Excellence

This concept should be one of the main guiding principles implemented by management practice. It is through the application of this notion that any business activity will produce the greatest benefits to the community, increase the reputation and prosperity of the business and foster the development of the individual.

Social Responsibility

Business management practice should stress the responsibility of each social and economic agent for the general well-being of the community/society to which it belongs. The scope and spread of the community or society with which one identifies will depend on the content of the prevalent value system. Regardless of size, management should take an active role in participating in the establishment of social services/utilities and encourage involvement of its own workforce in socially related activities.

People as an Asset

Management practice should recognize at its base that labour is not a cost to the business but, on the contrary, its main asset and as such needs to be nurtured and cared for. This reversal of attitude means accepting that the human is a multifaceted being whose needs are not only material, intellectual and physical but also social, emotional and spiritual. It is the balanced satisfaction of these needs that will foster the dedication and allegiance of a person to his or her business organization and to the wider community while promoting the full development of his or her potential.

This implies the implementation of practical measures from management, a theme which is, unfortunately, beyond the scope of this paper.

PROFIT SHARING

A general application of this practice would produce several positive effects. First, it would reduce, if not eliminate, the tensions between capital and labour which absorb so much of the energy that could be dedicated to more productive and constructive purposes. Second, it would promote a higher degree of dedication to and identification with the business by the employee. The principle of profit sharing can also be applied between the business organization and the wider community in which it operates. Indeed, the prosperity of any given rural business is based as much on the existence of demand within the community as it is on the work of its employees. Thus part of the profits should be redistributed to the community through fiscal methods but also using a voluntary mechanism. The latter has the great advantage of creating a spirit of responsibility and solidarity. The concept of profit sharing applied to management practice would be a great step forward in establishing higher standards of economic and social justice.

Conditions for the Application of Management Practice

Although there are certainly many more ideas which should lie at the core of any management practice of small rural businesses, the application of these proposals and the benefits they will achieve will depend to a large extent on two main factors: deliberate inducement policies at the macro level and the inspiration underlying management practice.

A FAVOURABLE ENVIRONMENT

In order for a small business sector to emerge and apply socially responsible management practices in the rural areas, several conditions must be established.

- Deliberate policies promoting the development of the small business sector should be implemented by the local/regional and national planning authorities. Such an inducement package should address such crucial questions as:

    - Fiscal measures to stimulate small businesses actively to hire employees, to distribute part of their profits to social ends, to integrate locally and so on. This is a very powerful tool when well used.

    - The provision of easier and more adaptable access to external finance sources.

    - The provision of counselling and advice services which can accompany and follow up emerging businesses.

- The provision of adapted professional training facilities focusing on the local mix of factors of production.

- The provision of technical research facilities capable of working hand in hand with the small business sector on process improvement.

- The provision of infrastructure, utilities and services necessary for the emergence of this sector.

- Authorities at all levels – local, regional and national – should provide the conditions that foster the smooth development of future entrepreneurs. This forward-looking role is one of the most fundamental played by public planners since businesses by their nature concentrate more readily on short-term objectives linked to the survival of their ventures. Thus the public sector should contribute to the creation in rural areas of appropriate and dignified conditions of life through the provision of basic services such as health and education facilities while promoting active measures for preserving the environment. This social and environmental focus of the public sector, added to the combined economic activity of the agricultural and small business sectors, will provide the conditions necessary for the development of the socially responsible entrepreneurs of tomorrow.

- One of the great, creative and far-reaching contributions that can be made by the public sector at the local, regional and national levels is the formulation and diffusion of a vision statement that can mobilize all social and economic actors behind shared objectives of development and the generation of the spirit that should underlie action. The latter should stress values such as unity, integration and solidarity as prime operational principles.

- The international context will also influence the capacity of individual governments to implement these policies. Indeed, international organizations such as the International Monetary Fund and the World Bank should soften their adjustment programmes to include significant social measures to offset the social cost of the transformation and transition process witnessed in the third world. More importantly, the recognition of the growing interdependence of the world should induce the adoption of new patterns of North–South relations where the medium-term goal of a unified world outweighs the present short-term, competitive model of relationships. The realization of such a goal, plus a more unified vision of purpose, will lead to a genuine acceptance of the need for a real transfer of resources from the North to the South. Indeed, as Bahá'u'lláh pointed out more than a century ago, 'The well-being of mankind, its peace and security, are unattainable unless and until its unity is firmly established' (Bahá'u'lláh, *Gleanings* 286).

A New Value System

Since it is the individual who directs and orients business activities, he or she will ultimately determine the impact of this activity on society as a whole. Thus if human actions, and more specifically businesses, are to reveal their full potential and contribute to an 'ever-advancing civilization', an ethic is required that will provide the framework within which management practice can be implemented. This ethic must, on the one hand, provide a vision through which human beings can find a sense of purpose and, on the other, establish a set of guiding principles or moral/spiritual values by which human action can be guided. It is only through an alliance with such an ethical package that management practice can hold to its promise of fostering real change and progress.

Source of This New Ethic

In order for this ethic to be operational, it must be reflected in the behaviour of the individual. If it remains only at the level of ideas it will not be translated into action. Victor Hugo once said that 'revolution changes everything except the hearts of men', observing that despite its declaration of human rights, the French Revolution exhibited the same oppression and lack of justice as the previous regime. Thus the required ethic must be based on a transformation which begins within people's hearts and recognizes love as the vital force behind human life and civilization. What other than the teachings of the religions have demonstrated the capacity to transform people in such a way that the most important advances of civilization have been achieved? A close analysis of history shows that the greatest civilizations have been founded on value systems based on love, justice and service derived from one or other of the great religions. The challenges that confront our decaying society can only find a solution in the moral and spiritual wisdom and principles of the great religions of the world, for 'The fundamentals of the whole economic condition are divine in nature and are associated with the world of the heart and spirit' ('Abdu'l-Bahá, *Promulgation* 238). Religion provides us with an ethic that sets out guiding principles and a value system as well as the power to transform our behaviour.

Guiding Principles for a New Management Ethic

The cornerstone of these guiding principles is the recognition of the spiritual as well as the material nature of human beings and, as a consequence, that human civilization is ruled by both spiritual and material forces. It is only through the equilibrium of these two forces that real, long-lasting prosperity will occur. 'Only when material and spiritual civilization are linked and coordinated will happiness be assured' (ibid. 109).

Unity of Humanity

The acceptance of the concept of the oneness of humankind at the base of all decisions by both individuals and the community implies the adoption of a whole set of new behaviours. Such new behaviours will foster solidarity and cooperation rather than the existing dominant forms of social relationships which emphasize conflict and competitive attitudes. Such a new spirit of unity will need to be applied at all levels of social and economic interaction, be it the business place, the community or the world. In addition to fostering these new attitudes, this principle of the unity of humanity will also promote the abolition of prejudice and discrimination, which have been such tremendously destructive forces. Such behaviours as racism, which 'retards the unfoldment of the boundless potentialities of its victims, corrupts its perpetrators, and blights human progress' (Universal House of Justice, *Promise*, para. 29) will, by the adoption of this principle, be entirely rooted out.

Values Other than Money

The dominant value in our society is money. It is the expression of both the capitalist model of competitive social and economic relations and of a world that increasingly relies on material criteria to measure success or failure of any human endeavour. The search for money has become an end in itself instead of serving a higher purpose. This material motivation has pervaded a management practice that has been geared solely towards maximizing profits for the business organization itself. All other purposes have been relegated to the background. This profit maximizing approach leads to the reinforcement of competitive behaviours where immediate benefits are emphasized even if achieved at the expense of other groups of people and future generations. Recognition of the interdependence of the human race and that the global challenges of our age require a unity of purpose and action will lead to the addition of other objectives to the concept of utility – objectives such as protection of the environment, social responsibility, promotion of diversity and the realization of the potential of the individual. The maximization of such utility will then become the main challenge of management practice.

Long-term Vision

The competitive model of relationships based on profit maximization provides a short-term vision at the expense of the longer perspective on which sustainable development and long-lasting prosperity can be achieved. Indeed, the greatest responsibility and contribution of today's economic and social agent is to promote a better world for future generations. As long as present conflict-based relationships predominate, society will be unable to free itself sufficiently from short-term objectives to face and prepare for the future. Every business, every manager must come to terms with the principle that future well-being has its roots in the present.

Empowerment of the Individual

In most organizations, the exercise of power and decision-making has been concentrated in the hands of a few. There is often a large gap between the few who take decisions and the many who live with them. This pattern of decision-making, on the one hand, suggests a lack of motivation and responsibility on the part of the many and, on the other, deprives the decision-making process of valuable contributions. However, when the individual's potential and his integration within a social organization or community are realized, he is empowered. Without such empowerment, a person can never take his destiny into his own hands and assume full responsibility for himself and the community or group to which he belongs.

Consultation

Within business organizations, the empowerment of the individual is achieved only through the use of candid, dispassionate and cordial consultation where the 'shining spark of truth' can emerge from 'the clash of differing opinions' ('Abdu'l-Bahá, *Selections* 87) and the expression of diversity. Consultation promotes the mobilization of everyone around an agreed objective and 'where a united will exists, nothing can effectively oppose and hamper the forces of constructive development' (Shoghi Effendi, in *Compilation*, vol. 2, 49). Consultation is the best vehicle for constructive and effective decision-making and proposes a framework and spirit under which it can operate.

Conclusion

As we have seen, the potential benefits to be reaped from the emergence of a small business sector can be very great. Indeed, agriculture alone will not be able to break the poverty spiral and the process of depopulation witnessed in most rural areas of the third world. The challenge of restoring pride in rural livelihoods and bringing back life to a decaying social structure calls for new forms of activity, grass-root participation and responsibility led by a new spirit of cooperation and service. These new forms of activity in the countryside should focus more and more on small non-farm activities structured as business organizations where individual development coexists harmoniously with a collective sense of purpose and vision. Successfully implementing this dual task is the challenge facing management practice. There are many guidelines that management practice can adopt to achieve this aim but the fundamental criteria for success will be the adoption of an ethic that will provide the motivation and liberate the energy required to translate these guidelines into action.

Works Cited

'Abdu'l-Bahá. *The Promulgation of Universal Peace*. Wilmette, IL: Bahá'í Publishing Trust, 1982.

— *Selections from the Writings of 'Abdu'l-Bahá*. Haifa: Bahá'í World Centre, 1978.

The Bahá'í World, vols. 1–12, 1925–54. rpt. Wilmette, IL: Bahá'í Publishing Trust, 1980.

Bahá'u'lláh. *Gleanings from the Writings of Bahá'u'lláh*. Wilmette, IL: Bahá'í Publishing Trust, 1983.

— *Tablets of Bahá'u'lláh*. Wilmette, IL: Bahá'í Publishing Trust, 1988.

The Compilation of Compilations. Prepared by the Universal House of Justice 1963–1990. 2 vols. [Sydney]: Bahá'í Publications Australia, 1991.

Lights of Guidance: A Bahá'í Reference File. Compiled by Helen Hornby. New Delhi: Bahá'í Publishing Trust, 2nd edn. 1988.

The Universal House of Justice. *The Promise of World Peace*. Haifa: Bahá'í World Centre, 1985.

Michel Zahrai took his first degree in International Development at Clark University in the United States and his Master's degree in Development Economics at the University of East Anglia in England. After completing his studies he worked for four years with a French non-governmental organization as the manager of a development project in Bolivia. For the last three years, he has been Controller, Europe, at the European headquarters of an American multinational corporation. Born into a Bahá'í family, Michel is involved in the European Bahá'í Business Forum and the International Society for Agriculture and Rural Development. He lives with his Bolivian wife and young family in France.

Reinventing the Village

Gary Reusche

Village Problems, Opportunities and Fundamental Needs
Fable

The morning light filters into the bedroom and slowly awakens the occupants. That night an owl had landed on the roof, not far from the bedroom window, its shrill cry startling the sleepers and interrupting their night's rest. It's time to get up and move slowly and peacefully in and out of the bathroom for the morning rituals and ablutions before walking the half kilometre to the Village House of Worship and the community prayer meeting and morning meditation. The air, as always, is fresh, now that internal combustion engines have been restricted. Even so, one is glad that in the morning they are not in use at all – even one of these engines produces a disagreeable smell and an artificial noise that spoils the beauty of God's nature and the expression of His perfections. This natural beauty resonates with the human soul; sometimes uplifting music or focused meditation has the same effect. Approaching the House of Worship, groups of people become visible, most quiet and meditative, but some quietly commenting on an event or thought with a loved one. Finally the villagers enter the assembly hall, quietly sit and prepare themselves for the dawn prayers.

After breakfast it's time to take care of the greenhouse, gardens and animals. First the fuel cell, the source of all the needed power, has to be checked. Its only byproduct is pure water, not noxious fumes. These tasks, mundane and manual, yet health-giving and satisfying, are difficult. The body works hard, lifting, moving, carrying. And veterinary services are needed today. Everybody these days has healthcare skills and practises health maintenance as the first defence against all disease – for animals no less than people. In the village all are trained in a variety of life skills because there is always some problem that creeps up and has to be dealt with, gently. When one does the morning work, it fulfils most requirements for food and exercise and provides some income for the family. Strange that even in this far northern clime, God has provided everything needed to prosper. And health problems are rare because of the exercise, the clean environment, the close association with the wonders of the world of nature and the lack of excessive stress.

After lunch, it's time to turn on the computer and research technologies related to the new small enterprise that looks promising for the village. New research has been done in Madya Pradesh. Using the ever-developing Internet, one can telecommute to work. The Internet is now accessible with practically unlimited speed by satellite links and radio nets from any remote farm, thereby connecting the rural inhabitants into a system of communication and information undreamed of until recently. The work accomplished by telecommuting is not only satisfying intellectually, it balances the more manual tasks of the morning and provides an additional source of revenue to pay for the modest requirements of the home, as well as the usual needs: health- care, saving for old age, money to contribute to the funds, music lessons or theatre tickets for the cultural centre located in the shadow of the House of Worship.

By 3:00 p.m. the workday is complete. After a short rest, it is time to practise a new violin composition, then off to the practice session for the latest village musical. It's amazing how creative people are when given the opportunity and the right environment. After dinner there is a meeting of the Village Store Foundation, an auxiliary institution of the House of Worship. This organization has acquired the trust of the villagers and the funds that flow to it are sometimes more than can be dispersed. Almost. There are so many difficulties in the village that need solutions, and although theoretically everyone can take care of themselves, in practice many families and individuals fall on hard times and turn to the foundation for help. Every case is different; each is individually considered in the light of the teachings of Bahá'u'lláh. And the systems assure that receiving help does not create dependence or humiliate those receiving it.

Current Trends

From a global perspective, the cultural and ecological conditions in the rural world can only be described in apocalyptic terms. Of the six billion human beings in the world, 1.3 billion live on less than one dollar a day, half live on less than two dollars a day. Looking at it from another perspective, 80 per cent of humanity alive today have no access to products and services that many of us consider to be human necessities (Gro Brundtland, Director General, WHO). Many of the world's poor live in rural areas or have migrated out of rural areas in search of a better life.

The world's urban population continues to increase and over the next three decades urban areas in less developed regions are expected to double in size. As a result, the world population will see a historic shift in its urban–rural composition: 35 years from today, nearly two-thirds of the population will be living in urban areas. In less than two decades, the number of cities with five million or more people will be about 60, with the large majority located in the developing world. Many cities will reach unprecedented sizes, exceeding 15 or even 20 million inhabitants (Chamie, press release).

Most of the 'power' in society has shifted from the rural roots of civilization to urban areas, where people either idealize country life or despise it for its cultural backwardness and lack of opportunity.

Industrialized Countries

Some focus on the poorer countries when thinking about rural problems. But negative processes are not limited to the poorer countries in the 'South' (Pinstrup-Andersen, *World Food*). Trends in North America show the family farm to be declining, giving way to corporate farming. Industrial farming practices, competition and efficiency in agriculture create low per unit margins. What this means practically is that the 'profit' has declined for each hectare of land. In order to stay in business, farms have to grow in size. The dynamics of this process are devastating to traditional farm families.

Over the past 50 years these processes have caused many rural communities in the industrialized world to lose their purpose. With fewer and larger farms, there is a concomitant decline in the rural population, resulting in a declining demand for local markets and locally purchased inputs and resulting in the economic decay of the rural community. Some communities have attempted to diversify their economy to reduce their dependence on agriculture and others have abandoned agriculture entirely as a basis for economic development. Industry hunting has become a preoccupation of many small town councils. Jobs, any kind at any cost, seem the primary development objective in some declining rural communities (Ikerd, Sustainable Agricultural Systems).

Many development activities in rural areas are rooted in the short-run exploitation of undervalued people, capital and natural resources. Large companies, although they may provide jobs in rural areas, often pay poorly and are expensive to attract and retain. The number of working poor in rural areas – workers with full-time jobs who live below the poverty line – has continued to rise. In addition, many manufacturing companies that initially relocated in rural areas in the industrialized world are now moving to poorer countries where labourers are willing to work even harder for far less money. This is the best interpretation of this trend. Uglier interpretations of this shift to the poorer countries find expression in terms thought to have disappeared from the life of the world: slavery, child labour, illegal and morally reprehensible exploitation of the resource base, and the use of corrupt government officials to obtain business advantage. Efforts to attract low quality, low paying jobs are increasingly regarded in the industrialized world as expensive and ineffective strategies for rural economic development.

Tourism, vacation homes, retirement communities and rural residences have helped some rural communities survive the harsh reality that they retained no major purpose during the industrial era other than, perhaps, to facilitate the forced migration of rural people to the cities.

Developing Countries

In the so-called developing countries, the circumstances and dynamics are different; often they result from technologies and changes in other parts of the world which impact with disastrous effect on rural communities in the developing world. Population increases in Africa, for example, brought about by improvements to healthcare and other technology-related factors, destroyed age-old agricultural systems. The 'slash and burn' agriculture practised for generations in Africa doesn't work any more. This traditional system was based on large areas of land that could lay fallow and were thus allowed to regenerate their fertility over long periods of time. In the traditional world, an area was 'slashed and burned', cropped for four to six years and then left fallow. Because land was available, the best areas were chosen for cropping. Now, owing to population pressures, there is not enough arable land to allow it to lie fallow for more than a few years, thus the underlying premise for the success of traditional agriculture has been undermined by circumstances. Dozens of similar examples of how the world of the traditional farmer has been irreversibly altered could be given. Yet few examples exist of new and sustainable ways to replace this lost world.

The typical rural household in the developing world can be typified as follows. The family farm is relatively small, consisting of perhaps a half hectare to one hectare of arable land. Part of this land is used as a homestead, with a small, simple home. The floors might be concrete, wood or even dirt. Electricity may or may not be available but if it is available it is used mainly for lighting. Food is prepared on fires; some are inefficient open fires and others are enclosed. The women of the household spend a lot of time preparing and making food. Water is not available in the house. The women often carry the water, if they are lucky, from a sanitary village well. If they are unlucky, they have to carry the water from long distances and the water is of extremely poor quality. Often, the water brings diseases to the family when it is not boiled, either out of ignorance or because there is not enough wood to boil it. Finding wood for the fire is a constant battle. Fuel wood is scarce and efforts to grow wood are inadequate. It's a constant struggle. An outhouse is an expensive innovation. Often the toilet is in the open. In this typical home there are a number of children, maybe three or four or even more. They attend the village primary school for a few years but it is hard to pay for the uniforms and the books. The agricultural activities are mostly subsistence. Even if there were theoretical opportunities to increase production, this would require credit, which is not available, or markets, which may not be accessible. In any case, the first priority is household food security. When this is achieved, the surplus will be sold for some cash to pay for schooling, medicine and other items that cannot be produced on the homestead. But subsistence needs predominate. Little is left over for cash purchases. And at the market the small farmer is often exploited at harvest by the traders, who pay the farmer a very low price.

The above description of rural life in the developing countries is meant to be illustrative of the type of extreme poverty and overwhelming difficulties of many rural families. It is not an exaggeration. More advantaged professionals, including the author, working in these areas and attempting to help these populations, often feel helpless in the face of the obstacles to development. For rural households, breaking out of this paradigm is extremely difficult and beyond the capacity of many that are suffering its consequences. For decades development projects have attempted to improve the lot of these rural families, and although some progress can be measured, too often what appears to happen is that extreme poverty is made less extreme. Achieving household food security is a major achievement. Even if the development projects are overwhelmingly successful and the farm families have the means to work their fields and homesteads effectively, and fair markets exist where their products can be sold, the fact that their resource base is perhaps one hectare limits the family income to near subsistence levels.

Nonetheless, development must take place; to maintain the status quo in the villages can mean freezing whole societies in lives of poverty and ignorance. Without development, whole populations may be prevented from attaining a sufficient standard of living or working successfully in their chosen professions. They may be unable to afford a reasonable level of security to ensure the well-being and health of family members or have sufficient human and financial resources to develop their communities. They may be unable to fully participate in the lifestyle offered by the Bahá'í teachings, in which all enjoy the minimum requirements for sustainability and for achieving their purpose in life.

Developing countries have made progress in expanding access to schooling: education statistics show primary school enrolments to have significantly improved over the last 30 years. However, there are still regional deficiencies, especially in Africa and especially with girls. The UN Millennium Development Goals call for universal primary enrolment by 2015 but this target is not likely to be achieved. These figures, however, refer only to primary education. What about secondary education and beyond?

> Consider carefully: all these highly varied phenomena, these concepts, this knowledge, these technical procedures and philosophical systems, these sciences, arts, industries and inventions – all are emanations of the human mind. Whatever people has ventured deeper into this shoreless sea, has come to excel the rest. The happiness and pride of a nation consist in this, that it should shine out like the sun in the high heaven of knowledge ('Abdu'l-Bahá, *Secret* 2).

The World of the Soul

Bahá'u'lláh once described the country as the 'world of the soul' (Bahá'u'lláh, quoted in Esslemont, *New Era* 33). But will the country be a place for rest and relaxation in the future, with life centred on the cities? Does the 'world of the soul' consist of recreation areas, nature areas and small populations of workers oriented to serve urban dwellers, interspersed with technologically very efficient 'industrial' farms? This seems to be the trend in the industrialized world. In the developing world, breaking out of the cycle of poverty seems unattainable in the near to medium term.

There is little discussion on sustainable rural communities or how such communities become sustainable places where people choose to live, can afford to live and where subsequent generations also find fulfilment and purpose. This is true not only among the relatively uninformed urban intellectuals but also among rural development professionals designing programmes to help these peoples. For example, in the Philippines a project designed to redistribute land resources and develop the economic life of poor farmers resulted in a modest but significant increase in the quality of life and the education of the youth. Then the youth escaped to the cities. This was a reported beneficial impact of the project. There was nothing to keep them in the village. And for the family, it was better if they got even a low paying job in the city and sent some of this money to the farm.

The response of the typical villager in both materially poor and rich countries is to look for ways to escape this bleak landscape. Thus the youngest and the brightest leave the village and go to the city. There they find ways to obtain more education and a job. In the developing world, the odds against success are high. This out-migration leaves villages even bleaker and their prospects for the future even dimmer.

Village Rights

An attempt has been made to describe some complex issues that are having an impact on rural areas and to show that the trends are not good. Large-scale rural development projects have taken place in many of the poor rural areas of the world, supported by a large group of bilateral and multi-lateral donors, but sustainable progress is slow and sometimes non-existent. It is popular to criticize these efforts but this criticism is rarely constructive and accentuates the difficulties of finding real solutions. A new paradigm for rural areas needs to be created and there are no easy answers. The 'world of the soul' must be a place where people live and prosper. It can be suggested from this phrase, and from other Bahá'í teachings about agriculture, that rural areas are actually very good for the human soul and the current situation is an aberration, the result of scientific and technological development without a concurrent development of a world value system, a juvenile expression of technology used because it exists, not because it produces a better life for the peoples of the world.

In order for the village to survive, fundamental rights need to be recognized and practised. Ironically, the success of scientific agriculture has diminished its priority in societal decision-making, created an underclass and disenfranchised the rural sector. To balance this, certain principles or rights need to be supported. Three are selected for discussion below.

Environmental and Social Justice

The teachings of the Bahá'í Faith recognize basic human rights, morals, spiritual and physical laws (Tahririha-Danesh, *Perspectives*). They are divine in origin, purposeful and the basis for correct solutions. They are woven into the fabric of the material world. The existing situation in rural areas is clearly unjust and contrary to these laws. If societies choose to marginalize the rural areas, exploit their relative weakness in democratic societies and let future generations pay for the ecological abuses, then this choice will determine an outcome. Possible outcomes include social instability, terrorism, ecological catastrophes and epidemics, hooliganism and disrespect for the law, and the dead-end and hopelessness of a life that is not centred on authentic values.

Without a consideration of justice and equity, a situation arises where, on one hand, a few have so much to eat that being overweight is a serious health problem, and on the other, there are millions of starving children. Or, in rich countries there are closets so full of clothes that it can be difficult to decide what to wear, yet in poorer countries most of the population struggles to have clean clothes to wear. There are houses in the industrialized West so big that some rooms are rarely used and numberless huts in poor countries with earthen floors and no toilets.

The chasm between those in richer countries and the extremely poor in rural areas is so great that it seems to produce a selective blindness. The rich countries, when exposed to rural suffering on the news, are ready to send aid and help. This is a normal human response to such need. But when the crisis is over and the news teams move to another crisis area, the human suffering of the extremely poor continues without the world's notice.

In order to create the necessary changes in the village, the question of social justice will need to be on the agenda of those advantaged populations that have the resources to support social change. The Bahá'í Faith teaches:

> O Ye Rich Ones on Earth! The poor in your midst are My trust; guard ye My trust, and be not intent only on your own ease (Bahá'u'lláh, *Hidden Words*, Persian 54).

From the macro level, one can argue that urban society has virtually assured the failure of rural communities by pursuing 'cheap food' policies and concentrating the development of resources on urban areas. Many cheap food policies are, explicitly or implicitly, designed to supply a greater prosperity for urban voters at the expense of rural farmers. Oftentimes, to feed his family, the farmer produces in non-sustainable ways, causing, for example, soil erosion, since the first priority is to survive. The environment in which the farmer is forced to operate controls him or her. In this way, so-called democracy, based wholly on material perspectives, and especially when power is concentrated in urban centres, creates an environment for failure at the rural level and indirectly destroys the environment. This is a spiritual problem. Ironically, many urban dwellers believe the farmer is the source of the problems associated with the degradation of the environment. It is not that simple.

Minimum Sustainable Standard of Living

Rural communities have to be more than a utopia. They have to, literally and figuratively, work. They must have economic justification.

The Bahá'í International Community in its statement *The Prosperity of Humankind* elucidates a view of prosperity that includes spiritual factors. Some aspects of a new view of prosperity include:

- considering efficiency together with equity, service, social justice, harmony and cohesion

- the creation and preservation of beauty (both man-made and natural)

- support for human rights

- finding the balance between the interests of the individual and of society

- fostering equality and partnership between women and men

- protecting and nurturing families

- sharing the fruits of science and technology for the whole of the human race

- safeguarding the world's ecosystems

- balancing work–life, health, spirit

and

- a values-based, or values-centred, framework

Prosperity at the village level raises the question of an acceptable minimum standard of living. When confronted with poverty in rural areas, few discuss a prosperous rural environment. The question of a minimum standard of living goes far beyond this paper but some things seem obvious:

- Rural children deserve to be born into a family of sufficient economic and spiritual strength to provide for their spiritual and material upbringing and permit them full integration into the life of the modern world. They have a right to an official registration of birth, needed for various purposes, such as school attendance or protection from trafficking.

- Rural residents must have the opportunity to live in a clean, well-lighted, warm home, with proper sanitary facilities and clean water.

- Rural residents must have food security, from birth to the grave, enough to assure good health, provide energy and honour the 'temple of the spirit' (Shoghi Effendi, in *Compilation* 12).

- Rural residents must have enough education to permit gainful employment and this implies a secondary, perhaps tertiary, education. Ways and means for everyone who has the capacity to develop their intellectual potential should be available and affordable. All should be able to read the writings of the major religions, to continuously grow in knowledge and wisdom in proportion to his or her efforts.

- Rural residents should have access to technical and time-saving devices that provide relief from drudgery and create free time that can be devoted to the family, to service and community activities, to membership on consultative bodies and to leisure.

- Rural residents should have the opportunity to develop and express their creative energies and to enjoy the beauty that is produced by others.

- Every person has the right to sufficient healthcare, starting with preventative health maintenance and including wise use of modern technologically advanced solutions to health problems when required.

- Every person has the right to live at the end of his life with dignity and to die in dignity, ideally surrounded by family and friends, and without excessive pain.

- Every person has the right to a burial plot, with a proper casket and a marker and a ceremony given by family and other loved ones.

Two things are noted when this list is compared with the current situation in rural areas. The most obvious is that most of humanity doesn't get close to these minimum standards. Less obvious is that it is unlikely that farming alone will provide sufficient income to make this kind of a life a reality for all.

Spiritually Viable Villages

Individually, a minimum standard of living is a right. But to attain this, more than individual initiative and effort is required. There is also a collective requirement to make the village viable. The village must have the potential to be sustainable. If there is insufficient public infrastructure, for example, there may be no realistic way to make the village sustainable. Without access roads to transport the harvest to market there is no basis for market activity.

The Bahá'í perspective for a viable village starts with the thesis that 'unless the development of society finds a purpose beyond the mere amelioration of material conditions, it will fail of attaining even these goals' (Bahá'í International Community, *Prosperity* 3–4). More specifically, the Bahá'í paradigm is that 'purpose must be sought in spiritual dimensions of life' (ibid. 4). Interestingly, given the relative simplicity of the village and its small scale in comparison with urban areas, this perspective may be more easily implemented.

From the developing world, there are endless examples of village development projects that have failed owing to the fact that their focus was material. For example, the development of village cooperatives is a common theme in many of the poorer countries of the world. Such village cooperatives are normally conceived as assistance to grass-roots organizations to improve the economic life of the members and usually focus on the agricultural sector. Villagers join together to buy some common assets, such as a storehouse, small tractors or grinding mills. In addition, the village cooperative can serve as a basis for extension education and training activities provided by the government, or a means in which the private sector can present their products and services to the rural sector. It all sounds very logical and workable. But too often these projects work only when there is external assistance, in the form of a project or direct government subsidies that are channelled via the cooperative. It would be too easy to say that the approach was not sufficiently 'bottom up' or 'participatory' and therefore it failed. There is also the spiritual dimension. In a large number of cases the cooperatives fail owing to dishonesty within the group, lack of unity and the inability to manage the assets for the good of all the members of the cooperative. These are spiritual problems.

The above-mentioned cooperative example will also fail if there is not enough prosperity to satisfy the legitimate needs of all its members. If agriculture is not enough, for example, to provide a reasonable standard of living for all the farmer-members and the cooperative is focused solely on agricultural possibilities then it is doomed to a competition for the available income, which is insufficient for all.

The Bahá'í perspective suggests that a paradigm shift towards development focused on the spiritual dimensions of life will produce an entirely different motivation among those involved in the development process (see Bahá'í International Community, *Prosperity*). Special consideration, it is suggested, needs to be given to the fundamental place of the village and its relative weakness vis-à-vis the urban masses. Such an orientation will create an enabling environment that transcends a constantly changing economic landscape. This constantly changing economic landscape is a business cliché in the 21st century. Businesses that cannot adapt and evolve will eventually lose competitiveness and decline. Viable spiritual villages, by definition, also must adapt, evolve and remain competitive. Forces internal to the village have to creatively find answers.

The foundation for creating such villages needs to be essentially developmental. To be more specific, economic planning should empower people and institutions to build a new social order where the limitless potentials of human consciousness can grow and blossom (Bahá'í International Community, *Prosperity* 22).

Given a spiritual focus, sustainable villages will have to provide an acceptable level of economic returns and sufficient quality of life to those who live and work in the community. Robert Reich (*The Work of Nations*) stresses that the world economy is no longer local or even national in scope. It is global. The 'artificially imposed division of human societies into "developed" and "developing"' is being overcome by the information and technological explosion of the late 20th century. Underdeveloped India is well-entrenched in materially abundant Silicon Valley. Neither communities nor nations can depend on capturing the benefits of local capital, local industries or even locally developed technologies in a global economy. Money, jobs and technology can and will move freely to anywhere on the globe where they can be used to the greatest advantage. This trend has the potential to revive the rural landscape.

Reich outlines two fundamental strategies for economic development in a global economy. First, he advocates investment in infrastructure, including such things as roads, bridges, airports and telecommunication access systems. Reich's second development strategy is to invest in people. People who work with their minds will be the fundamental source of productivity in a knowledge-based 21st century. If a nation is to be productive in the post-industrial economy, its people must be productive.

A similar thought is found in *The Prosperity of Humankind:*

> The most important role that economic efforts must play in development lies, therefore, in equipping people and institutions with the means through which they can achieve the real purpose of development: that is, laying foundations for a new social order that can cultivate the limitless potentialities latent in human consciousness (Bahá'í International Community, *Prosperity* 22).

Combining Reich's idea with those of the Bahá'í International Community creates a vision for the establishment of the spiritually viable village.

Given a spiritual focus, a development focus, an empowerment focus and an economic focus, it seems obvious these factors must operate within a community where the quality of life is high. As long as the village is considered culturally and intellectually backward, people will naturally move away to areas of greater potential for the full expression of the human spirit. Rural communities need to be so inviting that new workers are attracted and seek to relocate to the village. The primary attraction of rural communities for current and future workers will be the promise of a desirable quality of life. Quality of life is a product of the terms by which people relate to each other, socially, politically and economically; and the terms by which they relate to the other elements of their physical and biological environment (Ikerd, *Sustainable Agricultural Systems*).

The Bahá'í teachings and professionals in sustainable agriculture agree that the communities that survive and prosper during a rural renaissance will be culturally diverse. Diversity will be an important source of creativity, innovation and synergistic productivity and will be an important aspect of quality of life in rural areas (ibid.). Making this vision real is 'faith in action'.

Actions for Village Development

A Bahá'í vision of agricultural and rural areas would seem to find its basis in acknowledging their fundamental importance to both the individual and to society and thus the belief that current negative trends are temporary. Correcting the rural–urban imbalance would not actually involve designing a future because planning a future will have a large probability of error and involve 'linear thinking'. Just because something happened one way in the past, it does not follow that it will happen the same way in the future ('Designing a Future'). Although the following quotation is taken from another context, it seems relevant for solving the difficult problems that exist in the rural regions of the world.

> What Bahá'í institutions do, rather, is to strive to align the work of the Cause with the Divinely impelled process they see steadily unfolding in the world, a process that will ultimately realize its purpose, regardless of historical circumstances or events. The challenge . . . is to ensure that . . . Bahá'í efforts are in harmony with this Greater Plan of God, because it is in doing so that the potentialities implanted in the Cause by Bahá'u'lláh bear their fruit (Universal House of Justice, *Century of Light* 69).

Although the precise nature of the changes required might not be known from the onset, nevertheless action is needed to address the issues and create new circumstances so that the rural areas have the potential to bear their fruit. The balance of this essay attempts to describe courses of action that might help to bring this about.

Application of Spiritual Principles and Personal Transformation

Agriculture in the industrialized nations, although highly developed, is far from perfect. The list of areas where change is required is long. Major problems include the loss of prime agricultural land to non-agricultural purposes, irreplaceable soil loss from erosion, the non-sustainable use of aquifers for irrigation, the damming of rivers and streams thereby destroying ecosystems, gene manipulating technologies in plants and animals, the composition of animal feeds sometimes producing human disease, breeding focused on maximum yields with nutritional quality hardly considered, the reduction of genetic diversity in plants and animals, fertilizer and pesticide pollution in rivers and streams, the overuse of antibiotics in animal production, the use of toxic pesticides that disrupt the ecological balance and various post-harvest and processing activities that reduce the nutritional composition of products or introduce potentially harmful preservatives. Societal choices made in the industrialized countries have led to over-urbanization and a concomitant and unacceptable ecological 'footprint' for these societies. In order to create change, the basis for choice needs to change.

A whole range of 'implied' societal choices impacts on rural areas and only a sea change in values and their application can create the foundation for positive change.

> The Bahá'í approach to the problem of extreme poverty is based on the belief that economic problems can be solved only through the application of spiritual principles. This approach suggests that to adjust the economic relationships of society, man's character must first be transformed. Until the actions of humankind promote justice above the satisfaction of greed and readjust the world's economies accordingly, the gap between the rich and the poor will continue to widen, and the

dream of sustainable economic growth, peace, and prosperity must remain elusive. Sensitizing mankind to the vital role of spirituality in solving economic problems including the realization of universal equitable access to wealth and opportunity, will . . . create a new impetus for change (Bahá'í International Community, *Human Rights and Extreme Poverty*, para. 3).

Changing character involves individual growth and development – personal transformation. It needs to start from early childhood. The Bahá'í community has a full programme which supports individual transformation from birth to grave. Wholehearted involvement in these and similar programmes is required. This personal development process provides the proper basis for understanding the spiritual principles involved and thus finding solutions that are consonant with these principles.

Better Informed

Poverty and a declining standard of living in rural areas are intuitively unacceptable; after all, the rural areas are needed for urban life to exist. Yet contemporary society in the industrialized world, and oligarchs in the poorer countries, do far too little to make the situation better. The acceptance of extreme poverty is difficult to comprehend from the moral position of any of the world's major religions or the compassion inherent in human hearts. It suggests a spiritual 'schizophrenia', where the suffering and decline of rural societies are compartmentalized and ignored. Whatever the reason, we should be keenly concerned by the condition of the world and we should work towards its betterment. An interest in geography, history, current events, societal trends and political movements is one way to stay in touch with the requirements of the rural areas and to ensure that appropriate solutions are implemented and their needs are not forgotten. Study of spiritual principles needs to be combined with an accurate knowledge of the current situation. Too often urban dwellers know little about rural areas, upon which they depend for their sustenance and well-being, yet at the same time they may have very strong opinions about various elements of the problem. 'Be anxiously concerned with the needs of the age ye live in', says Bahá'u'lláh, 'and centre your deliberations on its exigencies and requirements' (Bahá'u'lláh, *Gleanings* 213).

Knowing more about the relationship between urban populations and farmers is important to society. For example, urban dwellers should understand that the market dictates the behaviour of farmers – and 'the market' is themselves. It is a cliché to agribusiness that the housewife searches for the cheapest product of acceptable quality. But does the housewife know that buying the cheapest product on the shelf creates a ceiling that limits the options of farmers to engage in more environmentally friendly production practices or to increase their income to levels consonant with others in society of equal education and workload?

If the awareness of urban consumers is increased, other factors may be included in the decision to buy, including nutritional quality, biodiversity, freshness and environmental preservation. Trends in the cities suggest that urban dwellers will support a healthy food supply and a cleaner environment even if it means the food budget is increased. There is an increasing awareness that many current agricultural practices are unacceptable. Organically grown products are commercially available for this market segment. If more is known about the issues, it will be easy to garner support for a viable village agricultural economy where urban dwellers will choose to pay the full price for food (including conservation costs and the elimination of questionable yet economically mandated production practices). They will do this because it is the right thing to do – it is a just action – and because they understand the situation.

Shop Green

Individual solutions to rural problems include the purchase of products from 'organic' or 'green shops' where the cost of the food is higher but the way it is produced and its quality is better. This is a very passive solution but still it is effective. If everybody shopped 'green', this would bring many improvements (Walz, *Organic*). Farmers will always produce for available markets and the method of production is typically secondary to markets and being able to make acceptable profit. Perhaps a more active variant would be to become better informed about agricultural production issues and begin to work with like-minded individuals to find even better solutions.

Activism and NGO Involvement

Rather than waiting for corrections, individuals can choose to be pro-active and to work for change. Although such activism may sound utopian and unproductive, to the Dutch such considerations are almost universally accepted and applied. Individually and socially, the Dutch consciously choose the public good over the right of unrestricted human or business choice and they pay for it in taxes and lifestyle options. For example, no one can build a new home on farmland in the Netherlands, even if this puts pressure on the housing sector. But they believe they are making the right choice, and although they may have less money to spend and live in smaller houses than Americans, the quality of life and individual security is considered to be better.

In organizational theory, organizations don't transform, individuals do. This theory can be extrapolated to larger social groups. Individuals need to support the spiritually viable village. An effective way to do this is to support one of the numerous non-government agencies working in this field. Passivity in the face of the current problems will cause the problems to worsen. Bahá'ís are called upon to work for a new world order. When the world is more just, the vision of a spiritually viable village becomes feasible. The current situation in the world, with a few enjoying the benefits of 'civilization' and many living in abject poverty, is destabilizing. Lobbying politicians and becoming involved in promoting resources for the development of the world's poor is something that everyone can do to generate resources for development. One can also volunteer time and energy to assist this worthy cause. Many people do.

Farming Options and SMEs

Farming is a noble profession. Modern agriculture in the industrialized world has steadily developed and gravitated towards large-scale production in one location where there are the best conditions for a particular crop, with consumption occurring elsewhere. This is the structure of the current system and producers and agricultural scientists do everything possible to make it work well. Decisions are grounded in solid economics. The scientists, businesses and communities involved are proud of what they do and their contribution to society. They are largely God-fearing and moral people. Nobody planned that the system would one day work so well that over-production would become a problem or that large corporations would have control over every aspect of production and marketing. The largest seed company in the world started as a family farm business. Producers, looking for ways to survive in this environment, started to overlook some of the environmental costs of using marginal areas for production, or the fact that the technology sold and promoted resulted in the nutrient pollution of ground water, rivers and streams, or that they incurred tremendous debts to buy the required equipment, leaving them very vulnerable to mistakes and bad weather.

In industrialized agriculture, every effort is made to train all the stakeholders and to be successful. In order to get a nice red tomato on the supermarket shelf, which stays bright red until it is bought and then consumed, a complicated chain of events is required. All the steps are thoroughly researched by competent scientists. Varieties have to be bred, not for nutritional value or for taste, but for redness, tough skins to allow mechanical harvesting, storability, often in a controlled environment, and high yield so that a good rate of return will be made on all the money invested. The logistics at harvest are phenomenal. The story of just getting bright red tomatoes to the urban consumer can fill pages. It is essentially a demand-driven system.

Farming options include family farms, corporate farms and collective farms. In the industrialized world, family farms are decreasing. Those that remain in business are generally long established; starting new would be very difficult. In the poorer countries, the family farms tend to be too small to be economically viable. In the industrialized world, many farm families remain on the farm as part-time farmers if they cannot make enough money by farming alone. If there is some additional off-farm employment available, this is a realistic and viable option to stay in business. The same dynamics could operate in the developing world if more off-farm employment opportunities were available.

The corporate farm is becoming the dominant force in the industrialized world. The corporate farm also exists in the poorer countries, side by side with the poorer subsistence farmers, which is an unstable situation. The corporate farms are efficiently governed almost solely on the principle of profit. The Bahá'í concept is that efficiency needs to be considered together with equity, service, social justice, harmony and cohesion (see Bahá'í International Community, *Prosperity*). Efficiency and profitability largely motivate corporate farms.

The corporate farm is backed up by increasingly sophisticated agricultural science, supporting both production and food processing, in order to mass-produce for urban areas. The corporate farm enables the urban masses, and the urban masses increasingly dictate (consciously or not) the way that food is produced and made available in the supermarket.

The collective experiment in the Soviet Union has left a bad image of this kind of farming. Soviet-era collective farms simply did not work, and since the break up of the Soviet Union, most are empty shells looking for ways to 're-engineer' their operations and revive their prospects. Some are breaking up into family farms; most are becoming corporate farms. Collective farming, on the other hand, is an effective way to farm in many traditional societies around the world. These traditional systems were based on mutual collaboration amongst the villagers. They had many different forms and were adapted to different circumstances. Such collective farming practices, where families group together for some of the farming tasks or the development of common infrastructure, would fit very well into the concept of the spiritually sustainable village. But collective farming to the degree practised under forced socialism does not seem to work.

Non-agricultural Income

If agriculture alone is not enough for a spiritually viable village, then it follows that other income-generating activities are required. In the book *Megatrends 2000* (Naisbitt and Aburdene) there is a discussion about new technologies that are changing economic dynamics in rural areas. It is suggested that individual entrepreneurs, or 'mind workers', can be an answer. The vision is based on economically viable, small and medium-sized enterprises (SMEs). Proofs are given of SME competitiveness, even when compared with large multinationals. For example, a recent US National Science Foundation study showed that small businesses produce 24 times as many innovations per research dollar as do large businesses.

Further, Naisbitt and Aburdene talk of an electronic heartland. This heartland is increasingly global. Nearly cost free communication networks will link the world. The technologies already exist and they are getting better and better. Free to live almost anywhere, more and more individuals will decide to live in small cities and towns and rural areas.

The suggestions of a reborn rural landscape, practising sustainable agriculture, created from advances in technology and based on the development of the human spirit, begin to sound more like a rural area that is 'the world of the soul'. The introductory fable is not as utopian as it looks at first glance. There can be very good reasons to abandon the cities for a rural life, reasons relating to quality of life and to the incorporation of new concepts of human prosperity that include a spiritual purpose for life. Many people, if options are available, may choose to abandon the suburbs for rural areas for quality of life or spiritual reasons: a better environment for the development of the soul, more living space, a cleaner environment, prettier landscapes or to live in a 'real' community. The challenge of rural economic development is to create places where spiritually aware 'mind workers' can develop, be productive and want to stay and become a part of the community.

All are Producers – At Least Part-time

Bahá'u'lláh stipulated, 'Special regard must be paid to agriculture,' noting 'Agriculture is highly developed in foreign lands, however in Persia it hath so far been grievously neglected' (Bahá'u'lláh, *Tablets of Bahá'u'lláh* 90). 'Abdu'l-Bahá states, 'The fundamental basis of the community is agriculture, tillage of the soil. All must be producers' ('Abdu'l-Bahá, *Promulgation 217)*.

Reflection on the meaning of these statements would lead many to think that they apply only to the poorer countries of the world. The statements are highly applicable to the majority of human souls inhabiting the planet, most of whom are extremely poor, but perhaps a bit puzzling to most people living in the industrialized world, far from agriculture and far from being a producer. On the other hand, the capacity to effect any change in the present system may well depend on those urban dwellers in the industrialized world who turn their efforts to building a new, more 'rural friendly' paradigm.

Producing some part of the family food requirement is entirely possible for nearly everybody on the planet. Self-sufficiency would not be necessary – the idea is not to eliminate trade or specialization or urban areas. There are possibilities to produce food in every region of the planet. (There are even web sites that describe agricultural production in totally self-contained systems for space travel.) There are many good reasons to be a producer.

Part-time farming is a solution for both the industrialized and the developing countries. With smaller scale technologies, many options are possible that cannot be done under the conditions of large-scale, industrialized agriculture. Not only can the food industry be re-oriented towards nutritional quality, biodiversity and human health, there are other indirect advantages of being producers. Producers do physical work. They get exercise, a requirement for a healthy body and mind. Producers observe the environment closely. Producers have to find solutions to their production problems and at the same time preserve the environment. They don't lose touch with the natural world around them.

Some benefits from part-time farming can be subtle. It is a cliché that farming is much more than a profession. It is a special, captivating way of life. It may even be that farming helps the individual to stay in touch with the Creator.

Nature is God's Will and is its expression in and through the contingent world . . . Indeed a man of insight can perceive naught therein save the effulgent splendour of Our Name, the Creator. Say: This is an existence which knoweth no decay, and

Nature itself is lost in bewilderment before its revelations, its compelling evidences and its effulgent glory which have encompassed the universe. (Bahá'u'lláh, *Tablets* 142)

There are many ways to get involved and work towards better economic opportunity in the rural areas. These include:

- Study agronomy and other agricultural sciences.

- Find employment on an industrialized farm and work for change from within.

- Study rural economics and business with a focus on those business or market opportunities that are appropriate for rural areas.

- Establish and grow a vegetable garden.

- Study SMEs, become an entrepreneur, start a business in a rural area.

- Telecommute to work from a home in a rural area.

and

- Study ecology and other environmental sciences, and the management of parks and recreation areas.

Participatory Development

Rural systems, like agriculture itself, involve many variables affecting the outcome of a particular event. Using state-of-the-art methodologies to study and plan a development intervention does not assure a positive outcome. For example, one would expect to increase household food security by assisting families to use more modern means of production, thereby increasing the food supply. Experience shows it is not that simple.

Between 1960 and 1990 many believed that the 'Green Revolution' was going to solve the food supply problems in India and other parts of the world. Prior to the Green Revolution, ships in the harbours of India were periodically queued up to deliver food aid. More than 40 years of agricultural development has dramatically increased the food supply in India. But the end result is that per capita food availability has simply kept pace with the increase in population. Village demographic studies near the Rabbani School in Madya Pradesh in the late 1980s and early 1990s consistently showed an abnormally high percentage of boys (resulting from the early childhood death of girls). This was attributed to insufficient family food supplies and then a preference for boys in the household. This example shows that well-intentioned, well-funded technological solutions may miss the mark.

Perhaps other strategies to improve food supply would have produced better results than simply focusing on food production. Facts show that below-replacement fertility characterizes 61 countries, virtually all the more developed countries (McCarthy, 'Examining Link'). The European Union stresses the strong interdependence between women's empowerment, their decisions on partnership, acknowledgement of their sexual and reproductive rights and resulting population growth. Education, particularly of girls and women, has a powerful effect on decisions about childbearing and childcare, as it enables real choices to be made about reproduction (Brito, 'Examining Link').

These and other corroborating facts from different contexts argue that the empowerment of people, especially women, has to be part of development planning. This approach appears to be difficult for development agencies, agencies that too often look for quick results, results that can be achieved in a project life cycle of two to five years. There is practically universal acceptance in development circles of the essential need for participatory, bottom-up approaches to development. But this intention is often inadvertently sabotaged by the political decision-making processes, budget processes and funding conditions.

The necessity of using participatory approaches to plan rural development interventions is now well established. Few rural development projects, from whatever agency, are funded unless they contain substantial components of community involvement in planning, design and implementation. Where these participatory initiatives have worked it is because individual communities and groups have been shown the benefits of working collaboratively, of developing a collective vision and learning and adapting their management practices together. Much has and is being learned by the families, communities and professionals that have been involved in these processes and the lessons are well documented.

However, despite the increasing numbers of participatory initiatives in different parts of the world, there are few examples of success. Often, what is called 'participation' is so in name or intent only. True participatory projects are those which build local skills, interests and capacities that continue even after the project ends.

In the Area Growth Programmes now practised by Bahá'í communities throughout the world, community development occurs in steps. Basic structures that are required for participatory planning are gradually developed. Ethical and moral principles are systematically studied and practical applications pursued. The communities gain skill in consensus-building and conflict management. The Bahá'í process of consensus-building referred to as 'Bahá'í consultation' not only requires the participants to give up conflict models of decision-making but also incorporates a spiritual and values-based decision-making process. Complex social and economic development projects are considered appropriate only when the community has attained sufficient consultative skills and maturity to manage them. Development efforts in the initial stages are gradual and stepwise, initially focused on the development of human resources and the spiritual element. Bahá'ís feel their approach is a good model that is applicable on a global scale.

It is suggested that full support of the Area Growth Programme in all its aspects is one of the best ways to create change in rural areas. It provides the foundation for subsequent development potential. It is based on decades of Bahá'í experience in community social and economic development throughout the world, including large numbers of communities located in the rural areas. It may even be that these Area Growth Programmes, as they gain in capacity and grow to include both Bahá'í and non-Bahá'í stakeholders in the village, may become logical partners for the development efforts of regional governments and international donors.

The concept of 'learning by doing' or 'adaptive management' accommodates uncertainty and complexity in the participatory process. As indicated above, rural development activities involve complex systems with many uncertain elements. Participatory approaches emphasize developing the knowledge and action needed to constructively change real situations. In practice, all these processes are cyclical and highly iterative, with many steps likely to be carried out simultaneously. There are also numerous entry points. You need to have a systematic approach and good methodologies to manage the process and assess its results (or lack of them).

The rural residents and beneficiaries of participatory development activities require a range of skills and training. In addition, supporting the Area Growth Programme, or other similar initiatives, can be a fulfilling mission for life. Those interested would start with themselves, to prepare themselves by acquiring the attributes, motivations and skills necessary to wisely assist the work. They might also choose an appropriate profession, facilitating their move to a region and their collaboration with the larger programme, thereby supporting the unfolding of the potentials of the community where they now live. A whole range of development skills can be acquired to facilitate the process of participatory development, examples of which include:

- spiritual leadership (where leaders become servants)

- consultation and consensus-building

- facilitation and empowerment

- understanding the dynamics of 'ownership'

- management to create ownership

- planning and process management

- project cycle management

- statistical methods

- monitoring and evaluation

and

• technical writing

The Vital Role of the Mashriqu'l-Adhkár

'Abdu'l-Bahá describes the Mashriqu'l-Adhkár (the House of Worship) as 'one of the most vital institutions in the world', and Shoghi Effendi indicates that it exemplifies in tangible form the integration of 'Bahá'í worship and service' (Bahá'u'lláh, *Kitáb-i-Aqdas* 190–1).

The Mashriqu'l-Adhkár is the complex of buildings and institutions devoted to the spiritual and social well-being of the community and to its education and scientific training, including a central house of worship, a university, a travellers' hospice, a hospital and drug dispensary, a school for orphans and a home for the infirm (ibid. 190).

It seems obvious that this institution must play a major role in rural development and one can hypothesize various spiritual, coordinating and developing roles that it will play. But, to date, the Bahá'í community has no real experiences with its application in village settings.

Not only will the Mashriqu'l-Adhkár play a major role in village development, it also has a social role. 'Abdu'l-Bahá, discussing the function of the economic institutions auxiliary to the Mashriqu'l-Adhkár, says:

Each person in the community whose need is equal to his individual producing capacity shall be exempt from taxation. But if his income is greater than his needs, he must pay a tax until an adjustment is effected. That is to say, a man's capacity for production and his needs will be equalized and reconciled through taxation. If his production exceeds, he will pay a tax; if his necessities exceed his production, he shall receive an amount sufficient to equalize or adjust. Therefore, taxation will be proportionate to capacity and production, and there will be no poor in the community ('Abdu'l-Bahá, *Promulgation* 217).

Microfinance and Microenterprise

Microfinancial services are proven practical measures to alleviate poverty. These programmes of credit, savings and related services for the resource-poor are known to have motivated activism from villages. The Microcredit Summit of February 1997 proposed a plan to reach half the world's severely poor families (100 million families), particularly the women of those families, with credit and other financial services by 2005. By the end of 2003, approximately 55 million families report having received microcredit.

Growth in the Implementation of Microcredit, 1997–2003

Year	Number of institutions reporting	Total number of clients reached	Number of 'poorest' clients reported
1997	618	13,478,797	7,600,000
1998	925	20,938,899	12,221,918
1999	1065	23,555,689	13,779,872
2000	1567	30,681,107	19,327,451
2001	2186	54,932,235	26,878,332
2002	2572	67,606,080	41,594,778
2003	2931	80,868,343	54,785,433

(Source: S. Daley-Harris, State of the Microcredit Summit Campaign Report 2004, 2004)

Microfinance programmes are based on the vision of united, prosperous communities by stimulating healthy civic engagement and strong community enterprise economies. With inculcation of universal values and ethics linked to sound economic principles, the microfinance movement works to create a sustainable model of human development and well-being.

The founding principle of the microfinance effort is the belief in the inherent dignity of people: of the integrity, innate capacities and commitment of the majority of the world's resource-poor to work hard, take responsibility for their own lives and to repay credit rather than depend on charity. From the universal principles of human dignity, trust, unity and the equality of women emerged practical measures that became the methodologies of successful microfinance programmes worldwide.

Grameen Bank in Bangladesh and FINCA's (Foundation for International Community Assistance) village banking model pioneered solidarity groups of women as the key to high loan repayment and social change. Another programme in Colombia, Fundación para la Aplicación y Enseñanza de las Ciencias (FUNDAEC), built upon the Grameen strategy and introduced pre-credit training modules on solidarity, unity, trustworthiness and service as the foundation of creating community. The results were profound. Not only did the introduction of these concepts raise the loan repayment rate, villagers also consistently emphasized that the greatest impact on their lives was a renewed sense of unity within the community. They found that the collective effect of the community working with a consciousness of unity and mutual support increased productivity, social bonding and activism. Beyond individual production, the results included numerous secondary economic effects.

Microenterprises are very small, informally organized, non-agricultural businesses that often employ a third or more of the labour force in lower-income countries. Enterprises involved in direct agriculture production, that is, small farmers in the context of their farming activities, do not fall under the microenterprise rubric. Farm household value-added and non-farm activities, however, are microenterprises.

There is a historical reason behind the exclusion of farmers from the microenterprise definition. Programmes directed at primary agricultural production did not reach the many microenterprise activities that were present in developing countries.

Many microenterprises employ just one person, the owner–operator or 'microentrepreneur'. Some microenterprises include unpaid family workers and others may have one or several hired employees. Although no single characteristic distinguishes microenterprises from small enterprises, a threshold of ten employees, including the owner–operator and any family workers, is used by some agencies as the upper limit for an enterprise to be considered 'micro'.

Clearly, such non-farm activities and enterprises are part and parcel of any strategy to create spiritually and materially viable villages.

Works Cited

'Abdu'l-Bahá. *The Promulgation of Universal Peace*. Wilmette, IL: Bahá'í Publishing Trust, 1982.
— *The Secret of Divine Civilization*. Wilmette, IL: Bahá'í Publishing Trust, 1990.
Bahá'í International Community. *Human Rights and Extreme Poverty. Statement to the 49th Session of the United Nations Commission on Human Rights*, 1993.
— *The Prosperity of Humankind*. New York: Bahá'í International Community United Nations Office, 1995.
— *Who is Writing the Future? Reflections on the Twentieth Century*. London: Bahá'í Publishing Trust, 1999.
Bahá'u'lláh. *The Hidden Words*. Wilmette, IL: Bahá'í Publishing Trust, 1990.
— *Tablets of Bahá'u'lláh*. Wilmette, IL: Bahá'í Publishing Trust, 1988.
Daley-Harris, S. 'State of the Microcredit Summit Campaign Report 2004', 2004 Microcredit Summit Campaign, viewed January 2005.
    http://www.microcreditsummit.org/pubs/reports/socr/2004/SOCR04.pdf
'Designing a Future or Tempting Fate'. Australian Broadcasting Corporation's Radio National. Sunday, 22 May 2005.
Brito, Nuno (Portugal, speaking on behalf of the European Union). 'Examining Link

Between Population, Gender, Development'. Commission on Population and Development, Thirty-Third Session, 27 March 2000 (POP/759).
http://www.scienceblog.com/community/older/archives/L/2000/A/un000457.html

Chamie, Joseph (Director, Population Division, Department of Economic and Social Affairs, UN). Press Release POP 759, 2000.

Commission on Population and Development, Thirty-Third Session: 'Examining Link Between Population, Gender, Development'; 27 March 2000 (POP/759).)
http://www.scienceblog.com/community/older/archives/L/2000/A/un000457.html).

Esslemont, J.E. *Bahá'u'lláh and the New Era*. London: Bahá'í Publishing Trust, 1974.

Ikerd, John. *21st Century Agriculture: The End of the American Farm or the New American Farm?* Partnerships for Sustaining California Agriculture, Woodland, CA. 27–8 March 2001. University of Missouri's Sustainable Agricultural Systems Program, 2001.

— Economics as if People Mattered: Farming for Quality of Life. 2000 Midwest Small Farm Conference and Trade Show, sponsored by Sustainable Earth, Noblesville, IN. 17–18 November 2000. University of Missouri's Sustainable Agricultural Systems Program, 2000.

'Improving the use of collaborative approaches within natural resource management: multi-stakeholder processes'. Massey University, New Zealand.
http://nrm.massey.ac.nz/ch; angelinks/co_man.html http://www.massey.ac.nz/

McCarthy, James, Heilbrunn Professor of Public Health, Colombia University's Mailman School of Public Health. 'Examining Link between Population, Gender, Development'. Commission on Population and Development, Thirty-Third Session, 27 March 2000. (POP/759).
http://www.scienceblog.com/community/older/archives/L/2000/A/un000457.html

Naisbitt, Johan and Patricia Aburdene. *Megatrends 2000*. New York: Avon Books, 1990.

Pinstrup-Andersen, Per; Rajul Pandya-Larch and Mark W. Rosegrant. *World Food Prospects: Critical Issues for the Early Twenty-First Century*. Washington DC: International Food Policy Research Institute, 1999.

Reich, Robert B. *The Work of Nations*. New York: Vintage Books, Random House Publishing, 1992.

Tahririha-Danesh, Tahirih (ed.). *Bahá'í-Inspired Perspectives on Human Rights*. Hong Kong: Juxta Publishing, 2001.

The Universal House of Justice. *Century of Light*. Thornhill, ON: Bahá'í Canada Publications, 2001.

UN Commission on Population and Development. *Proceedings from the Thirty-third Annual Session* 2000.

UN Commission on Sustainable Development. *Proceedings from the Eighth Session*. 2000.

Walz, Erica (Programme Coordinator). *Third Biennial National Organic Farmers' Survey*. Santa Cruz, CA: Organic Farming Research Foundation, 1999.

Dr Gary Reusche has been an agronomist, development and management specialist since 1975. His career started as an academic in agricultural sciences in the United States and was followed by increasing experience as a development consultant, evolving in the mid-1980s into privatization issues, agribusiness and microfinance. His specialization in agronomics includes the seed industry, extension and training, and management. He has gained project experience in some 50 countries over a range of rural development subjects and has worked for a wide range of clients, including the European Union, IFAD, World Bank, GEF, USAID, FAO/UNDP, the SENTER (Netherlands), DGIS (Netherlands), DFID (UK), Abu Dhabi Fund, and the private sector. He is currently director of the EU funded project 'Support to SMEs in the Rural Sector' which works to develop the cooperative credit system in Ukraine.

The Genetic Modification of Crops: A Bahá'í Scientist's Perspective

Paul Olson

Agricultural practices have evolved in many parts of the globe since the 19th century and the time of Bahá'u'lláh. The purpose of this essay is to point out that the Revelation of Bahá'u'lláh offers guidance regarding a recent agricultural technology, the application of genetic modification (GM) to crop species. A Bahá'í approach to the subject neither glorifies nor vilifies the technology. Instead, in assessing the risks and opportunities associated with this technology, it calls for a broad understanding of creation and an emphasis on building ethical values, institutions and processes that promote and safeguard the interests of the entire human race and the environment.

Discussions throughout the essay will interweave Bahá'í themes of unity, interdependence, justice and consultation. Bahá'í analyses emphasize a perspective of process; this analysis of agriculturally-related genetic engineering will follow that tradition. The first section defines the relationship between GM and agriculture. In the second section a brief review of the Bahá'í writings sheds light on the related concepts of nature and science; later in the second section Bahá'í perspectives on creation are outlined with particular attention to the plant and animal kingdoms. In the third section transformations in both physical and legal spheres are outlined to help the reader relate genetic engineering to other models of system change. The last section borrows a framework often employed by the Universal House of Justice to examine the impact of agricultural genetic engineering upon three interacting levels – community, institutional and individual.

Introduction
Clorinda Minor's New Old World Frontier

The story of a Christian woman, Clorinda Strong Minor, and her agricultural exploits in 19th-century Palestine may seem like an unusual starting point for a Bahá'í perspective on agricultural GM but her story provides a useful springboard into a discussion of the subject (Kreiger, *Expectations*). Briefly, Clorinda Minor, along with many of her fellow Philadelphian Millerite friends, faced a spiritual crisis in 1844 after fulfilment of the prophecies of Christ's return did not meet her specific expectations. Undeterred by disappointment, in the 1850s she left her husband and committed herself to the establishment of an agricultural settlement in the Holy Land where Jews, Christians and Muslims laboured side by side. She believed that agricultural revitalization of the region would foster the restoration of the Jews that would lead to the return of Christ. In the last few years of her life she transformed the Palestinian agricultural genescape with introductions of improved cultivars of various horticulturally important plant species (e.g. cabbage) and she introduced the wheelbarrow and the American pitchfork to the suite of Palestinian agricultural implements used at the time. Moreover, she inadvertently helped to precipitate Zionist agricultural settlements.

Clorinda Minor's innovations provide a historical example of how spiritual principles guide human endeavour in agriculture and land use. Her life can also serve as a metaphor for genetic engineering. Clorinda's beliefs pulled her from her community in Philadelphia and reintegrated her into Palestinian society in much the same way technological enthusiasm inspired recent transfers of insect-resistant genes from a bacterial genome into the corn genome. The consequences of moving one system component – be it a visionary person or a DNA sequence – into a new context may trigger lasting changes to a system, be it a society or a genome. Finally, Clorinda's story reminds us of how the intertwined web of agriculture and geopolitics has been dramatically transformed in the last 150 years, concurrent with the young Bahá'í era.

Purpose, Outline and Limitations of This Article

Since Bahá'u'lláh's mission began, agricultural development options across the globe have proliferated far beyond introductions of cabbage cultivars, pitchforks and wheelbarrow technology. The emerging technology of genetic engineering, made possible by rapid growth in the fields of biology and molecular genetics, is one such recent development. A variety of contemporary voices advocate that genetic engineering may extend development options, enhance efficiency and contribute to the production of wealth; on the other hand, some contend that socioeconomic, safety and ethical issues call for extreme caution or total bans on application of the technology.

This article seeks to examine genetic engineering in the broad and balanced context of guidance found in the Bahá'í Revelation. The article will focus on Bahá'í perspectives on the specific example of genetically modified agricultural plants. It is hoped that it will broaden the reader's understanding of issues to consider in making decisions about the roles of agricultural genetic engineering in enhancing the means and ends of agricultural development. This discussion has certain limitations. At present, no one can claim to write the Bahá'í perspective on agricultural genetic engineering. The author of the article, a research scientist employed by a commercial seed company, admits to a North American bias in many of the specifics and emphases. For example, individual rights to land ownership may be defined differently in different systems. Furthermore, other Bahá'ís working in this field may view genetic engineering differently. What will be agreed on is the idea that the Bahá'í perspective provides values, principles and processes that will assist humanity in making decisions about the applications of this technology.

The Relationship between Genetic Modification (GM) and Agriculture

To the author's knowledge, the Bahá'í writings never explicitly define agriculture. However, according to 'Abdu'l-Bahá, 'The fundamental basis of the community is agriculture, tillage of the soil. All must be producers' ('Abdu'l-Bahá, *Promulgation* 217). This implies that agriculture encompasses most of society's confluence with land, plant and animal resources. It extends to the production, processing, storage and distribution of food, fibre, medicine, pigments, fragrance and other raw materials.

For purposes of this discussion, genetic engineering in plants refers to technology that allows a novel DNA sequence to be incorporated into a plant population or species without pollination. To date the technology has been applied in agriculture with the aim of creating new traits or enhancing existing ones of agricultural crops. Genetic engineering has been used in crop plants with varying degrees of technical success to improve disease resistance, control insect damage, confer resistance to herbicides, enhance drought resistance and bolster the nutritional and industrial appeal of specific crops. As a relatively new technology, the frontier of applications for genetic engineering has yet to be fully explored; vaccine production and environmental remediation serve as examples of other areas where genetic engineering might offer opportunities.

The Bahá'í writings imply a value on innovation, efficiency and productivity for agricultural activities – within the bounds of 'moderation in all things' (Shoghi Effendi, *Dawn* 193). For example, Bahá'u'lláh states: 'Agriculture is highly developed in foreign lands, however in Persia it hath so far been grievously neglected. It is hoped that His Majesty the Sháh – may God assist him by His grace – will turn his attention to this vital and important matter' (Bahá'u'lláh, *Tablets* 90). Also, 'Abdu'l-Bahá noted that 'From the Caspian Sea to the River Oxus there stretch wild and desolate plains, deserts, wildernesses and valleys . . . Formerly that plain bore the fruit of the finest civilizations of the past. Tokens of development and refinement were apparent all around . . . commerce and agriculture had reached a high stage of efficiency . . .' ('Abdu'l-Bahá, *Selections* 288) and further, 'Wealth is praiseworthy in the highest degree, if it is acquired by an individual's own efforts and the grace of God, in commerce, agriculture, art and industry, and if it be expended for philanthropic purposes' ('Abdu'l-Bahá, *Secret* 24). Thus technologies with the potential for enhancing the development of agriculture should not be ignored, although they must be promoted with the utmost care for humanity.

Nature, Creation and Science

Both nature and science are terms that frequently enter discussions about genetic engineering, thus a rigorous examination of their meaning will help lay a foundation for further discussions of agricultural GM.

Nature

Bahá'u'lláh exalted nature:

> Say: Nature in its essence is the embodiment of My Name, the Maker, the Creator.
> Its manifestations are diversified by varying causes, and in this diversity there are
> signs for men of discernment. Nature is God's Will and is its expression in and
> through the contingent world. It is a dispensation of Providence ordained by the
> Ordainer, the All-Wise . . . Indeed a man of insight can perceive naught therein save
> the effulgent splendour of Our Name, the Creator (Bahá'u'lláh, *Tablets* 142).

'Abdu'l-Bahá further expounds upon the magnificence of nature and upon humanity's relationship with it, stating that:

> Nature is that condition, that reality, which in appearance consists in life and death,
> or, in other words, in the composition and decomposition of all things.
>   This Nature is subjected to an absolute organization, to determined laws, to a
> complete order and a finished design, from which it will never depart . . . from the
> smallest invisible atom up to . . . great stars and luminous spheres, whether you
> regard their arrangement, their composition, their form or their movement, you
> will find that all are in the highest degree of organization and are under one law
> from which they will never depart.
>   But when you look at Nature itself, you see that it has no intelligence, no will
> . . . there are no voluntary movements except those of animals and, above all,
> those of man. Man is able to resist and to oppose Nature because he discovers the
> constitution of things, and through this he commands the forces of Nature; all
> the inventions he has made are due to his discovery of the constitution of things
> ('Abdu'l-Bahá, *Answered Questions* 3–4).

But even though humanity can change the course of nature – at least temporarily
– at the same time humanity represents just one extension of nature. 'Abdu'l-Bahá
states, 'One of the things which has appeared in the world of existence, and which
is one of the requirements of Nature, is human life. Considered from this point of
view man is the branch; nature is the root (ibid. 4). In the words of Robert White,
'the Bahá'í writings offer a vision of wholeness in our relationship to Nature . . .
that empowers individuals to become agents of transformation in developing an
ecologically sustainable global civilization' (White, *Spiritual Foundations* 24).
    Consistent with Bahá'í values, one might consider that humanity's power to
channel the forces of nature, including the introduction of novel or foreign genes
into a crop plant, is not any less 'natural' than is the nature of a wheat grain to
grow and mature into a harvestable plant outside its centre of origin. Opponents
of genetic engineering have often dismissed the technology as 'unnatural' or not
'organic' and therefore inherently dangerous. Denouncing a product as 'unnatural'
has little meaning because composition and decay are both organic conditions. To

brand a set of technologies as 'unnatural' seems more like prejudice than a legitimate statement of truth.

A review of history shows that pre-Columbian agriculturalists selected, recombined and subsequently propagated unique lines of maize from wild progenitor populations against the tides of 'natural' evolutionary forces. Other ancient maize innovators dispersed these newly modified maize lines to new habitats. Over generations, newly modified maize lines lost both their resemblance to their ancestors and their ability to compete in their ancestral habitat. The composition of domestic maize populations changed radically owing to human intervention, yet few would denounce these selection practices as 'unnatural' or insinuate that it was a dangerous enterprise – many in Mexico treat the genesis of maize as a sacred event. In many ways the selection and transformation of genes by contemporary genetic engineers for the subsequent development of unique transgenic lines of maize from individual cell lines echoes the selection, recombination and propagation that ancient maize growers exercised on maize populations. The types of processes are parallel, although the level of modification shifted from the plant population level to the genome level. Despite radical modifications to composition of maize populations prior to transgenic technology, few completely avoid corn on the grounds that it is unnatural.

To understand a Bahá'í perspective on nature also necessitates an understanding of Bahá'í perspectives on creation. Agriculture derives from the interaction of several kingdoms of nature. The Bahá'í writings acknowledge the diversity of nature and creation. Bahá'í cosmology organizes natural diversity using the concepts of mineral, plant and animal kingdoms. 'Abdu'l-Bahá delineates kingdoms of nature based on unique processes demonstrated in each kingdom:

> If we look with a perceiving eye upon the world of creation, we find that all existing things may be classified as follows: first, mineral – that is to say, matter or substance appearing in various forms of composition; second, vegetable – possessing the virtues of the mineral plus the power of augmentation or growth, indicating a degree higher and more specialized than the mineral; third, animal – possessing the attributes of the mineral and vegetable plus the power of sense perception; fourth, human – the highest specialized organism of visible creation, embodying the qualities of the mineral, vegetable and animal plus an ideal endowment absolutely absent in the lower kingdoms – the power of intellectual investigation into the mysteries of outer phenomena. The outcome of this intellectual endowment is science . . . ('Abdu'l-Bahá, *Promulgation* 29).

Even though the mixing of genes between plant and animal kingdoms becomes possible with genetic engineering, it may reassure some (and seem esoteric to others) that Bahá'í kingdoms concepts can still apply. For example, a cell line containing the genome of a plant and a few animal-derived DNA sequences is still a plant because 'Abdu'l-Bahá defines these kingdoms in relationship to process and emergent properties, not in terms of components.

'Abdu'l-Bahá explains at another time that the processes of nature that sustain the kingdoms are fundamentally spiritual and driven by the expression of love and attraction:

> We declare that love is the cause of the existence of all phenomena and that the absence of love is the cause of disintegration or nonexistence. Love is the conscious bestowal of God, the bond of affiliation in all phenomena . . .
> . . . As this [the human kingdom] is the superior kingdom, the light of love is more resplendent. In man we find the power of attraction among the elements which compose his material body [as in the mineral kingdom], plus the attraction which produces cellular admixture or augmentative power [as in the plant kingdom], plus the attraction which characterizes the sensibilities of the animal kingdom, but still beyond and above all these lower powers we discover in the being of man the attraction of heart, the susceptibilities and affinities which bind men together, enabling them to live and associate in friendship and solidarity ('Abdu'l-Bahá, *Promulgation* 255–6).

From this spiritual perspective of creation, genetic engineering might be viewed as diversifying the expression of love in the plant kingdom. Genetic engineering is an innovative means of nature by which novel combinations may arise with potential for creating benefits to humanity. Genetic engineering, like any natural process, may affect composition and decomposition of organisms; like all natural forces, agricultural GM requires attention to safety and moderation. As with any form of love, responsibility comes with the power of humanity to partner with the forces of nature.

Science

Science provides tools for humanity to prosper creatively and safely in partnership with the rest of nature. 'Science is the governor of nature and its mysteries, the one agency by which man explores the institutions of material creation ('Abdu'l-Bahá, *Promulgation* 29). Science is a process that distinguishes humanity from the rest of nature. Science occupies an important role in Bahá'í life. 'The first teaching of Bahá'u'lláh is the duty incumbent upon all to investigate reality' (ibid. 62). '[Science] is especially characteristic of man. This scientific power investigates and apprehends created objects and the laws surrounding them. It is the discoverer of the hidden and mysterious secrets of the material universe and is peculiar to man alone. The most noble and praiseworthy accomplishment of man, therefore, is scientific knowledge and attainment' (ibid. 29). Thus, science 1) increases knowledge and understanding of creation, 2) opens paths of service to humanity and 3) can empower all levels of society by creating an expanding, participatory process of human advancement.

1) First, numerous passages in the Bahá'í writings laud the pursuit of scientific investigation and the acquisition of new knowledge, which can include genetic engineering.

Strive as much as possible to become proficient in the science of agriculture . . . the acquisition of sciences and the perfection of arts are considered acts of worship. If a man engageth with all his power in the acquisition of a science or in the perfection of an art, it is as if he has been worshipping God in churches and temples ('Abdu'l-Bahá, *Selections* 144).

2) Second, scientific investigation affords the believer another path of service for the progress of humanity.

Science should, therefore, be pursued to improve human life, and have as its conscious and ultimate goal the establishment of world peace and the unification of the human race.
Unfortunately, science can similarly perfect instruments of war, support the concentration and abuse of power, undermine social and cultural values, and endanger the existence of humankind. It is not sufficient, therefore, by itself, to guarantee progress. It must be directed by the civilizing aims and values of the society it is intended to serve (Bahá'í International Community, *Science*).

Clearly, the warning applies to genetic engineering, as it does to other areas of scientific application. Mere imitation or blind application of technologically complex and esoteric techniques does not constitute science. Science is a process of knowing and discovering that leverages the practice of known techniques to extend beyond current limitations. Both the potential benefits and hazards of genetic engineering warrant scientific investigation. Ideal scientists are 'busy by night and by day with meticulous research into such sciences as are profitable to mankind, and they devote themselves to the training of students of capacity' ('Abdu'l-Bahá, *Secret* 21).

3) Recent statements from Bahá'í institutions have emphasized that the current inequities in the distribution of scientific capacity across societies must be broadened to involve participants from all circles of global society. Application of technology and science by an elite few will not promote the progress of civilization. In many ways, the process of scientific accomplishment is as important as what is accomplished. After all, new scientific discoveries continually reframe the context, significance and utility of previous discoveries.

Regarding social and economic development strategy, noted a recent statement from the Bahá'í International Community:

. . . the issue rather is how scientific and technological activity is to be organized. If the work involved is viewed chiefly as the preserve of established elites living in a small number of nations, it is obvious that the enormous gap which such an arrangement has already created between the world's rich and poor will only continue to widen, with the disastrous consequences for the world's economy already noted. Indeed, if most of humankind continues to be regarded mainly as users of products of science and technology created elsewhere, then programmes ostensibly designed to serve their needs cannot properly be termed 'development'.

A central challenge, therefore – and an enormous one – is the expansion of scientific and technological activity. Instruments of social and economic change so powerful must cease to be the patrimony of advantaged segments of society, and must be so organized as to permit people everywhere to participate in such activity on the basis of capacity (Bahá'í International Community, *Prosperity* 17–18).

Current access to genetic engineering investigation and many other technologies remains out of reach for all but a limited few. Clorinda Minor's example of participatory development may even offer clues for how to effectively organize scientific activities.

In summary, agricultural genetic engineering, as the intersection of several kingdoms of nature, must comply with natural laws that science seeks to understand. As an application of the scientific process, agricultural GM has potential to enhance understanding of nature and expands opportunities for service to humankind. Increased access to the scientific process will multiply the possible benefits and better define the safety parameters needed to effectively apply the technology.

Parallels in Recent Transformations of Land and Genetic Resources

From discussions of the interrelated concepts of nature and science, the ground is now prepared for an exploration of the parallels in recent agricultural transformations of the mineral kingdoms (i.e. land) and the plant and animal kingdoms (i.e. genetic systems, referred to as genescapes). This section aims to aid the reader to see agricultural genetic engineering in a fresh light by examining parallel changes that have occurred and continue within both physical systems and legal systems of ownership. The perspective offered here is not intended to convince the reader to blindly accept all applications of GM; rather the parallels outlined here may help anchor considerations of GM to less novel models of transformation. An appreciation of known models of system transformation may aid future consultation in determining appropriate regulation and application of the technology. Bahá'u'lláh exhorts, 'In all matters moderation is desirable' (Bahá'u'lláh, *Tablets* 69). Neither a wholesale rejection of the technology nor a policy of unbridled experimentation with it seem to represent a moderate approach.

Parallels in Physical Transformations of Land and Genetic Systems

Rhetoric advocating a wholesale ban on GM has given the impression that crop genomes need to be spared from any alterations. In contrast, the Bahá'í writings suggest that mineral, plant and animal systems undergo and catalyse constant alteration. Many forces shaped evolution of geologic and genetic systems even before humankind's capacities developed to their present state. 'Abdu'l-Bahá explains:

All beings, whether large or small, were created perfect and complete from the first, but their perfections appear in them by degrees. The organization of God is one; the evolution of existence is one; the divine system is one. Whether they be small or great beings, all are subject to one law and system. Each seed has in it from the first all the vegetable perfections. For example, in the seed all the vegetable perfections exist from the beginning, but not visibly; afterward little by little they appear. So it is first the shoot which appears from the seed, then the branches, leaves, blossoms and fruits; but from the beginning of its existence all these things are in the seed, potentially, though not apparently . . .

Similarly, the terrestrial globe from the beginning was created with all its elements, substances, minerals, atoms and organisms; but these only appeared by degrees: first the mineral, then the plant, afterward the animal, and finally man. But from the first these kinds and species existed, but were undeveloped in the terrestrial globe, and then appeared only gradually . . . When you consider this universal system, you see that there is not one of the beings which at its coming into existence has reached the limit of perfection. No, they gradually grow and develop, and then attain the degree of perfection ('Abdu'l-Bahá, *Answered Questions* 199).

Subsequent to their appearance and development – and now for millennia – humans also have acted as agents of change to landscapes and genescapes alike. The juxtaposition, transfer and mixing of components of mineral, plant or animal kingdoms from one context to another drives the transformation of the system in whatever agricultural system that is considered. Materially, 'Nothing is new under the sun' (Ecc. 1:9) – the re-assemblage of the ancient system components often spawns change throughout the system. As for the plant kingdom, even without the knowledge of genetic theory, agriculturalists have practised recurrent selection for millennia in order to domesticate and improve crop species that originated from wild species. For the mineral kingdom, an evolution of landscapes catalysed by humanity has been going on since early recorded history; the drainage and irrigation of cultivated land such as the Tigris, Euphrates and Nile serve as ready examples (Toynbee, *Mankind* 592).

While human-catalysed transformations of the world's landscapes and genescapes are nothing new, the dimensions of exploration, characterization and transformations in the last 150 years, since the time of Bahá'u'lláh, have been unprecedented – with both positive and negative consequences. With regard to spiritual, social, economic, political, ecological and even geological systems, one might say, with Bahá'u'lláh:

> The world's equilibrium hath been upset through the vibrating influence of this most great, this new World Order. Mankind's ordered life hath been revolutionized through the agency of this unique, this wondrous System – the like of which mortal eyes have never witnessed (Bahá'u'lláh, *Kitáb-i-Aqdas*, para. 181).

Clorinda Strong Minor, as a contemporary of Bahá'u'lláh who remained unacquainted with his Revelation, provides one small example of the explosive advance in the area of agricultural/biological science since the dawn of his Revelation. First, Clorinda Strong Minor's introductions of novel cultivars illustrate one type of transformation that impacts genetic resources at the macro level. Second, her transformation of land stewardship by introducing the wheelbarrow – facilitating the removal of rocks – provides a simple example of innovations that transform mineral resources.

Beyond this example, land stewardship practices across the globe have altered the condition of land and water systems with increased use of farm chemicals such as fertilizers and micronutrients. Similarly, pesticides have altered both the genetic and mineral features in an agricultural system. Moreover, introduction of the mouldboard plough to the Great Plains of the North American continent catalysed enormous changes in the mineral, plant, animal and human kingdoms. Beyond the mineral kingdom, stewardship of genetic resources impacted the plant and animal kingdoms well before the advent of genetically modified organisms. Swidden subsistence agriculture – where forest parcels are burned to clear the ground to plant local varieties of crops – provides a historic and contemporary example of plant kingdom transformations. Analogously, the extinction of certain species and the introduction of crops into new regions offer other examples of genetic transformation.

In many cases of transformation the components of the systems that are changed are tangible, obvious and macro-scale. In the GM of plants, however, the components to be juxtaposed are microscopic and subtle. GM of plants juxtaposes micro level genetic elements, from one cell line into another. The seeming intangibility of genes and of the altered physiological processes within crops may seem more mysterious than the establishment of a novel cultivar in a new environment. Yet the relocation of genes between genomes is analogous to relocation of species or plant populations from one ecosystem to another. From this perspective, agricultural GM is simply an extension of existing transformational processes and genetic engineering becomes simply another vehicle of transformation – change that brings about varying magnitudes of both beneficial and harmful consequences.

From a broad perspective that sees components – be they at the macro or micro level – as interacting elements of a united system, the physical process of GM appears to be an extension of ongoing physical changes. The profound magnitude of transformation in the past 150 years is similar for both land and genetic resources but is not easily quantifiable because the catalogue of examples is so vast. One cannot deny that much of the past 150 years of transformation of geologic and genetic systems has had seemingly disastrous consequences. For example, the draining of wetlands may have endangered many biological populations and compromised hydrological systems. But preservation of the status quo may not be neutral either. Difficult choices have to be made. Protection of swampland might lead to disease and the suffering of innocent children, for example.

Change and innovation define much of life. The important choice resides in how change is managed. Bahá'í principles of moderation, consultation and a focus on justifying the means, rather than merely the ends, will help humanity to manage transformation. Both Clorinda Minor's ideas and the genetic information used in transformation were novel to their respective new landscape but the origins of the novelty could be traced through history to coalesce in a common motive. Both ideological and pragmatic motives fuelled Clorinda Minor's transformation of Palestinian agriculture; similar motives animate many plant scientists working on genetically modified crops today.

Parallel Transformations in Ownership of Land and Genetic Systems

Discussion now shifts from the physical realm to the concomitant, less tangible, but nevertheless powerful transformation in applications of ownership concepts that has occurred since the time of Bahá'u'lláh. The applications of the concepts of property and ownership to land and living systems also have evolved in the past 150 years. Ownership of greater domains of genetic and land entities is possible in a way that it was not during the time of Bahá'u'lláh. The socioeconomic systems of agricultural resource control have changed as dramatically as the components (land, plants, processes) subject to control; rights of access to and protection of intellectual property associated with the utilization of genetic engineering components and processes have been altered in ways that parallel changes to the rights and access to the North American landscape during the decades following the arrival of Europeans on that continent. This segment covers three subtopics: the concept of private ownership, what is considered legal property and Bahá'í guidance on land and genescape ownership.

From a Bahá'í perspective the practice of private property ownership is acceptable, as long as ownership does not override the principle of collective trusteeship. In a statement by the Bahá'í International Community:

> Since the body of humankind is one and indivisible, each member of the race is born into the world as a trust of the whole. This trusteeship [the principle of collective trusteeship] constitutes the moral foundation of most of the other rights – principally economic and social – which the instruments of the United Nations are attempting similarly to define. The security of the family and the home, the ownership of property, and the right to privacy are all implied in such a trusteeship (Bahá'í International Community, *Prosperity* 12).

Across the globe, in many cultures communal 'ownership' of landscapes and ecosystems has evolved into practices of individual ownership. In the US, for example, common lands and bison herds have been replaced by deeded parcels of real estate and traded commodities of livestock and crops. Similarly, whereas in past times genetic resources were freely exchanged and governmental or communal curation of genetic resources was common, nowadays individual gene variants and plant varieties can be owned – at least for a limited duration, generally less than two decades – via patent law systems. The rights of *temporary* ownership afforded by patent systems creates incentives to allocate resources to describe, understand and develop useful new crop lines that might not otherwise occur. Patent systems are not perfect but they tend to foster innovation.

At least in the US, for more than 200 years property ownership has signified – justly or unjustly – the right of use, control and disposition that one may lawfully exercise over objects or land. Adequate systems to describe property make ownership possible; a description of property lets the owner delineate her domain of use and control. The ability of humanity to describe more and more features of the natural world has opened up the possibilities of temporarily owning plant varieties, genes and processes involved with genetic engineering. The limits of available property for legal ownership have stretched as the 'kingdom of names' has expanded owing to scientific explorations of wilderness landscapes and of microscopic genescapes.

Both individual people and legal entities such as governments, non-governmental organizations, multinational corporations and trusts can own most property types. Governments may impose limitations on property, such as its limitation for certain purposes.

Evolution within systems continues without ceasing. With the turnover of human generations, what seemed like startling, unusual or even unnoticed changes at one point in history may become the expected, commonplace and celebrated features in future generations. The socioeconomics of genetic and geologic systems have changed in parallel since the time of Bahá'u'lláh and Clorinda Minor. More than one hundred years after the death of Clorinda Minor, a plot of disease-resistant cabbage or a parcel of rock-free farmland may not elicit much attention by inhabitants or visitors to the Holy Land. The web of ownership of land and plant varieties has grown more complicated than it was during Clorinda Minor's time. Viewed through a 21st-century filter, Clorinda Minor's innovations – the cabbage cultivars and wheelbarrows that changed Palestine – may seem minor or even laughable but those and similar, incremental innovations occurring across the globe have made the world a different place. Only the future will show how agricultural GM will further drive humanity's evolving partnership with other kingdoms of creation.

Agricultural GM and Its Impact at the Levels of Communities, Institutions and Individuals

The consequences of agricultural GM ultimately reach to all levels of society. Relevant and interacting issues include food safety, environmental protection and the interdependence of the world food supply. In light of broad ramifications, the implications of agricultural GM will be examined at community, institutional and individual levels; the same three levels that the Universal House of Justice highlights when providing guidance to the interdependent, worldwide Bahá'í community. At all three levels one finds opportunities to apply spiritual principles of unity, interdependence, justice, truthfulness, moderation and purity of motive to questions raised by agricultural GM.

Agricultural GM and Its Impact at the Community Level

A community is of course more than the sum of its membership; it is a comprehensive unit of civilization composed of individuals, families and institutions that are originators and encouragers of systems, agencies and organizations working together with a common purpose for the welfare of people both within and beyond its own borders; it is a composition of diverse, interacting participants that are achieving unity in an unremitting quest for spiritual and social progress (Universal House of Justice, Riḍván 1996, para. 25).

As a primary means of production, agriculture intercalates into socioeconomic issues of development and access to wealth. Tillage of the soil for food and other products is a community issue. Clorinda Minor believed that her agricultural agenda would even hasten the return of the Messiah and some posit that some of the characteristics of Israeli society and Zionism can be traced to her activities. Similarly, agricultural genetic engineering may both shape the structure of society and vice versa – an example of interdependence.

Agricultural self-sufficiency has become almost an oxymoron over the millennia; across the globe, most community structures have tended toward specialization. 'For none is self-sufficiency any longer possible,' 'Abdu'l-Bahá writes, 'inasmuch as political ties unite all peoples and nations, and the bonds of trade and industry, of agriculture and education, are being strengthened every day. Hence the unity of all mankind can in this day be achieved. Verily this is none other but one of the wonders of this wondrous age, this glorious century' ('Abdu'l-Bahá, *Selections* 32). Granted, some contemporary communities and individuals have been able to vertically integrate their local food stream and achieve some degree of self-sufficiency but globally agricultural interdependence has become the dominant paradigm.

In writing about the effects of the agricultural and industrial revolutions of the last two centuries, Toynbee's (*Mankind* 563) observations corroborate 'Abdu'l-Bahá's statements:

Some traditional but relatively inefficient ways of working – for instance, small scale subsistence-farming . . . were put out of action permanently. Production, both agricultural and industrial, was now organized in elaborately and expensively equipped large-scale units. These simultaneous changes started a flow of population out of the countryside into the new industrial cities. At the same time, it deprived most of the migrants of any shadow of economic independence that they may previously have retained. In the rapidly increasing population the percentage of employees whose only means of subsistence was the sale of their services rose steeply by comparison with the percentage of employers and of self-employed persons.

This ongoing specialization – just one facet of unity in diversity – has ultimately led researchers to unlock and alter the biological systems of crop plants through genetic

engineering. Genetic engineering innovations will likely lead to further specialization in crafts, sciences and professions. As interdependence and specialization
increase, so does the need for process-focused community consultation (decision-
making).

Need for Consultation within Communities

With interdependence comes the need for consultation to guide community
through cycles of action and reflection. Current decision-making tends to cede
first to the interests of the most powerful sub-segments of communities rather
than moving towards what is best for the community. Political power struggles, not
human values, dictate the features of the vast majority of contemporary communities. Strident local and international debate over agricultural genetic engineering,
food safety and agricultural sustainability has done little to illuminate constructive
paths for agricultural innovations.

Consultation is needed to find 'spiritual solutions to the world's economic problems', to further realize an ever-advancing civilization. The practice of consultation
requires detachment. It requires attention to process rather than to single silver
bullets; neither a global ban nor wholesale deregulation of genetic engineering will
serve humanity. Decision-making bodies must consider how agricultural GMs will
'extend to the provision of employment . . . physical health care . . . fair wages, rest
and recreation, and a host of other reasonable expectations on the part of the individual members of society' (Bahá'í International Community, *Prosperity* 12). For
example, genetically modified crops can impact community health both negatively
and positively. Genetic engineering may introduce new, potentially harmful aller-
gens into the food supply. On the other hand, genetically modified crops may serve
as a new public health tool to deliver vaccines or to alleviate vitamin deficiencies.
Also, in some cases agricultural GM may diminish use of widely used but toxic
pesticides.

A major challenge in employing consultation to agricultural GM rests on the
fact that most experience and knowledge about GM resides in the employees of
private enterprises. Many critics of GM have been excluded from free access and
familiarity with confidential projects that companies may have under development.
In most cases, only after a new genetically modified product nears commercializa-
tion stages do the opponents of GM have the opportunity to acquaint themselves
with details. The lack of transparency in the development process, owing to a
competitive business environment, can lead to distrust that manifests itself as opposition to the technologies.

Only consultation led by ethical and informed organizations can effectively
canalize the needs and perspectives of humanity to safeguard natural entities such
as ecosystems and gene pools. Ethical decision-making must go hand in hand with
research and technological innovations. For example, concern has been voiced
that widespread use of genetically engineering *Bacillus thurengensis* (Bt) in crops
may lead to resistant insect populations, thereby resulting in an end to topical

applications of Bt by growers serving organic markets. Some have speculated that introgression of transgenes into gene pools such as Mexican maize land races could have unforeseen consequences. Consultation, rather than polemics, can identify the spiritual principles involved as communities consult on myriads of such issues.

Agricultural GM and Its Impact at the Institutional Level

Many institutions participate directly in tilling the soil. Neighbourhoods, families, collectives, universities and corporations are among them. The activities of some of these agricultural institutions extend beyond cultivation. For example, some corporations have expressed ambitious visions of vertical integration that spans 'the farm gate to the dinner plate' on regional if not international scales. And genetic modification of crops increases the extent to which traditionally non-agricultural institutions such as laboratories, both public and private, become involved in agricultural plant research.

Some of the institutional impacts of agricultural GM involve motivational snares that test government, university, special interest non-governmental organizations and business institutions. Each type of institution can play constructive roles in agricultural GM. However, the following cases serve 1) to caution institutions against acting upon self-serving motives and 2) to emphasize that institutions must promote the advancement of civilization and foster unity in diversity – core Bahá'í values.

Even though universities aim to foster investigation and education, academic elitism and institutional self-promotion are easy traps to fall into. In a retrospective of the 20th century, the Universal House of Justice noted 'The academic world, once the scene of great exploits of the mind and spirit, settled into the role of a kind of scholastic industry preoccupied with tending its machinery of dissertations, symposia, publication credits and grants' (Universal House of Justice, *Century* 89). Similarly, when extremism supplants 'moderation in all things', NGOs (including labour, environmental and religious groups) may sometimes support special interests to the detriment of wider humanitarian considerations. Businesses may sometimes be blinded by profit motives and serving a narrow customer base whose self-interests conflict with the general interests of citizens. Governments aim to support the protection and welfare of the public through the rule of law and social programmes but an over-valuing of regional interests or other prejudices may corrupt these aims. Pure institutional motives promote the best interests of the public, contributing to the prevention of the misuse of agricultural genetic engineering while enabling humanity to enjoy its benefits.

Proliferation and Redefinition of Regulatory Agencies

Beyond pure motives, other institutional issues include changes in the agendas of governmental regulatory agencies, issues related to institutional access of GM technology and the role of the technology in development. In these cases

Bahá'í principles of international cooperation, innovation and honesty apply. The emerging systems of governmentally-regulated releases of new genetically modified crops require each country to reconsider how to allocate resources to agricultural, environmental and food agencies. Regulatory agencies aim to guarantee public safety. Unfortunately, regulatory approvals are not well coordinated; dozens of governments may scrutinize a single genetically-engineered product with much duplication of effort. A more globally coordinated system of product regulation could be equally effective in terms of safety and make more efficient use of both public and private resources. A key will be to have a truly global system, rather than one dominated by one or a few powerful nations or other agencies.

Moreover, genetic engineering may redefine the domains of regulation because the technology may blur boundaries between disciplines such as medicine and agriculture. Genetically engineered nutraceuticals and vaccines in plants foist agricultural institutions into pharmaceutical roles. Government medical agencies will face new challenges in covering this area. Institutional cooperation will be needed. Finally, governments may use their authority to use regulations as a ploy to protect sectors of their economies. In cases where trade restrictions are thought to be in the best interests of a geopolitical region, the true reasons for these restrictions should be stated, otherwise falsely invoking science to support a policy violates ethics, fosters mistrust and undermines the value of science in the eyes of the public.

Access to Technology: Legal and Economic Considerations

Genetic engineering has also presented new challenges to legal institutions, research organizations and seed companies. Litigation in the agricultural arena has proliferated as battles over patent rights have extended from debates over plant varietal ownership to battles over the DNA sequence. Agriculture's foray onto the legal landscape has both drawbacks and benefits. Institutions may compete with each other in attaining coveted and often confidential research goals; in some cases, duplicated efforts lead to waste. Or, to avoid patent infringements, some institutions may pursue less efficient routes to achieve research objectives.

The complexities of patent law add many wrinkles to the decision-making process that public and private institutions must follow to be successful. Despite these drawbacks, most multinational corporations contend that patenting of GMs is necessary to recover a fair amount of the investment that was required to create the invention. In fact, some posit that without such patent protection research investments in agricultural genetic engineering would not occur.

Patents on genes and processes are not the only factors to limit institutional participation in agricultural genetic engineering. Successful research programmes in agricultural GM require significant resources to pay costs of lab, field and informational infrastructures and for the cadre of researchers, product stewards and patent law specialists. Only a handful of multinational corporations and government-funded laboratories have chosen to divert resources to explore the area. Hopefully, economies of scale will change and access to participation will broaden as the technology matures and patents with key claims expire. If monopolization of the technology persists, specific new policies and laws may be required to safeguard appropriate access to benefits of the technology ('Abdu'l-Bahá, in *Bahá'í World Faith* 281).

On this issue the Universal House of Justice comments:

> Increasingly, globalization assumes political, social and cultural dimensions. It has become clear that the powers of the institution of the nation-state, once the arbiter and protector of humanity's fortunes, have been drastically eroded. While national governments continue to play a crucial role, they must now make room for such rising centres of power as multinational corporations, United Nations agencies, non-governmental organizations of every kind, and huge media conglomerates, the cooperation of all of which is vital to the success of most programmes aimed at achieving significant economic or social ends (Universal House of Justice, *Century* 132–3).

Solutions to Poverty Lie Beyond Technology

Finally, in the socioeconomic development arena, various institutions have touted the value of genetic engineering in advancing material civilization. Even though genetic engineering has the potential to enhance agricultural success and material prosperity, it should not be construed as the solution to hunger or poverty. ' . . . scientific and technological advances respond to a set of priorities only tangentially related to the real interests of the generality of humankind,' comments the Bahá'í International Community. 'A radical reordering of these priorities will be required if the burden of poverty is finally to be lifted from the world. Such an achievement demands a determined quest for appropriate values, a quest that will test profoundly both the spiritual and scientific resources of humankind . . . To participate effectively in the struggle to bring material well-being to humanity, the religious spirit must find – in the Source of inspiration from which it flows – new spiritual concepts and principles relevant to an age that seeks to establish unity and justice in human affairs' (Bahá'í International Community, *Prosperity* 23).

The cultivation of human dignity, mutual aid, empowerment of individuals and stakeholders, plus attention to institution- and community-building, will have greater positive impact than single-minded promotion or opposition of transgenic cultivars. Indeed, wholesale rejection of agricultural GM by some segments of society may stem from a sense of marginalization; remoteness from scientific investigation and applications has resulted in distrust. In this regard, the Bahá'í International Community has said that 'the training that can make it possible for the earth's inhabitants to participate in the production of wealth will advance the aims of development only to the extent that such an impulse is illumined by the spiritual insight that service to humankind is the purpose of both individual life and social organization' (ibid. 21).

Agricultural GM and Its Impact at the Individual Level

Finally, at the individual level, agricultural GM touches individual lives in the areas of service to humanity, personal health and obedience to certain food taboos.

SERVICE

Service to humanity is the primary motivator for an individual who is cognizant of the unity of humanity. As institutions evolve to accommodate GMs, so too the individual's options for service to humanity and worship. Bahá'u'lláh writes: 'Blessed is he who . . . will engage in handicrafts. This is a bounty from God, for in this Most Great Dispensation it is acceptable in the sight of God for man to occupy himself in a trade which relieveth him of depending upon charity. The craft of every craftsman is regarded as worship' (Bahá'u'lláh, in *Compilation* 1). As a new craft, genetic engineering offers new frontiers for investigation and may be considered a new dimension to the craft of plant breeding. But as in many facets of 21st-century life, the reflective individual who seeks to heed Bahá'u'lláh's exhortation to 'Be anxiously concerned with the needs of the age ye live in' (Bahá'u'lláh, *Gleanings* 213) may face the question of whether expending resources on GM research is a reasonable path to improving the human condition.

HEALTH

In terms of impact on health, one can argue that GM itself has little impact on personal health if the composition of the harvest has been properly tested – although what constitutes proper testing is a hotly contested issue. Allergenicity to new proteins has been a main concern but new genetically-engineered crops are not the first instance where novel proteins have been introduced into food supplies.

Introgression of agronomically valuable genes from wild relatives into food crops by classical breeding methods poses similar challenges but receives little public attention. As one health safeguard, persons may have the choice to eat or not eat foods from genetically modified organisms (GMOs). Extensive testing may be required to validate GMO-free claims or producers; and proof of a negative, such as no adventitious presence, can be difficult. Moreover, some may contend that adventitious presence of genetically modified grain will occur in putatively GMO-free foods owing to lapses in seed purity, inadvertent pollen drift and inattentive grain handling. From a free market perspective, however, it would be in a corporation's best interest to thoroughly test genetically modified products prior to release: promoting products that precipitate allergic reactions in their customers would quickly result in a company's demise.

Our individual and visceral communion with agricultural products volatilizes the debate surrounding genetically modified foods. The results of the technology are taken into our bodies. In contrast, other recently harnessed natural forces that pass through our bodies – such as electromagnetic radiation – are less tangible and so receive less public scrutiny. Consumer education and adequate product testing, in combination with more inclusive consultation prior to the release of genetically modified species, would go far to allay concerns over genetically modified foods.

RELIGIOUS DIETARY OBEDIENCE

Beyond physical health, GM raises ethical and religious questions related to dietary choices. Both Jain believers and Seventh Day Adventists (the spiritual descendants of Clorinda Minor's Millerite co-religionists) may continue to debate whether to consume food from plant genomes containing animal genes. Genetically modified crops may also spawn uncertainty among Jewish and Islamic religionists about how to adhere to kosher and halal guidelines. Additionally, should adherents to Christian Science avoid consuming foods made from grain that delivers a vaccine? Bahá'ís do not face such dietary questions. Moreover, the earlier discussion on process-defined kingdoms makes clear what is a plant or an animal.

Conclusion

Agriculture will continue to evolve and the fundamental importance of agriculture acknowledged in the Bahá'í writings warrants efforts to facilitate its advance. In the past two decades genetic engineering accelerated the evolution of one sector of agriculture, the genetic alteration of crops. Most issues raised by agricultural GM have parallels and precedents from other agricultural innovations. Bahá'í perspectives on the subject take a moderate, open-minded and judicious approach to the technology.

Bahá'u'lláh often noted that humankind was reaching the age of maturity. The possibilities of genetic engineering may be another small metaphor for humanity's approach to this developmental stage. After all, maturity confers the ability both to do great, expansive things and also appreciate refinements and subtleties. Maturity also implies the capacity to synthesize reductionistic and holistic approaches to issues. Humankind has reached the stage where it is possible, indeed necessary, to postpone short-term rewards (e.g. financial gain from prematurely released genetically modified crops) in exchange for the long-term benefits potential in powerful new technologies (a global ability to enhance food production when and where it is needed). Effective development, testing and utilization of genetically modified organisms for the prosperity of humankind will require no small feat of coordination; it will require coordination among many disciplines across global society.

This article shows that the Revelation of Bahá'u'lláh offers guidance to the application of GM. Unity, justice and consultation will lead to increasingly effective applications of GM and other technologies. The Universal House of Justice clarifies that:

Unity is not . . . merely a condition resulting from a sense of mutual goodwill and common purpose, however profound and sincerely held such sentiments may be, any more than an organism is a product of some fortuitous and amorphous association of various elements. Unity is a phenomenon of creative power, whose existence becomes apparent through the effects that collective action produces and whose absence is betrayed by the impotence of such efforts. However handicapped it often has been by ignorance and perversity, this force has been the primary influence driving the advancement of civilization, generating legal codes, social and political institutions, artistic works, technological achievements without end, moral breakthroughs, material prosperity, and long periods of public peace whose afterglow lived in the memories of subsequent generations as imagined 'golden ages' (Universal House of Justice, *Century* 41).

The controversy over genetic engineering and other technological novelties must be considered in terms of the larger spiritual challenges of our time. As the House of Justice points out, 'However important the application of legal, sociological or technological expertise to such issues [pollution of the environment, economic dislocation . . . and epidemics that ravage whole populations] undoubtedly is, it would be unrealistic to imagine that efforts of this kind will produce any significant recovery without a fundamental change of moral consciousness and behaviour' (ibid. 90).

Genetic engineering is another technological innovation. To the author's knowledge, none of the Bahá'í writings – including communications from the Universal House of Justice – suggest a ban on technology. The principles of the Bahá'í Faith and the development of a global commonwealth that operates under such principles have much to offer in appropriately and effectively applying and regulating the technology for the betterment of human society. Just as the endeavours of Clorinda Strong Minor to improve agriculture in the Holy Land contributed to political change in the region, so too will the efforts of other agricultural innovators such as agricultural genetic engineers lead humanity into new experiences from which to learn more about the application and interconnectedness of the oneness of God, humanity, the natural environment, science and religion.

Works Cited

'Abdu'l-Bahá. *The Promulgation of Universal Peace.* Wilmette, IL: Bahá'í Publishing Trust, 1982.
— *The Secret of Divine Civilization.* Wilmette, IL: Bahá'í Publishing Trust, 1990.
— *Selections from the Writings of 'Abdu'l-Bahá.* Haifa: Bahá'í World Centre, 1978.
— *Some Answered Questions.* Wilmette, IL: Bahá'í Publishing Trust, 1981.
Bahá'í International Community. *The Prosperity of Humankind.* London: Bahá'í Publishing Trust, 1995.
— *Science and Technology for Human Advancement.* New York: Bahá'í International Community United Nations Office, 1979.
Bahá'í World Faith. Wilmette, IL: Bahá'í Publishing Trust, 2nd edn. 1976.
Bahá'u'lláh. *Gleanings from the Writings of Bahá'u'lláh.* Wilmette, IL: Bahá'í Publishing Trust, 1983.
— *The Kitáb-i-Aqdas.* Haifa: Bahá'í World Centre, 1992.
— *Tablets of Bahá'u'lláh.* Wilmette, IL: Bahá'í Publishing Trust, 1988.
The Compilation of Compilations. Prepared by the Universal House of Justice 1963–1990. 2 vols. [Mona Vale NSW]: Bahá'í Publications Australia, 1991.
Holy Bible. King James Version. London: Collins, 1839.
Kreiger, Barbara (with Shalom Goldman). *Divine Expectations: An American Woman in 19th-Century Palestine.* Athens: Ohio University Press, 1999.
Shoghi Effendi. *Dawn of a New Day: Messages to India 1923–1957.* New Delhi: Bahá'í Publishing Trust, 1970.
Toynbee, Arnold. *Mankind and Mother Earth.* Oxford: Oxford University Press, 1976.
The Universal House of Justice. *Century of Light.* Thornhill, ON: Bahá'í Canada Publications, 2001.
— *Riḍván Message to the Bahá'í World.* Haifa: Bahá'í World Centre, 1996.
White, Robert A. *Spiritual Foundations for an Ecologically Sustainable Society.* Ottawa: Bahá'í Studies Publications, 1998.

Plants, genetics and horticulture have occupied many of Paul D. Olson's waking hours since 1970. He encountered Bahá'u'lláh's challenging message for humanity in 1986. Subsequently he worked and studied in the Philippines, Colombia, Ecuador and Costa Rica. Paul completed his PhD in Genetics at Washington University in St Louis, Missouri, USA, in 1997 and now works as a research scientist for a commercial seed company. In addition to striving to be a source of love, joy and understanding, he endeavours to contribute his skills to improving global agriculture. He gratefully acknowledges early editorial input from another plant biologist, Laurie Landry, PhD.

Section 3

Bahá'í Perspectives in Practice

Igi Oko: The Tree Farms at Sapoba, Nigeria circa 1927

Richard St Barbe Baker

This chapter, an excerpt from Richard St Barbe Baker's 1944 book, I Planted Trees *(London and Redhill: Lutterworth Press), describes experiments in agroforestry that Baker carried out around Sapoba, Nigeria in the late 1920s. His experiments and musings about alternative economic systems were well ahead of their time and in many ways consistent with current thinking in sustainable economic development. The passage provides a glimpse into the socioeconomic development activities of an outstanding early Bahá'í.*

Richard St Barbe Baker (1889–1982) was a pioneer of the modern environmental movement. A graduate of Cambridge forestry school, he was assistant conservator of forests in Kenya and Nigeria for the British Colonial Office in the 1920s. He later became an international forestry consultant, popular lecturer and best-selling author. He was dubbed 'Man of the Trees' by the broadcaster Lowell Thomas and travelled the world for over 60 years to promote conservation and tree planting.

Baker was well ahead of his time in advocating sustainable forestry and predicted the local and global impacts of deforestation decades before the problem was widely acknowledged. He started one of the first international environmental non-governmental organizations – The Men of the Trees – at one time active in 108 countries. His extraordinary network of contacts included heads of state, leaders of thought, visionaries, eminent scientists and ordinary people everywhere who loved trees. He had a particular affinity with indigenous people, especially in Africa, where he was the first white man inducted into the secret society of Kenya's Kikuyu elders. In collaboration with these elders, he formed the first society of Men of the Trees among the Kikuyu youth by sponsoring a new ceremonial dance, the Dance of the Trees, as an initiation rite. By adopting traditional cultural forms, Baker was able to collaborate with the Kikuyu in reforestation, which until then had been considered 'God's work'.

Like his uncle, explorer Sir Samuel White Baker, St Barbe (as friends called him) had a taste for adventure, which he indulged in every corner of the world. A pioneer homesteader, cowboy and lumberjack in Saskatchewan, he was among the first one hundred students of the fledgling University of Saskatchewan. His relationship to this university was ongoing: in the 1970s, he was awarded an honorary doctorate from the University of Saskatchewan, presented by his friend John Diefenbaker, the university chancellor and former prime minister.

After recovering from war wounds and completing his forestry training at Cambridge, he began his career as a conservationist in Africa's tropical forests. At one point the territory he administered was as large as France. A promoter of racial justice, he was fired from the colonial service for his interventions on behalf of Africans, after which he began his ceaseless planet-wide activities to promote forest conservation and tree planting.

In 1929 he succeeded in 'tricking' the warring factions in Palestine into a collaborative reforestation scheme. He crossed Africa twice by land, before there were roads. In his sixties Baker crossed the Sahara on a groundbreaking ecological survey. At the age of 74 he travelled the length of New Zealand (more than 1,500 kilometres) on horseback. In his eighties he took up the study of Chinese, intending to cross the Gobi on a Mongolian pony (he never obtained permission). However, in his nineties he did tour China. His greatest obsession was the idea of reforesting the Sahara by way of a military-style campaign requiring an army of 25 million tree planters. Twice he travelled around this desert, visiting every Saharan leader to promote the project. His efforts to encourage tree planting were recognized with the Order of the British Empire (OBE).

Baker first learned about the Bahá'í Faith in 1920 on a ship while travelling to Africa for the first time. The faith influenced his deep sympathy with the African peoples and his understanding of ecology and development.

Baker supervised an experimental station in Sapoba while working as forest conservator on one hundred different concessions ranging from nine to two hundred square miles. The logging by British firms was heavy but good management helped to alleviate stress on the forest. More detrimental, Baker believed, was the clearing of the forest by indigenous farmers, whose networks of small tracts already honeycombed the forest. Yams, their staple, quickly depleted the soil and the farmers then moved on to a new area of virgin forest where the process began again. Population pressure was beginning to accelerate the impact of this traditional farming system.

The solution Baker devised and implemented on a small scale was called Tree Farms, Igi Oko.

Fifty-two of my forest workers needed land in which to grow their crops, so instead of allowing them to select their own sites at haphazard wherever they might be inclined in the virgin forest, I persuaded them to agree to a site adjoining the young plantations. We chose an area of twenty-six acres of inferior bush which in years gone by had been cultivated but now contained only inferior growth. This they cleared in their spare time, and we divided it into half-acre plots, oil palms being planted first to make the boundaries of each allotment. In between their food crops they planted an economic selection of the most valuable trees available in the nurseries ... In among the mahoganies, as nurse trees, they planted soil improvers such as *Ricinodendron africana* and *Pentclethera macrophylla*, both of which provide also useful timber while acting as nurse trees to the mahoganies. Besides the mahoganies we planted African walnut, *Lovoa Klaineana*, which, although not a true walnut, has that characteristic black streak which gives it the appearance of English walnut and has suggested its use in the making of gunstocks. We found also places for Obeche, *Triplochitin* species, a soft white wood used for making ply-wood. It has a huge cylindrical bole, and before the war was finding a good market in Hamburg for the manufacture of packing cases.

In addition to the indigenous trees, we experimented with Burma teak,

Tectora grandis. I used to get the Forestry Department in Burma to supply us with quantities of seed, which was shipped to Lagos. For ground cover and as a soil improver and nurse tree we planted *Cassia siamea*, a welcome exotic. All these were planted by the forest cultivators in between their food crops at a distance of six feet by twelve feet. When I inspected their allotments at the end of the season there were on the average 300 trees flourishing, and one allotment had 366.

Among the farm crops grown for food were corn, yams, gourds, okra, peppers, iklogie, beans and ground-nuts, the latter are one of the best nitrogenous crops and great soil-improvers. Each year a new farm is allotted to successful cultivators, so that in time they will create considerable areas of new forest for the growing benefit of their country. I should add that as an incentive to obtain the best results I gave a small bonus to those farmers who succeeded in establishing not less than 500 trees to the acre. That number is sufficient to take possession of the land and provide the requisite silvicultural conditions to produce the best timber.

I have dealt with this particular experiment at length because it is one of the simpler ways of protecting land from serious erosion and desiccation and an example which might be followed throughout the whole of equatorial Africa, bringing untold good and well-being to millions of people. I believe the best name for this is the simple one of TREE FARMS, *Igi Oko*. It is one that can be easily translated into every dialect and clearly suggests what it is. It is not a measure that can be enforced by law, but requires the voluntary co-operation of the people. I believe it should be introduced by farmers of their own race who should be trained cultivators and act as distributors of the young trees raised in local nurseries.

. . . Mistakes have been made in the past by planting fast-growing exotics with a view to producing timber quickly. It cannot be too strongly emphasized that the degree of rationalization even in forestry is determined by what is profitable – that is, by economic factors. 'Profitableness' as I use it here is considered from the point of view, not only of the individual, but the society and, of course, the fertility of the land, which is the very basis of human existence. The rhythm of growth must be manifested by approximating the conditions found in the natural forest – that combination of tree species which by natural selection has survived or adapted itself to its surroundings through the centuries . . .

In many parts of Africa forests are of primary importance in checking the destructive forces of Nature, such as violent winds which cause the soil and sand and even stones to shift and drift. If created with knowledge and skill, the forest may not only conserve moisture and regulate stream flow, but actually increase the amount of precipitation in their vicinity. The established and correct practice of forestry in sparsely populated areas may be the means of reconditioning the land and saving whole populations from racial suicide. If, as a result of my initial experiments at Sapoba, in the Southern Province of Nigeria, the proved systems of management are adapted and adopted throughout the most necessitous regions in the equatorial zone, I shall feel that the sweat, toil and physical suffering will not have been in vain. It remains for young Africa to turn the tide of destruction and, by means which are now at the disposal of all, to reclaim their paradise so nearly lost. It may be that some of my young African friends scanning these pages may think that I am exaggerating the evil consequences of old methods of nomadic farming. If they are living in the Southern Provinces of Nigeria they are fortunate, for there is still forest cover and in consequence an ample rainfall. But away to the north, even on the southern borders of the Northern Provinces, in many places the orchard bush is giving way to the *savannah* type, and still further north the rainfall is insufficient to maintain tree growth apart from stunted thorns and a few inferior species.

The old French Equatorial Africa has already become a graveyard for dying races, resulting to a great extent from thoughtless forest destruction by past generations of shifting cultivators. In many of those parts the few poor tribesmen that still remain are constantly being pushed south by the drifting sands of the desert which is the heritage of past forest destruction. Let my young African friends take warning and co-operate in the task of stemming the tide of the oncoming desert. No amount of talk, politics or legislation will remedy the dire plight of those who have been caught in a wedge of the desert. It needs a great army of foresters, devoted men fired with the ideal of 'service before self', men who through serious application to the work in hand have equipped themselves for the field of their labours backed by the knowledge that science can offer them . . .

We must not try to impose our worn-out methods in our African colonies. I learnt of one well-known business concern that has lost something in the neighbourhood of £2,000,000 sterling, solely because, in my opinion, it was trying to introduce a form of wage slavery, which the African native would not accept. I should like to substitute co-operation for the wage system, rather on the lines of the first Men of the Trees, which has proved so successful in Equatorial Africa. That indeed might form the basis of an African co-operative movement, and follow on from afforestation to food-production and the development of handicrafts. Many of the tropical and sub-tropical products would find ready sale in the home market. Labour would readily be derived from African pupils in co-operative schools of forestry and farming. The pupils would all be Men of the Trees, having first been initiated into the order by the usual ceremony. In return for their work, they would be provided with food, plus a small number of tokens per month which they could bank or exchange for the extra luxuries of life if they so desired at our local depot or stores. At the close of each season when the books were made up, they, in company with those who had invested in the money for the establishment of the centre, would share in the profits made from their labours. The association might also provide for the organization of centres where native tribes, under their own chiefs and our resident representative, would be formed into groups of workers who would cultivate small-holdings in their own tribal land of their own free-will, and would be allowed to dispose of their crops to our local resident, who would ship them against instructions from London headquarters. In London there would be a corresponding headquarters with a co-operative depot to deal with the disposal of shipments and products received from our colonial centres, to purchase stores and ship them to our agents abroad, provide a centre in London at which our members would be able to obtain the best domestic supplies, such as coffee, tea, cocoa, nuts and sugar from our own plantations, on the best terms.

I visualized a travel service for our members who wished to visit outlying stations; permanent camps would be available and provide quarters and servants. If they wished it, fresh *bandas* could be built at short notice to suit individual taste and requirements. Subscribers to the Men of the Trees at home would be given the opportunity of becoming shareholders in the trading branch of the organization on the most favourable terms . . . this business side of the Society would be in a position to render service to associates in a hundred and one different ways. At the same time it would give them an opportunity of rendering a practical contribution to the development of the African peoples on sound lines. It should continually be borne in mind that the primary duty of the Men of the Trees in Africa is to protect their native woodlands and ensure that whenever a tree is cut down or destroyed a new one is planted in its place. This idea is sufficiently valuable in itself, but beneath it lies the foundation of a much wider ideal. This is but a starting point for the introduction of improved methods of agriculture and for the substitution of fixed settlements and the introduction of crop rotation to take the place of the old nomadic farming. With the introduction of improved methods of agriculture, living in fixed localities will become possible. Village life would soon spring up around our co-operative farms and conditions would become better suited to modern requirements (St Barbe Baker, *I Planted Trees* 105–15).

This passage from I Planted Trees *by Richard St Barbe Baker, published by the Lutterworth Press in 1944, is reprinted here by the kind permission of the publisher.*

Strengthening Local Economies and Community Identity: FUNDAEC's Experience

Pascal Molineaux

The increasing force of social and economic globalization during the last decade has undoubtedly been a phenomenon with great impact on the community-sustaining network of human relations throughout the world. Numerous studies demonstrate how human relations inspired in an essentially competitive spirit with market-oriented values – actively promoted by global enterprises whose main goal is short-term maximization of economic profits – are penetrating into the social and cultural value systems of people, displacing traditional values and eroding essential community-based identity structures.

Historically, the human being has always had a deep-rooted communal identity. Gradually constructed through a complex network of interdependent human relations based on common beliefs and value systems, trust built through social interactions, a common history and spontaneous solidarity, this identity until very recently still gave orientation and purpose to life. A child grew – and should continue to grow – embedded in and protected by a nuclear family, itself positioned within an extended family in which cousins, aunts, uncles and grandparents play a fundamental role, and set within a healthy community of neighbours and friends. It is in these three social contexts – of close family members, distant family members and community – that the child develops a sense of belonging, a sense of identity and purpose in life. These, each in its own particular way, serve to educate and guide the child through life.

In its interaction with the world of which the individual is a part, access to and generation of relevant knowledge is no doubt of fundamental importance. Real participation in the life processes require that one may contribute to advancing existing knowledge and to an understanding of one's reality. Only then will a human being reveal his or her hidden potentialities for the benefit of society as a whole and contribute both generously and significantly to the advancement of his or her family and community.

Organization and Knowledge: Cornerstones of Education

It is in this context that FUNDAEC's (Spanish acronym for *Foundation for the Application and Teaching of the Sciences*) experience in developing an appropriate educational system initially rooted in a given rural reality and with the aim of strengthening local economies and community identity can be analysed. Fundamentally, this experience is centred in the creation and evolution of a relevant educational content and method, involving locally based learning institutions and economically oriented structures that belong, in a true sense, to the local communities themselves. Access to and generation of knowledge and organizational skills are considered by FUNDAEC as the main elements needed for people to fundamentally take charge of their own development processes and begin to interact as equals with the outside world. The learning institution that evolved to pursue this purpose was called the University for Integral Development, a community-based system for the development of human resources. The University sets in motion a series of learning processes in which the knowledge generated by the participants helps to strengthen a sense of identity, pertinence and purpose, and to create and increase the forces necessary to resist social disintegration and, eventually, to achieve positive change.

Tutorial Learning System (SAT)

The Tutorial Learning System (SAT in Spanish) is a high school equivalent curriculum embedded in the reality and needs of rural life. Now approved by the Ministry of Education in Colombia, it has close to 25,000 students in Colombia and seven other countries. It offers an interesting experience in the creation of a locally rooted (and relevant) educational system connected to a national – and now international – movement of NGOs, public institutions and communities. The local SAT groups, of 15 to 20 students guided by a trained tutor from the same community, have demonstrated their potential as they apply the service-oriented principles and concrete knowledge gained through the study of the SAT texts to become active groups in the strengthening of a community's identity. Their activities – which reflect an enormous diversity – cover the implementation of sustainable production systems; educational activities with younger children; environmental activities; and educational, artistic, cultural and sporting events. These serve, directly or indirectly, to create a sense of community, of belonging. These activities have shown a great potential, especially among the participants and other youth in the community, in developing a sense of worth, a sense that rural community-based life is possible and can be improved using local resources and know-how. This is remarkable in the context of a country known for its high rate of violence and insecurity, accelerating an already high rate of rural out-migration. No doubt, such a feat is, in each local context, a much-needed contribution to peace and understanding.

Moreover, the SAT educational movement strives to connect the participating students and institutions – close to 40 NGOs and public institutions in Colombia alone – to the reality of a world advancing towards greater levels of unity. Achieving this, which is at once the promise and challenge of globalization, can only be done if the local, regional and national identities and value systems are strengthened and recognized. If not, globalization will continue to cause havoc in local economies, traditional value systems and community rooted identities, as it has been doing everywhere. Giving the SAT students – most of them living in marginal and isolated rural villages – access to modern knowledge systems is indeed a tremendous challenge, as this has to be done while respecting their own empirical understanding of life's purpose. This is, in essence, what the programme strives for: providing a learning space in which the students, with their own life experience, can participate in the generation and application of knowledge relevant to their own social and cultural contexts.

The Development of Alternative Small-Scale Production Systems

The challenge of developing an educational system that helps to produce in the participants the capacities needed to become active change agents in their communities involves the creation of a social learning space in which traditional, empirical knowledge systems and 'modern' knowledge systems may interact, thus generating new, locally relevant knowledge. It also involves the integration of theory and practice centred on the concept of service. It is expected that the participants will 'discover', as they advance in their learning process, that a service-oriented life is extremely empowering. No doubt, true learning only takes place as one is constantly challenged to apply what one has learned in theory to a real-life situation and share this newly acquired knowledge with others using one's own words. As the participants do so, they also become active community members, increasingly knowledgeable about a complex community reality and wanting to contribute to the strengthening of community life processes.

As this is a vast and open field, and many life processes are no doubt worthy of investigation, we will analyse how such knowledge is generated, systematized and incorporated in the Tutorial Learning System in the development of sustainable small-scale intercropping and animal husbandry systems.

The general method of the FUNDAEC University is to initiate learning processes that run parallel to important life processes of the population. The investigations of the 1970s and 1980s in the North Cauca region of Colombia in the search for alternative smallholder production systems was carried out by an interdisciplinary team headed by an agricultural scientist. The working method included three sets of activities: 1) immersion of the interdisciplinary group within the smallholder logic and rationale, 2) the development of alternative subsystems and 3) the strengthening of other community structures that facilitate the reproduction and further enrichment of the knowledge thus generated.

Formal investigation methods are available to help the investigator understand, make explicit and value the technological culture of a smallholder community and analyse its socioeconomic reality. However, the initial challenge is more down to earth: the group initiating investigation–action activities must insert itself in the life of the population they will work with and *learn to look at the world from their viewpoint*. The smallholder has firsthand knowledge of those socioeconomic and natural conditions that day by day shape his or her life. However, both groups, the smallholders and the external participants, must make more explicit the knowledge systems of the population as well as the possibilities and restrictions that the social and natural environments present to the smallholder production process. The group can introduce to this experience certain instruments of systematization. For example, FUNDAEC has always used what has been called *the description of families*, in which a family, with the help of a student or professor at the FUNDAEC

University, describes its resources, human and economic, its limitations, aspirations and goals in the short and long term. This is done at an individual, family and community level. Later, when specific areas are in need of a more detailed description, other more formal types of interview are carried out.

In the case of the North Cauca region, this continuous interaction and analysis has helped to make explicit, gradually, a set of complex conditions. A list of aims that will guide the search for alternative smallholder production systems was developed. It is worthy of note that such aims agree to a great extent with what can be found in the conventional literature, as a result of other investigations:

- Improve the production of food crops, in the hope of improving the nutritional balance of the family.

- Make a more efficient use of the resources of the smallholders (labour, land, secondary agricultural products, etc.).

- Increase the species diversity of both plant and animal elements and reduce the risk factor.

- Regulate the use of the family labour available throughout the year, avoiding periods of excess or deficit.

- Diminish the use of those external inputs that are costly and improve productivity using appropriate technologies.

- Help to regulate the flow of income and food, insuring that traditional harvesting periods are distributed throughout the year.

- Ensure that the benefits of alternative production systems are not restricted to a few families but contribute to the progress of the whole community.

As mentioned previously, continuous efforts are made to make more explicit the production conditions and smallholder rationality; moreover, permanent attention has to be given to the rapid changes taking place in the rural areas, changes which generally affect rural life processes negatively. However, the aims just mentioned are sufficient to initiate a set of activities in the development of alternative subsystems.

Originally FUNDAEC tried to design, with several smallholder families, new total production systems that would satisfy the aims mentioned. However, it rapidly became evident that the complex life of the smallholder of the North Cauca region did not allow him to dedicate all his time to the development of such a production system. He or she had already developed a balance between work on personal land and work outside. Moreover, the recommended alternative systems implied a much greater infrastructure and more complex management requirements than were possible only if the rhythm of change was slowed down somewhat. Thus the need arose to develop alternative subsystems.

In the literature on agricultural investigation, the term 'subsystem' is often used to refer to the different components of the total system. For example, the family can be considered a subsystem, the soil can be yet another subsystem. At the FUNDAEC University the term is used with a different meaning in mind: it refers, simply enough, to a clearly defined physical space within the total landholding of the smallholder, with a set of species, plant and/or animal, and a management plan through time. In the case of the North Cauca region, the size of the optimal subsystems in this first phase of development was between 500 and 2000 square metres, depending on the characteristics of the subsystem.

The aim of the second set of activities is to develop, with several smallholder families, subsystems that are feasible for the conditions of the region. Any given smallholder family, taking into account its specific situation regarding the availability of land and family labour, will be able to choose and gradually establish four or five subsystems that will finally constitute the totality of its production system.

To illustrate the concept of a subsystem, we briefly describe two examples.

The Subsystem of Maize–Short Cycle Leguminous Plant–Green Beans–Pumpkin

A land area of 500 to 1000 square metres is sown. For the North Cauca region, the maize is sown simultaneously with a leguminous plant, which can be the common bean, soybean, cowpea or mungo, depending on the fertility and condition of the land used. The green bean is sown at the same time as the maize and the pumpkin when the leguminous plant has reached its physiological maturity. This subsystem, which is explained in greater detail below, has been designed to last six months.

The Subsystem of Cassava–Short Cycle Leguminous Plant–Maize–Pumpkin

This is established in an area of 500 to 2000 square metres and is designed to last one year. The cassava, leguminous plant and maize are sown simultaneously and the pumpkin is sown when the leguminous plant reaches its physiological maturity. Two of the products of this subsystem, cassava and soybean (cooked), can be mixed and used as feed for pigs.

The Design of the Subsystems

In analysing the experience of FUNDAEC thus far in the design and development of alternative subsystems, one can conclude that there are essentially two possible paths. The first option is that an agricultural technician, along with several smallholder families, chooses a common crop of the region and in consultation identifies other species that can be grown together to constitute a viable subsystem. All the variables that are related to the vegetative cycle of each crop, the possibilities of competition or symbiosis, the land cover, the reduction of labour needed, etc. are analysed to insure the viability of the subsystem. The other option is to design the subsystem in a gradual, step-by-step way, centred around a crop already grown on the smallholder plot and adding to it other crops over time until a whole subsystem is eventually developed.

FUNDAEC has chosen to work according to the first option; the subsystems are thus redesigned several times during implementation.

Trials

Once designed, with full smallholder participation, the group prepares a set of trials to determine the agronomic, economic and social feasibility of each subsystem. Here again, the trials are made directly on the smallholdings; the smallholders are investigators in the process. FUNDAEC finances the input costs, while the harvest and its products are given to the smallholder family. During this phase of the investigation, the trials are fairly simple and essentially work with three variables: density and management of space, times of sowing and other labours, and choosing appropriate varieties for the combination. In further trials, other technological details are also incorporated, such as fertilization levels, plant pathology management, and land and soil management.

Selection of Best Alternatives

The essential challenge is to develop criteria to decide if a subsystem is appropriate for the region and which subsystems the smallholder can adopt as part of a total production system. Clearly, there are many possible indicators but the University has worked with four. The first is to determine the land area needed to produce, in the same time span, exactly the same quantity of products produced in the subsystem but as monoculture crops. Obviously, this indicator must be greater than 1 and for those subsystems that have proved most feasible, the indicator has been between 1.5 and 2.5.

The second type of indicator is economic. Generally, two indicators have been used, both with problems of a theoretical and practical nature. The first number is the net gain of the subsystem in the local currency, divided by the number of days worked. The second number must reflect in some way the risk factor. It can be calculated by supposing that, for agronomic reasons, 50 per cent of the production of the crop with higher economic value is lost; in that case, what is the percentage of loss relative to the total economic gain of the subsystem? This number is then compared to a number obtained by calculating a 50 per cent crop loss of a monoculture of the same high-value crop.

No doubt the dependency of these two indicators on the changing prices of a market – that is generally speaking unfair – makes the task of interpretation somewhat difficult. In a certain way, the acceptability of a subsystem increases if the net gain per day worked increases. However, defining the bounty of a subsystem cannot depend on this criterion alone. For example, at a given time the price for cassava in the region was so high that – in terms of net gain per day worked – any intercropping combination would have produced lower economic gains than a monoculture cassava field. A few months later, the price of cassava fell to much lower levels, making the cassava subsystem with two or three other species much more attractive than a monoculture cassava field. Moreover, the smallholder himself does not consider, within his rationale, that this economic indicator is the only valid one, as there are several other criteria that also need be taken into account.

The third type of indicator is social in nature and the University has not felt the need to quantify it. The investigation process itself helps to pinpoint those subsystems that have greater social acceptance. The factors that influence the producer in his decision are varied: for example, the producer values the greater availability of food crops throughout the year and the fact that the subsystem requires a greater amount of labour over time (compensated by higher productivity). A negative factor that can affect the social acceptability of the subsystems has to do with their difficult management requirements and, generally speaking, only those producers with greater skills are successful. However, the complexity does not constitute a factor of rejection; the smallholder accepts the subsystem theoretically, as he understands its logic and conception within his rationale. Very few, however, confront the full complexity of the subsystems from the beginning. For example, the *maize–bean–green bean–pumpkin* subsystem can be developed in two or three step-by-step trials in which the green bean is not included in the first or second trial. The design of the subsystems must consider these possibilities and insure it fulfils the agronomic, economic and social acceptability criteria.

A fourth criterion, which has lately proved to be of great importance, has to do with the conservation and reconstruction of the soil. The continuously decreasing soil fertility in smallholder lands is no doubt a factor that greatly limits productivity. Subsystems that include leguminous plants that produce edible seeds and low-lying shrubs for cover are essential to improve soil fertility, structure and erosion-resistance. Obviously, this soil improvement can only be measured in the long run: moreover, it is difficult to find indicators that can be easily measured under the living conditions of the smallholder producers.

Community-learning Structures

In the initial diffusion of the subsystems that have proved most successful, two paths are taken. First, the University produces a series of easily accessible educational materials and shares the experience; second, 'learning plots' are established. These learning plots still have a strong investigative component. To establish one, a small producer enters into an agreement with the University to gradually develop, according to his needs and possibilities, a total system that consists of a number of subsystems already tested in the region. The University again helps to finance the external inputs needed but on the condition that the producer opens up his land to the community and allows regular smallholder meetings to be held to discuss and analyse the advance of the subsystems. Furthermore, other producers can participate in the decision-making involved in the further development of the subsystems.

In the North Cauca region, in the mid-1980s, ten small producers initiated the creation of such community learning plots. The initial impact was so great that within six months a hundred smallholders requested to be included. It is important to note that in spite of the enthusiasm of the producers, the gradual adding on of other subsystems in the design of a total production system is not easy. When a producer chooses four or five subsystems based on the possibilities, it is necessary to reevaluate a year later, considering such factors as labour distribution throughout the year and subsystem planting and growth according to rainfall patterns. As a result of such observations, revisions and modifications to the subsystems will be made. On the other hand, the increase in production thus achieved implies that other community processes have to be strengthened, including the development of community-owned stores, creation of food-processing microenterprises, the management of money flows, etc. Thus the concept of community learning plots owned by one producer, although important in initiating the diffusion and further improvement of the subsystems, loses importance as the need for other community-based structures, such as a community fund, and other plots dedicated to permanent investigation are identified.

A factor of utmost importance in all these processes of the University is the continuous creation of human resources. It is very common in programmes dealing with agricultural development efforts to direct all training to the adult population, leaving the youth out, precisely the population that is most vulnerable to the disintegration processes at work in rural communities. The FUNDAEC University, on the contrary, has decided to direct most of its attention to the youth. Thus the establishment of the Tutorial Learning System allows for a greater diffusion of the subsystems developed, the methods used and the further investigations of the communities themselves, within a formal educational system.

Positive Results

The FUNDAEC educational programme is seen to be truly revolutionary and to provide very positive results. Graduates of the SAT programme emerge with comprehensive knowledge of agriculture, animal husbandry, soil chemistry and other fields traditionally associated with rural vocations. Many have implemented, with slight variations in composition, time and space, and with help from their tutor or a local agricultural technician, some of the subsystems detailed in the SAT textbooks. They have learned to value productive diversity and a greater degree of self-sufficiency. They also acquire knowledge about how to create microenterprises and have a greater degree of consciousness of the value of living in and serving their community. As such, they can, and do, initiate and participate actively in community development processes. As rural youth, who would otherwise have left in search of work elsewhere, the SAT students are now staying back, setting up small enterprises within their own communities and earning their own living. SAT graduates in many communities have begun to take up some of the key public posts, such as running the public telephone office, the public library, the local pharmacy or the kindergarten, or have become highly valued local resource persons in the implementation of sustainable production systems, and so on. These are the types of positions for which municipalities once had to find people from outside the community.

Solidarity Groups

The other programme in which FUNDAEC has developed noteworthy experience is in the creation and strengthening of solidarity groups in a wide variety of rural communities. As the subsystems became successful, the challenge was to strengthen community organizational structures that would ensure a greater number of producers and the community as a whole would benefit. The other challenge was to develop a credit-based system that could make the subsystems available to all, despite the often high initial investment required. Finally, a third challenge was to strengthen those community values that give meaning to the concept of 'community' and have recently undergone severe erosion under the ever-increasing presence of a market-oriented economy and values emphasizing the competitive, individualistic spirit.

The programme started in 1990, inspired by the Grameen Bank of Bangladesh, with the help of a long-term loan from the Inter-American Development Bank. The credit was used as an instrument to create local solidarity groups in the belief that the traditional values of reciprocity, interdependence, trust and mutual help could be greatly strengthened and thus contribute to enhancing a sense of collective iden-tity in each community.

As the programme has grown the groups have shown great potential. Each group received basic training in solidarity-based value systems and the technical aspects of the productive project they planned to implement. On the one hand, the small productive projects have increased the welfare of and given a greater sense of security to the participants. On the other, they have helped to foster or strengthen in the participants those essential values that gave and must continue to give meaning to the concept of community.

Finally, these solidarity-based productive efforts have generated important firsthand knowledge and experience, creating an increased sense of worth and dignity in the participants and providing knowledge essential in the design of a specialization degree programme at FUNDAEC University in the strengthening of rural economies. Again, the essential purpose of working with community-based groups of producers was the production of knowledge, which would be systemati-cally incorporated into educational materials, thus sharing the experience as widely as possible. It is this constant interaction between the University staff, students and community that provides the experience needed to further advance the local knowledge systems – exactly what human resource centred development is all about. In this context, in 1998 FUNDAEC initiated two specialized degrees in

'Education and Social Development' and 'Strengthening of Local Economies', with close to a thousand students in Colombia participating so far.

Return to Community Values

Members of solidarity groups support each other by sharing resources, knowledge and labour. Solidarity, in this case, is not confined to a group but reaches out to other groups and the community at large. A few examples will suffice. One group member, in the village of Padilla in the Cauca department of Colombia, became aware that an elderly woman living in a small house in very poor conditions had a leaking roof. The rainy season was soon to start. The group decided to provide a helping hand, as they had previously established a small solidarity fund. They all participated, over the course of one day, in rebuilding the roof. The women prepared juice (the day was hot) and food in abundance. Each group member brought some element for the reconstruction of the roof – nails, wood, tiles. In one day the elderly woman discovered she was member of a community that cared for her, the participants rediscovered how powerful the principle of unity is and the community recovered a long-established tradition of mutual help – the MINGA – that had of late been abandoned to a great extent.

Another nucleus of five solidarity groups in the neighbouring village of La Arrobleda decided to pool their resources to buy a bull for their 30 or so milking cows. One person was responsible for taking care of the bull and costs were shared among all. They also decided to make the bull available for a small fee to any community member who might need it. In another community, one of the group members lost her cow when it consumed a sugar cane-based sweet she produced. After the group members and other members of solidarity groups in the community chipped in, she was able to negotiate the reimbursement of the credit she had received to buy the first cow and receive further credit to acquire a second. Again, this was possible because the network of human relations making up community life and identity was alive and strong, thanks in part to the solidarity-based groups previously established in the community.

Challenges for the Future

Recently there has been an expansion of the SAT programme to other countries, initially to neighbouring Latin American countries but also to countries in Africa and elsewhere. In Zambia, for example, a sister institution has initiated the implementation of the SAT programme as part of its educational efforts. A project is underway to rewrite and translate the textbooks of the SAT programme into English, which may afford a greater application in an even wider context. This demands time and a great deal of careful analysis and evaluation of contents and methods. Moreover, in Brazil a sister institution that has adopted the SAT programme for the Amazon indigenous populations has undertaken the translation of the first level textbooks into Portuguese.

The essential challenge for FUNDAEC is two-fold:

- To continue to foster systematic learning in each group and institution that has adopted the SAT programme (there is an annual meeting of participating institutions for such a purpose).

- To ensure that all other institutions may find their own learning thus enriched, continuously integrating the learning generated in the textbooks and complementary materials.

The solidarity production programme is also entering in a new phase, in which four or five solidarity groups in a given community form a core group, with a governing board and a treasurer. Those core groups that have proved to be dependable and have maintained themselves have been given a long-term loan with which they may assume the functions of a local credit bank. They take on the responsibilities of administering the credit and ensuring technical assistance to local projects. So far, the experience has been very rewarding. Again, the challenge for FUNDAEC is to ensure that the knowledge and experience being generated at the local level is systematically integrated into the educational materials for the benefit of all the institutions and groups of students working with the SAT programme.

Strengthening Local Communities

FUNDAEC's experience points clearly to two essential aspects that must be considered if local communities are to confront the great – and potentially destructive – force of social and economic globalization. One involves access to knowledge in all its complexity, along with its generation and application as it interacts with locally-based knowledge systems. The other involves efforts to create local structures that serve to strengthen local economies within the context of a community value system and identity. These two aspects go hand in hand.

Pascal Molineaux was born in Ethiopia and grew up in Switzerland. He pursued a Bachelor's degree in Botany and Plant Pathology at the University of New Hampshire and a Master's degree in International Agriculture and Development at Cornell University. After becoming a Bahá'í in 1988 and serving at the Bahá'í World Centre in the Gardens Department, he went to Colombia to work with FUNDAEC. Since then he has been a teacher in the FUNDAEC Rural University, helping to develop the content of courses on development at both the undergraduate and postgraduate levels.

Balancing Science with Inspiration: A Bahá'í Scientist's Struggle to Discover the Hidden Secrets of Restoring Corals and Fish to Degraded Coral Reefs
Austin Bowden-Kerby

Coral reefs are among the most endangered ecosystems in the world. Their erosion in turn leads to the depletion of fisheries, undermining the economies of fishing communities. Austin Bowden-Kerby's methods for restoring coral reefs are winning acceptance, as evidenced by the number of grants and awards for his Coral Gardens Initiative. In 2002 the project was chosen as a reef conservation 'demonstration site' by the International Coral Reef Action Network (ICRAN). In 1999 it won the prestigious Henry Award for Partnerships in Coral Reef Conservation. The project has also received significant grants from the MacArthur Foundation, the David and Lucile Packard Foundation, the Government of New Zealand and, most recently, the European Union. In this essay Bowden-Kerby discusses the role the Bahá'í writings have played in the development of his work. Content is also derived from the article 'In Fiji, a new approach to the restoration of coral reefs draws notice', *in the October–December 2002 issue of* One Country, *the newsletter of the Bahá'í International Community.*

This paper explains how as Bahá'ís, scientists in agriculture, forestry and fisheries must learn to transcend modern scientific thought and begin using a combination of the scientific method and inspiration. This is my story about how I was able to break the mould and discover revolutionary methods for restoring coral reefs, replanting corals on reefs shattered by careless blast fishing and transforming barren sand flats into actively growing reefs crowded with diverse and valuable fish species. These methods have been called 'Johnny Coral Seed' methods, in reference to the American legend Johnny Appleseed. Other methods for other natural systems await discovery by Bahá'í and like-minded scientists in our attempt to increase the prosperity of rural communities, as well as the health of the planet.

The Coral Gardens Initiative

How the Project Emerged

While working and studying in Micronesia and Fiji in the mid-1970s and early 1980s, I began to consider the problems facing fishing communities dependent on coral reefs. I saw a lot of suffering and nutritional deficiencies related to reef decline caused by over-fishing and dynamite fishing. Damaged reefs were not recovering.

    I began to study what could be done and the Bahá'í writings inspired me with the idea of direct interventions such as replanting corals.

The Bahá'í writings and publications based on them contain passages and concepts that challenge the materialistic philosophy prevalent in science today. In *The Prosperity of Humankind*, for example, the Bahá'í International Community (BIC) states: 'As the twentieth century draws to a close, it is no longer possible to maintain the belief that the approach to social and economic development to which the materialistic conception of life has given rise is capable of meeting humanity's needs' (Bahá'í International Community, *Prosperity* 3).

Being the product of an educational system steeped in this philosophy, I had unwittingly become influenced by this materialistic philosophy myself.

Another strong influence from my background was the prevalent philosophy which 'deifies' nature, considering nature (when left alone by man) to be absolutely perfect. In contrast, the BIC comments: 'The earnest hope that this moral crisis can somehow be met by deifying nature itself is an evidence of the spiritual and intellectual desperation that the crisis has engendered' (ibid. 25).

'Only a breakthrough in understanding that is scientific and spiritual in the fullest sense of the terms', says the BIC statement, 'will empower the human race to assume the trusteeship [of the earth] toward which history impels it' (ibid.). Taking this statement from the BIC into account, as a Bahá'í scientist, and through much search, I began struggling to understand some of the more challenging truths regarding the 'imperfect' condition of the world of nature, as spoken of by 'Abdu'l-Bahá in *Some Answered Questions*. I focused on one of the most diverse and 'perfect' systems on the planet, the coral reef, and identified several of its important natural limitations or weaknesses, such as:

- It is fragile and easily damaged or destroyed.

- It is slow to recover following major damage.

- Coral larvae are unable to colonize barren sandy areas.

- Reef damage may cause fish to become poisonous (ciguatera).

- Over-fishing causes ecological imbalances, including sea urchin erosion, *Acanthaster* plagues, and algal overgrowth kills corals.

With this clarified awareness, major breakthroughs began occurring in my research on coral reef restoration methodologies. The Coral Reef Restoration and Development Project (CRRDP) is the direct result of these breakthroughs, whereby village people learn how to conduct simple experiments on the reefs and study first hand how to 'train' the coral reef ecosystem to produce more abundant resources.

These methods were developed over many years of research. They are based on the increasingly accepted idea that the best way to save endangered reefs is not necessarily by eliminating human impact but rather by carefully managing it, with a special emphasis on working closely with the local people who know the reef best and who still depend on it for their livelihood.

More specifically, the methods go beyond simple management and seek actively to 'cultivate' the reef by weeding out overabundant predators such as the octopus and the coral-eating Crown of Thorns starfish, while at the same time 'planting' missing or low-count species that are friendly to the reef, such as the giant clam, and then encouraging their regeneration in special protected areas.

Perfecting the Coral Reef Ecosystem

Methodologies designed to overcome the natural limitations of the coral reef, to enhance its productivity and to accelerate its recovery were developed in Pohnpei (Micronesia) and in Puerto Rico.

Dynamite fishing damages many reefs. If you dynamite a coral reef, it cannot repair itself since the coral larvae cannot settle on the rubble. But my research has found that if you mimic a hurricane by scattering broken branches of live corals onto the rubble, the corals often attach to the rubble and begin reestablishing themselves. In this way we work with nature to help it recover.

Experimentation involved scattering unattached coral fragments onto damaged reefs and planting larger coral branches in barren sandy areas. The results surpassed all expectations, with high survival rates and coral growth rates far exceeding all published records for both the Pacific and Caribbean. The coral transplants recruit numerous juvenile reef fish and crustaceans, transforming formerly unproductive areas into important fisheries habitat within only a few months.

In my mind, these breakthroughs confirmed my reliance on spiritual as well as scientific modes of inquiry. As Bahá'u'lláh stated, '. . . this Wronged One hath, at all times, proclaimed . . . that which will serve as the key for unlocking the doors of sciences, of arts, of knowledge, of well-being, of prosperity and wealth' (Bahá'u'lláh, *Tablets* 96).

Social and Economic Implications of the Project

Many coral reefs are presently over-fished and have lost much of their productivity owing to damage to living coral cover, often caused by unwise use. A decline in overall prosperity and health in the local community is the inevitable result. Rural subsistence fishing/farming communities often have few opportunities for human advancement, especially for youth and women. This is particularly true for resource-poor environmentally depleted areas. In such areas, village people are often faced with the dilemma of how to survive in a crumbling culture, where the new focal point of social activity may be gambling and alcohol and where there is a lack of vision as to the possibilities for constructive action.

Simplicity is the most striking aspect of the new coral reef restoration and enhancement methods, making them ideally suited for introduction to rural village communities on tropical islands and coasts. The project seeks to involve village fishing communities in their own realm of experience and cultural strength, taking advantage of local experience and knowledge, recognizing that 'the immense wealth of cultural diversity achieved over thousands of years is vital to the social and economic development of a human race experiencing its collective coming of age. It represents a heritage that must be permitted to bear its fruit in a global civilization' (Bahá'í International Community, *Prosperity* 13).

Development projects to create and enhance coral reefs may help communities located near reefs demonstrate the transformational nature of the Bahá'í teachings. Bahá'í development projects demonstrate a firm belief in a secure and prosperous future, a belief that is essential for progress and is a refreshing contrast to the 'end of the world' paralysis that has affected many societies.

The Unfolding Project

The Bahá'í Faith's emphasis on consultation, cooperation and community participation led me to see the importance of involving the local community in any effort to restore the reefs.

Developed under guidance from the Bahá'í Office of the Environment and the Bahá'í World Centre's Office of Social and Economic Development (OSED), the coral project seeks to empower village people involved in subsistence coral reef fisheries to begin to understand and solve local resource depletion problems for themselves. Since the technique is based on local observation and trial and error and requires no elaborate instrumentation, it is an appropriate way to introduce scientific approaches into rural communities, which could over time become expert in the management and improvement of their own reefs.

The project involves:

- identifying sufficiently mature Bahá'í fishing communities

- holding small village workshops and consultative sessions

- working with local people to establish demonstration sites

- returning after one year for evaluation and consultation

- offering advice for expanded local initiatives

Consultation at the grassroots level is consistent with the Bahá'í approach, as outlined by the BIC: 'Indeed, the participation of the people on whose commitment and efforts the success of such a strategy depends becomes effective only as consultation is made the organizing principle of every project' (ibid. 16).

The approach is not dependent on merely getting local people to do the work of reef management or simply following rules such as 'don't fish here' or 'leave the large clams to reproduce'. Rather, the project strives for the active participation of coastal residents by drawing on their own knowledge of the reef and its diverse interactions.

For instance, local fishermen once told me that branching corals can actually move, something not realized by academically trained marine biologists. I didn't believe it at first but I tagged some corals and found they did move during a storm, some over 400 feet. Further study proved that coral branches can break off and roll across the lagoon floor like tumbleweeds, reestablishing in new places.

The fisher knows things that the scientist doesn't. Being unschooled and being uneducated are two entirely different things. Island people, in fact, have a knowledge-base dating back thousands of years. The project is designed quite specifically to draw on traditional knowledge by using consultative methods that promote the participation of the entire community.

At the start of the project we bring the entire village together – the fishers, men and women, old and young – and we go through a series of exercises to detail the history and problems of the reef. The participatory process is based in part on the principles of Bahá'í consultation, a distinctive non-adversarial decision-making system used by Bahá'í communities worldwide.

In the case of the Cuvu-Tuva sites in Fiji, this type of community-based process has led to the creation of resource maps, some dating back to 1942, showing where the major fish species and coral types used to exist. The combination of applied academic knowledge and local knowledge makes for a very creative process.

Resource maps have been an important step in the creation of special no-fishing areas on the reef, which are key elements of the coral restoration strategy. The idea of establishing no-fishing 'marine protected areas' is not new. Indeed, chiefs in Fiji traditionally had sacred 'taboo' areas, putting certain sections of the reef off limits, a practice that eroded under British rule.

What makes the no-fishing zones in the project distinctive is the way in which they are once again defined and managed by local chiefs and scaled to local needs through active community participation. The five no-fishing areas in Cuvu-Tuva have been established following a consultative process; they have been designed to be consistent with the natural topography and also ensure that people who are dependent on reef fishing for their livelihood still have some access.

The taboo areas are relatively small, since small no-fishing zones, if managed properly, can create a 'spill-over' effect, whereby fish and shellfish in the protected areas grow, reproduce and eventually migrate into the non-protected areas, helping to restore the once bountiful harvest. Indeed, the Cuvu-Tuva Environment Committee, a group of area chiefs appointed to manage the no-fishing zones, says fish are coming out of the taboo areas and migrating species, like the mullet, have returned.

Another distinctive element of the project is the involvement of women, who are encouraged to participate in community consultations. This is critically important because the inshore reefs are predominantly women's fishing areas. They have seasonal knowledge about where things are and where they breed. They are also the ones who must be convinced to follow the no-fishing rules if success is to be achieved in restoring and managing shallow areas. It is also much more effective for a woman to talk to another woman than for a man to tell women what to do. Seeing things are for the good of their children is convincing to them.

Site Selection and Requirements

At the suggestion of the OSED, a number of National Spiritual Assemblies of the Bahá'ís were contacted about the project, seeking sites where Bahá'í communities are ready for this effort.

As this is a self-help project, the commitment of a group of interested people and one or a few boats/canoes are needed for three to five days at each village workshop site. Workshop discussions mainly occur in the evenings, while days are occupied with hands-on field trips. Where reefs are owned by individuals, or where a traditional or elected authority controls the reefs, permission from these individuals must be obtained. Additional site prerequisites are:

- cordial relations between the Bahá'ís, the local population and leaders

- ample coral reef and sandflat sites, unaffected by serious siltation or pollution

- local ownership and control of the reef areas

Working with local Bahá'í communities is consistent with the directive of the Universal House of Justice in its message to the Bahá'ís of the world of Riḍván 1989, which called upon Bahá'í communities to make the conservation of the environment an integral part of their ongoing activities by 'assisting in endeavours to conserve the environment in ways which blend with the rhythm of life of our community'.

The Current Status of the Project

The first local training for the project was conducted in July 1996, in Ukupseni village, Kuna Yala (San Blas Islands, Panama), under the auspices of the National Spiritual Assembly of Panama. The project was a success, resulting in two community education meetings called by the local chief and the planting of seven reef sites where corals had been destroyed by a tsunami some one hundred years before.

In 1997–8 funding was secured for travel to South Pacific sites in the Solomon Islands and Fiji. On Malaita Island, Solomons, three Bahá'í communities were trained to replant corals destroyed by the traditional harvest of coral for the production of betelnut lime. Four non-Bahá'í communities were also trained to restore reefs and grow corals for the coral trade, three in Fiji and one in the Solomons. Follow-up visits to the sites were made in six months. The results are very encouraging, with juvenile fish recruiting to the rapidly growing corals on restored reefs and with two communities beginning the process of establishing marine reserves for the reestablishment of over-fished resources.

Anare Mudunavere, chief of one of the villages actively involved in the project, observed that plenty of fish are coming back. 'You could not find them here a few years ago', he commented, 'but they are coming back now, every kind of fish.'

An illustrated handbook on methods is being written so that widely scattered individuals and groups will be able to apply the exploratory aspects of the coral reef project to local conditions, as educational projects initially but with potential to transform local subsistence economies. At the end of the day, the goal is to make this process self-managing, so that it becomes part of everyday life,

The project has been adopted by a like-minded NGO, Foundation for the Peoples of the South Pacific International, and a regional five-year project is envisioned. The Coral Gardens approach can easily be replicated in other areas, not only on Fiji but also throughout the South Pacific. Projects are already under way. On Malaita Island, in partnership with the Solomon Islands Development Trust (SIDT) and ICRAN, communities are beginning to establish small-scale conservation areas similar to the taboo zones in Cuvu.

Thoughts on Environmentally-based Bahá'í Development

The Bahá'í teachings offer an alternative model for development and seek to transform society from the inside out. Once the required spiritual foundation has been laid, the question of what to do to positively affect society confronts Bahá'í communities. The old-world development models are often inappropriate but are frequently applied in Bahá'í situations for lack of understanding or simply owing to lack of alternatives.

Degraded resources must be restored and this will require understanding of the causes of degradation as well as of the natural ecological recovery processes. Bahá'í environmental projects aimed at both preventing human-induced environmental degradation and accelerating natural recovery processes will result in restoring the natural balance and abundance in nature. Prosperity will increase where natural resources have been restored, and increased understanding and improved interactions with the natural world will be the end result of restoration projects. Physical transformation of the planet will not only reflect the spiritual transformation of rural communities, it will reinforce and heighten the depth of this transformation.

New approaches towards development must be formulated and this is where individual initiative is required to seek out, identify and experiment with the application of new information, towards the goal of identifying, resurrecting or, if necessary, formulating new models and systems of sustainable production. Individuals and students should be encouraged to study the present ecological, agricultural and economic models in the light of the Bahá'í writings, freeing themselves from the constraints and failings prevalent in these knowledge systems. These individuals especially need to study the indigenous knowledge systems regarding the particular situation or ecosystem of interest.

Works Cited

Bahá'í International Community. *The Prosperity of Humankind*. London: Bahá'í
     Publishing Trust, 1995.
Bahá'u'lláh. *Tablets of Bahá'u'lláh*. Wilmette, IL: Bahá'í Publishing Trust, 1988.
The Universal House of Justice. Letter to the Bahá'ís of the World, Riḍván 1989.

Dr Austin Bowden-Kirby is a marine biologist and director of the Coral Gardens Initiative centred in Fiji.

Gardens for Mongolia:
Growing the Capacity of Mongolia's Families
The Mongolian Development Centre

The Mongolian Development Centre is a Bahá'í-inspired non-governmental organization established in April 1993 with the objective of translating the spiritual principles found in the Bahá'í writings into practice for the betterment of Mongolian society. This chapter was written by MDC staff.

Mongolia's challenges in ensuring its scattered peoples have an adequate diet are as daunting as they are complex. According to the *Mongolian Human Development (UNDP) Report 1997*, a number of related factors marginalize the Mongolian people as 'the poorest of the poor'. These include a national diet historically limited to animal products (as a consequence of a nomadic lifestyle); a recent history of dependency on the centralized policies of the former Soviet state to provide a broader diet; limited access to the benefits of an effective educational system; and a climate which offers an extremely short growing season. In addition, a paralyzing resignation to the existing standard of living has resulted in a situation in which, with the exception of some hardy optimists, few have had the courage to seek substantive change.

Among the group of optimists is the Mongolian Development Centre (MDC). MDC is a non-profit, non-governmental organization dedicated to serving society by empowering individuals and families to develop to the fullest their inherent intellectual, material and spiritual capabilities through a process of education. The organization derives its positive outlook from a vision that human consciousness is a storehouse of untapped potential and latent capacities.

Since its formation in 1993 MDC has worked primarily in the domain of children's rights and capacity-development for families, aiming to effect positive change in both the family circle and the community at large. Its overall vision is focused on promoting a culture of service.

MDC programme is based on several concepts found in the teachings of Bahá'u'lláh:

- The nature of the human being is basically noble.

- This nobility takes the form of latent capacities that are 'inestimable in value'.

- The role of education is to develop these 'gem-like capacities'.

- Education and development have the same goal.

- The needs and aspirations of any group of people involve a range of factors that must be addressed in an integral way.

- Knowledge is a vital requirement of development that helps create the volition to act and to change.

The main goal of MDC is, therefore, to facilitate the process of human resource development.

Capacity-Development of Families and Their Neighbourhoods

MDC's major programme – Capacity-Development of Families and Their Neighbourhoods – is designed to develop the capacities of families to work in groups for the betterment of their neighbourhood. Capacity-development is realized through systematic training, which initiates a participatory learning experience focused not only on the transfer of know-how but also on honing effective consultation and decision-making skills among project participants. The approach is based on the conviction that true development first takes place within individuals who are empowered to recognize, enhance and employ their own abilities to be of service to themselves, their families and their communities.

The programme is devised to support such national governmental initiatives as the National Green Revolution Programme, the Poverty Reduction Programme and the National Programme on Child and Family Development, in addition to international initiatives such as Learning for Life, UNESCO's non-formal, basic distance education project, and the UN Convention on the Rights of the Child (CRC). Families who participate in the programme are selected in consultation with community leaders and local government authorities.

Projects started in 1993 have been implemented thus far at five locations in four different provinces (Darkhan, Hovsgol, Baganuur, Zavkhan and Eastern Gobi). They seek to promote the rights of children, to support healthy attitudes and habits related to nutrition, hygiene, health and family relations, to improve the nutritional content of the diet of low-income families and children, and to empower family groups to enhance and employ their own abilities to be of service to themselves and to society.

Significantly, these projects have a strong demonstration effect within a community, whereby families not directly enrolled in a project are encouraged to undertake similar activities. The programme for family capacity-development has also enlisted strong government support at the local level.

Elements of the Programme

MDC has used two components of the course 'Social Enterprise', produced by the Badí' Foundation in Macau, in its training initiatives. The component 'Transformation of the Heart' deals with aspects of human nature and assists the process of self-discovery and self-respect. 'The Art of Consultation' assists project participants to acquire communication and decision-making skills. These course components form the basis of an empowerment process. Once the participants are armed with communication and decision-making skills, they are then encouraged to use and further develop these skills in initiating a community/family group service project. Service projects, however, often require some technical knowledge and skills and MDC meets this need by providing instructors. For the past few years the main domain of skill learning has been gardening, which has been taught with the assistance of MDC horticulturists.

MDC subscribes to the concept of the bio-intensive method of growing vegetables, which is ideally suited for small-scale, family and/or community gardening and has been shown to be effective for local conditions. Using the bio-intensive approach, high yields can be sustained year after year with fewer inputs than are usually needed. The approach relies on resources found nearby or produced in the garden itself through the composting of all garden refuse, thereby creating a healthy environment for plant and gardener alike.

The family vegetable gardens, as well as the demonstration gardens, serve to promote bio-intensive gardening practices, such as adding compost to the soil, companion planting, crop rotation, deep soil preparation, the use of raised beds and cover-cropping – all practices which promote sustainability and harmony with the natural environment while maintaining high yields on small pieces of land. In addition, seed collection, food storing, pickling, preserving and cooking techniques are demonstrated.

The Greenhouse Project

MDC's first development project was initiated in 1994–6 in Baganuur, a subdistrict of Ulaanbaatar, in response to UNICEF's Child Nutrition Survey of Mongolia. The Greenhouse Project began with the restoration of a run-down, abandoned greenhouse belonging to School No. 64 in Baganuur. It was intended to serve as an educational facility for the training of 60 school children who then proceeded to produce a variety of vitamin-rich vegetables. The project, which emphasized hands-on training and learning by doing, was later continued as a means of researching the practicality and economic feasibility of the use of family-size greenhouses for improving the diet of children. The Swiss Municipality of Bellevue provided funding for both projects with the assistance of the 1% for Development Fund of the United Nations in Geneva. Owing to interest on the part of the Baganuur district government to participate in a joint project with MDC, a programme funded by the German Embassy in Ulaanbaatar was initiated in 1996. It involved ten poor and single-parent families who were provided training in gardening and the construction of mini-greenhouses.

The Darkhan Project

A project in Darkhan has evolved progressively and organically over the past five years, starting in 1997 with the Family Gardening and Greenhouse Project. This project, also funded by the German Embassy in Ulaanbaatar, was initiated owing to the interest shown by Darkhan's University of Agriculture to have a joint gardening project with MDC. In the first project MDC was not directly involved in family selection and priority was given to the families of lecturers, not the most needy. At the same time, the director of the Darkhan Charity School, which accommodated street and orphan children, also expressed interest in involving his school in the project. This led to MDC's decision to use the school gardening plot as its demonstration area. Because the 30 children involved in the project were small, the families decided to supervise the gardening of their children's plots.

MDC conducted three main training seminars for the families. They dealt with soil preparation, planting, transplanting seedlings and harvesting and included other aspects of training, such as an appreciation of the CRC and nutrition, as well as the standard course components in human development.

In the second year of the project, 1998, two groups, one of eight and another of six families, were selected with the assistance of the local government of Darkhan. The criteria for selection were a common interest in gardening and a willingness to work in groups. The Charity School continued to participate and the Australian Embassy in Beijing funded the project.

In the third year two groups of eight families each were selected through application and in consultation with local government authorities. Darkhan Charity School also formed a group of 15 children and a teacher, who actively participated in the training. Another 80 children in the dormitory participated in the project. The local government then requested MDC to conduct the training of one hundred families from their category of the 'poorest of the poor' and AusAID at the Australian Embassy in Beijing funded the project.

In the fourth year, owing to a tremendous response from local government authorities – who requested MDC to become more involved and extend its services to larger segments of the population through capacity-building training – more than a hundred families participated in MDC's Human Development Seminar. As developing capacity to become more self-reliant is effectively achieved through the Social Enterprise workshops, the project for the year 2000, Integral Human Development, focused mainly on fulfilling capacity needs both on a community and a group level. The project had several components: gardening, capacity-building at the community and group levels, and the Darkhan Charity school component. Thirty-two families (in groups of eight) and two groups of children (from the orphanage of the Charity School and the Provincial Children's Centre) participated in all training sessions. More than 130 children and their families participated in this project, which was funded by AusAID and the Embassy of Luxembourg.

In addition, MDC conducted training for two groups of families (60 in all) in Baganuur and Sainshand, a town of the East Gobi province, where 15 families were selected for the project in response to requests from a group of families and their local government.

In the fifth year the project Poverty Reduction through Family Group Capacity-Building was initiated. According to interest expressed by the Darkhan, Baganuur and Sainshand governments, MDC has conducted a series of workshops on Human Development and Social Enterprise training entitled 'Human Development – Realizing Individual Potential'. After approximately 130 people in Darkhan, 35 in Baganuur and 30 in Sainshand participated in the seminar, MDC in consultation with the local government and community leaders, chose 38 families in Darkhan, 16 families in Baganuur and 13 families in Sainshand to participate. The selection criteria were interest in working in groups to grow vegetables in backyards and income level. One group of eight families who live in apartments has grown vegetables in common land allotments (1.5 hectares) which was provided by the local government for MDC's use as a demonstration/training area. In 2002, in support of the project and owing to an increased number of interested families living in apartments with no land, the local government increased the size of common land allotments. The Embassy of Luxembourg funded this project.

Impact and Achievements

Project participants noted that the seminars on human development made them 'think in new ways' and provided a new model and perspective on human relationships, including their ability to transform their own characters, and thus their relationships, and to influence the character development of their children. In addition, their capacity to contribute to the betterment of their families and their community became apparent.

They noted that the training and the work itself had changed the behaviour of their children, a fact which had not escaped the observation of non-participating neighbours, who also wished their children to engage in such activities rather than waste their time in the streets.

Following their training, when the participants immediately had cause to put what they had learned about consultation and problem-solving into practice in group work, they noticed how it assisted them to achieve unity and unity of vision in the group. This was reinforced and ensured by the continual presence of MDC field staff at regular meetings. The staff helped them recognize where and how to apply the principles they had learned in real-life situations. The unity achieved in the groups is reflected in their desire to continue working together after the termination of the project.

One group of landless families working on common land saw the value of their newly-acquired capacity in problem-solving in concrete terms when, despite problems involving water, security, distance and poor soil, they were able to reap a harvest as a result of their work.

The participants also noted that the involvement of the members of their families in the work increased their motivation. They observed that all members of the family not only participated but also benefited. The women had more responsibility during the growing season and the men were more responsible at the beginning and the end of the gardening work. While the project had an impact on all family members, MDC observed that mothers and daughters were the most actively involved.

Increased Capacity for Learning

Intrigued with the new idea of approaching work using a scientific method, some village families were inspired to carry out their own experiments in which they used the traditional way of gardening side by side with the new bio-intensive method. As a result of their own observations, they chose the latter. Individual initiative in experimentation led some families to discover that they can harvest some vegetables twice during the summer. Others found more innovative ways of making preserves, such as the invention of a watermelon and pumpkin jam or the perfecting of a vegetable pickling method which enabled one woman to progress from 40 jars last year to 130 this year. She anticipates that she will be able easily to triple her effort next year.

This gradual acquisition of expertise has led to increased self-confidence and pride among participants, which gives them more confidence and enthusiasm to share their learning with their neighbours. Such participants are now chosen as MDC resource people and used to promote the programme.

The same enterprising spirit has now led to training in bookkeeping and small business management, and some old and new participants are discussing the initiation of new small enterprises, such as the building of a permanent greenhouse or tree nursery plot with MDC's support.

What the participants noted from their experience was their capacity and potential to improve their lives through their own efforts, as well as their increased feelings of confidence to help others do so. Some participants have expressed a feeling that the skills they have learned have become an 'intellectual investment' for their family which will be passed down to the next generation.

An Increase in Self-reliance

Owing to traditional perceptions of 'development', many families understandably expected to receive hand-outs or money for participating in the project and when this was not forthcoming from MDC declined to take part. However, when they saw the results of a project in which the major investment was the hard work and innovative spirit of their neighbours, it provided food for thought. An MDC impact evaluation showed that whereas five years ago families often demanded materials, better quality tools, etc., in more recent years, after observing their neighbours' participation they joined the project for the benefit it would have on their lives, seeing the value of developing new skills and capacities.

One participant from the common land project reported how difficult it was at first to accept that the participants themselves would have to do all the work of building fences, providing water and other arduous chores. However, when they experienced the intense satisfaction of seeing the concrete and positive results of their own labour, they understood the value of self-reliant development.

During evaluation meetings, the governors, community leaders and government representatives who took part stressed in particular that the project empowers the needy to recognize, enhance and employ their own abilities and resources to be of service to themselves, their families and their communities. One participant commented that he was an orphan and that all his life he had worked for others – it was only during the project that he learned what it was to work with people of different backgrounds in a group and in a spirit of unity.

Nutritional Improvements and Increased Income

The concrete results of gardening activities were measured. Participating families in three areas harvested a total of 34 tons of vegetables this year, with each family consuming about 300 kg of vegetables during the period of growing and harvesting. They also benefited in the winter from the preserves set by and the cooking methods learned.

The success of the participants' gardening efforts resulted not only in better nutrition; in addition, surplus produce was preserved and then sold. The capacity for food preservation was extended and improved when a heating system was employed to enable participants to store their vegetables and seeds for family use in winter and also to sell products at times when higher prices could be charged.

Government Collaboration and Recognition

From 1993 to 1997 MDC operated with the support of the Mongolian Chamber of Commerce and Industry and was licensed by the Mongolian Ministry of Education. Since 1998 it has been registered with the Ministry of Justice of Mongolia. Collaboration with government has been an important ingredient in MDC's success.

MDC's impact on society is reflected in the local and provincial government requests for MDC to extend its approach to a much larger segment of the population and in more diverse domains of development. One local government offered office space for an MDC branch; governors and other officials made periodic visits to view activities and project sites in each area; and local governments helped MDC solve its problems by providing land, water and other supports. Community leaders participated in MDC's human development training, which has facilitated dialogue among the three major partners in development: community, NGOs and government. National and local media reported on and broadcast the training sessions.

The World Bank mission on civil society, which visited the project site in Darkhan and interviewed MDC staff and the governor, cited this project as an example of NGO–government dialogue and close collaboration. MDC also cooperated with and shared its experience in the development field with other like-minded national and international organizations and governments.

MDC has been actively working in the fields of child and family development since 1993 and since 1995 has been at the forefront of promoting in Mongolia the rights enshrined in the Convention on the Rights of the Child (CRC). It engages in joint activities with UNICEF and the National Centre for Children (NCC) – now the National Committee for Children – which was the first Mongolian response to the introduction of the CRC. The first two governmental and non-governmental organizations meetings on the CRC in 1995 and 1996 were organized at the initiative of MDC, together with UNICEF and the NCC, and the concert on the occasion of the 50th anniversary of UNICEF was jointly arranged with these organizations. MDC has been a member of the National Coalition of NGOs for Children since it was established in 1999.

MDC was the only representative NGO from Mongolia at the Millennium Forum of NGOs at the United Nations in New York and its suggestions and comments were included in the Millennium Forum Declaration and Agenda of Action Plans. On a national level – in support of the Millennium Forum and to sensitize fellow citizens to the main agreements reached – MDC and the Coalition for Children initiated a meeting of NGOs and government leaders in 2000. MDC has been invited by UNICEF Mongolia to contribute to the development of its main strategies for the next five years because UNICEF considers MDC to have extensive experience in implementing CRC-related activities and family development programmes. More recently, UNICEF has invited MDC to contribute to and start off a new Moral Attitudes programme for junior youth. MDC has also contributed to government strategies to reduce poverty.

MDC anticipates that its third stage of development will be institutional capacity-building. While MDC needs more training and support itself to enter this stage, an interesting phenomenon is that MDC gardening projects in Darkhan and Erdenbulgan, which started as community projects, are now at a stage where they could be strengthened and assisted to become independent entities, either as a commercial or economic activity or as a NGO. MDC will be involved in supporting this phase of development.

Works Cited

Mongolian Human Development (UNDP) Report 1997

Five Project Summaries

The five short articles making up this chapter offer glimpses into several social and economic development programmes and projects which are either sponsored by Bahá'í institutions or are carried out by non-governmental organizations inspired by the Bahá'í teachings. Dozens of such projects operating throughout the world are geared to locally identified needs and each employs principles promoted in the Bahá'í writings. The Office of Social and Economic Development at the Bahá'í World Centre and national or local spiritual assemblies provide advice and in some cases funding support for many such projects throughout the world.

An Investment for Well-being: Restoring the Agricultural Environment on Bolivia's Altiplano

From *One Country**

In the Andes mountains, just to the west of the central Bolivian city of Cochabamba, is the altiplano: a high, rugged plateau on which only the hardiest of peoples can survive. In isolated valleys small communities of Aymara and Quechua people eke out a subsistence living, growing potatoes during the wet season and grazing sheep on the marginal pasturelands that cling to the slopes. They are among the poorest of the poor here, in this poorest of Latin American nations.

Among their problems is a scarcity of water. The wet season is only about three months long and even then dry spells sometimes cause the potato crop to fail. Any trees which would have helped to hold the rain were cut for fuel or building materials long ago.

'It's really a mountainous desert here,' said William Baker, director of the Dorothy Baker Environmental Studies Centre, a Bahá'í-sponsored initiative which is devoted to exploring how appropriate technologies and education for sustainable development can be applied to improve the social, economic and environmental conditions in the Bolivian altiplano. In its early years the Centre focused on helping families in the region build inexpensive solar-heated greenhouses, enabling them to grow vegetables and fruits inexpensively at high altitudes and during the off-season.

More recently, the Centre has sought to encourage altiplano communities with a simple yet potentially far-reaching project to build small check dams which can catch and hold the scarce rainfall. The promise – which is starting to be fulfilled in some areas – is that periodic dry spells will no longer mean disaster for potato crops, that the pasturelands themselves will become more verdant, that the slopes can be to some extent reforested and that, ultimately, year-round supplies of water will be established.

'In reality, the soil in the region has a lot of fertility, but because of erosion and the fact that it dries out, many of the plant species that used to thrive no longer survive,' said Dr Baker during a recent interview. 'But with water conservation there is the possibility of changing the whole ecology of the area back towards what it once was and to use this as an environmentally sound base for other projects in agriculture and animal husbandry.'

The foundation for the Centre's efforts comes from a programme of environmental study classes for adults and preschool classes for children. These classes have been important in helping communities adopt new technologies. The accent is on showing a community how to help itself. Classes at the Centre underscore the inherent dignity and worth of all human beings, for example, as well as emphasizing the essential unity and equality of all peoples – teachings that help tap into the underlying aspirations that all humans share, empowering them to become increasingly responsible for their own development.

'In our classes, we advocate an idea of "investment for well-being",' said Dr Baker. 'The idea is based on basic principles of conservation and respect for nature. It also emphasizes the idea that we live in one world and that we really don't have the right to destroy it, since that affects the rights of other people too.'

Empowered by the knowledge that they gained in classes sponsored by the Centre, graduates from four communities in Tapacari Province organized their friends and neighbours to help build more than two thousand small check dams during 1994 and 1995. In all, more than three hundred people have participated in the project in these communities, which lie about 120 kilometres west of Cochabamba.

The simple rock and fill dams, which take three or four people a few hours to build, are designed to help slow the rainfall runoff, so that the water filters into the ground and leaves precious soil in catch basins behind the dam. The effort also seeks to control the heavy erosion that has washed away much prime pastureland in recent years. Small tree nurseries have also been started in these communities to supply seedlings that can be used to reforest areas behind the dams once they fill in.

Although the project is less than two years old, it is already beginning to show results, said Dr Baker. 'In one community, we have quite demonstrable new wetlands, while in another we have increased the area of wetlands,' he said. 'In all, we probably have 500 or more dams that are now filling in with soil and starting to filter water. We have planted many with new trees.'

'Now several other communities are asking to enter the programme because they see the results,' Dr Baker added.

*Reprinted from *One Country*, the newsletter of the Bahá'í International Community, volume 7, issue 3, October–December 1995.

A Tanzanian School Promotes Self-reliance

From *One Country***

Asked what makes their school different from others in the tropical East African nation of Tanzania, students at the Ruaha Secondary School are quick to point to the total absence of 'caning', as corporal punishment is known here. But when administrators, teachers, parents and local officials are asked what distinguished Ruaha, a private, non-profit school operated by the Bahá'í community of Tanzania, they see the 'no caning' policy as merely one sign of a distinctive approach to education, one that strives to create a learning environment based on the application of spiritual and moral values to the challenges of daily life.

In particular, those who know Ruaha talk about the school's emphasis on promoting qualities like patience, diligence, courtesy, trustworthiness, compassion and justice, while at the same time helping students develop the capacities, attitudes and skills – such as knowledge of appropriate agricultural techniques, computer literacy and basic commerce – that are geared to help students survive in one of the poorest countries in the world. On top of it all, they also speak of the school's strong sense of mission when it comes to educating girls and proudly note its record of academic excellence.

Although located in this relatively small and remote capital of the Iringa Region, the school draws students from all over Tanzania. The roughly four hundred currently enrolled, for example, come from 17 of Tanzania's 21 regions, as provinces are called here. Founded in 1986, the school is owned and operated by the National Spiritual Assembly of the Bahá'ís of Tanzania, the freely-elected governing body of the Bahá'í community. Overall, the school's primary mission is to serve the wider Tanzanian community by providing quality education at an affordable cost.

'We want to provide students with an education which is not only theoretical but also practical so they can be agents of change in their communities, so they can be examples of high moral rectitude, educational, academic and moral excellence, and so they can try to serve their communities and establish attitudes of service,' said Becky Fairley, the principal at Ruaha. 'Our fees are moderate. We are not here only to serve the elite, though some elite choose Ruaha for their children. We are open to people of moderate means also. We attract students of different economic statuses,' she said.

Focus on Girls

More than two-thirds of those students are girls, a testimony to the school's success at achieving one of its major goals. 'We are really focusing on the education of girls, which is very important here, where traditionally only boys are educated, where traditionally boys are put first,' said Ms Fairley, noting that nationally less than half of the students enrolled in secondary school are girls. 'We try to encourage girls, to improve their performance. We believe this contributes to raising up the status of women. It changes the way they raise children and this makes a tremendous difference in the community.' Ms Fairley said the school requires an entrance examination and girls are given preference in the scoring of that exam. She said the school also has a special scholarship programme for girls and that it participates in the government-sponsored Girls Secondary Education Support Programme funded by the World Bank, which gives educational opportunities to girls of low income.

Providing a good education is a difficult task in one of the world's poorest countries, where the majority of people are struggling to find enough food to eat. The average annual per capita income in Tanzania is about US$450 a year. The average annual tuition at Ruaha is US$175 a year, a fee which is higher than government schools but quite low compared to other private secondary schools of similar quality. 'It is difficult to help students see the importance of education,' said Angresia Ginga, who teaches agriculture at Ruaha. 'They see their university-educated relatives sitting at home jobless.' Ruaha strives to overcome these motivational barriers by focusing on subjects that will give students a better chance of finding a job. In addition to standard, nationally required subjects like English, Kiswahili, geography, history, mathematics, physics, biology and chemistry, Ruaha's curriculum also covers agriculture, commerce, computer literacy and 'self-reliance'.

One element of the self-reliance programme focuses on practical experience in agriculture. Each student is assigned a plot and different crops are raised by each class. They also sell their produce to the catering programme, so that students learn to see the 'fruits' of their efforts. 'The self-reliance class helps because I can help my parents at home to farm in the fields and to clean and do other small jobs,' said James Iddi, a 17-year-old Form III day student. 'The computer classes help because now there is email, Internet. If you go to other countries, they use computers. I think it's better to learn now so I will be equipped later on.'

Spirit of Teamwork

Another problem faced by virtually every school in Tanzania is how to motivate teachers. In government schools, teachers are poorly paid and many skip class because they need to find alternative means to earn money. Ruaha seeks to overcome this by promoting a spirit of teamwork among the teachers, a spirit that is enhanced by the school's policy of making salary payments on time. One result of the faculty's sense of teamwork has been solid academic performance, something especially noteworthy considering the school's high percentage of girl students, who often come under-prepared because of traditional neglect of girls in Tanzania.

Based on the 1998 National Form IV Examination results, Ruaha School ranked third in the region, fifth in the zone and 35th out of 611 schools nationally. Another measure of the school's success can be seen in the percentage of students who are selected by the government to go on from Form IV (11th grade equivalent) to Form V (12th grade equivalent). Nationally, the average acceptance rate is about five per cent. In 1998, however, 26 out of 33 Form IV graduates at Ruaha were selected to go on, a rate of 78 per cent.

Moral Education

Ruaha is also notable for its incorporation of moral education into the curriculum. Using an activities-based approach, the moral education programme, for example, might employ a tree-planting session to teach the importance of environment and ecology, as well as team decision-making. Ms Fairley said the school seeks to integrate moral education into every subject. 'We have a virtue of the week programme, stressing qualities such as "honesty", for example, to bring to the students' attention one virtue each week.' Students learn to be service-oriented by taking turns cleaning the school compound, gardening and doing other maintenance work. The moral education programme also stresses the importance of religion, taking an interfaith approach and teaching about all of the world's major religions. In religious beliefs, the Tanzanian population is evenly split between Christian, Muslim and traditional religions, and the school's effort to teach about all religions has helped to foster tolerance among students, who are likewise quite diverse in their religious and ethnic backgrounds.

'Ruaha School is different because it is a religious school,' said Moza Said, a 17-year-old female student. 'This religion unites people instead of differentiating between them. Our moral education class helps us learn to live with different people in society.'

Ruaha itself also stresses service to the wider community by operating several ongoing social and economic development projects. A shop was built recently to serve both students and the surrounding community. It sells products at comparable rates to town and was built to provide students with the things they might need on a day-to-day basis. A dairy farm provides milk to the catering department and to the teachers and surrounding community. Computer classes are available to the public in the evenings for a small fee, which helps improve skills in the wider community. In interviews, students and parents acknowledged all of these distinctive points about Ruaha and more.

'If anything stands out at Ruaha, it is the overall sense of respect for students as human beings,' said one former teacher. 'That is what is different. That they respect each person and try to empower them in a country where life is quite hard.'

**Reprinted from *One Country*, the newsletter of the Bahá'í International Community, volume 12, issue 3, October–December 2000.

Rural Education in Northern Honduras

Ineke Gijsbers

What do a community first-aid kit, pigs and chickens, election to a village council, vegetable gardens, cassava processing and inter-community football matches have in common? Simple; they all relate to the activities of SAT groups and achievements by SAT students in northern Honduras. This list could also include reforestation projects with coconut and fruit trees, adult literacy projects and tutoring primary school children with learning difficulties.

Background

SAT is the Spanish acronym for 'Tutorial Learning System', a rural, non-formal secondary education and development programme developed by FUNDAEC in Colombia (see chapter 9 of the present volume). The Bahá'í-inspired non-profit and non-governmental organization Bayán (the Association for Indigenous Social and Economic Development) is implementing the SAT programme in Mosquitia, one of the most remote areas of Honduras. The area is at the meeting point of two indigenous societies: the Garifuna people, of mixed Carib and West African origin, and the Miskito Indians of northern Honduras.

Some seven to ten thousand people inhabit the Mosquitia, living mainly on the coast and by inland waterways which cut through the jungle-like coastal marshland. The communities depend on the sea and farming for their livelihoods. Particularly among the Garifuna, the men undertake fishing using rudimentary technology – casting nets from dugout canoes – while the women are the main farmers. In both Garifuna and Miskito communities the men are often at sea for long periods, employed on the deep sea vessels which ply the Gulf of Mexico fisheries; thus households are normally headed by women for a significant part of the time.

The area is environmentally important since it is in the buffer zone of the Rio Platano Biosphere Reserve declared by UNESCO in 1980. It was the first biosphere reserve in Central America and at 525,000 square hectares it is easily Honduras' largest protected area, with possibly the largest area of tropical rain forest in Central America.

Bayán was established in the mid-1980s by two pioneering Bahá'í families. They focused at first on building a small rural hospital in the remote town of Palacios, as the people in the area at that time had no health services. Over the years, while improving the range of health services to the surrounding population, Bayán realized the need for a more integrated approach to the region's problems.

In 1996 Bayán started to implement SAT in villages surrounding Palacios (the project headquarters) with technical assistance support from FUNDAEC and financial support, initially from the Kellogg Foundation and the Canadian International Development Agency (CIDA) and later from the British Department for International Development (DFID).

The Integration of Bahá'í Principles with SAT

The SAT curriculum is taught by locally trained tutors and is organized around the concept of service to the community as the basic motivating principle, as opposed to individual material gain. It emphasizes moral values like honesty and trustworthiness. SAT students carry out literacy and health service projects with a number of neighbouring families as part of their practical studies. The students use highly interactive workbooks originally developed by FUNDAEC, which are now being adapted to Honduran conditions. As it has evolved in Honduras, SAT has two main levels which together comprise the complete secondary education equivalent. The course units and textbooks cover such areas as agriculture, mathematics, sciences, service to the community, readings about society and language. The texts especially aim to help the students in the development of their conceptual thinking and critical faculties: essential aspects of the independent investigation of truth and the realization of human potential.

Almost 80 per cent of the SAT students in Mosquitia are female, largely as a result of the occupational structure. This means that there is a unique opportunity to promote the empowerment of women in the development process, although it can be more difficult for women with young children to devote sufficient time to their studies. The education of women is emphasized in the Bahá'í writings.

Agriculture and Natural Resource Management

An important component of SAT is the agricultural 'subsystems' unit oriented to the search for more diversified and appropriate small-scale farming systems. This involves the development of a number of agricultural systems using a range of crop combinations with varying production cycles which complement each other, such as the use of soil nutrients, labour inputs and the timing of crop revenues. Here the principle of unity in diversity ties in with ecologically sound farming practices.

Each SAT group has a research plot, which usually belongs to one of the students but may be land loaned by the community. The students help design the research plots, thus reflecting respect for the farmers' traditional knowledge and experience. The aim is to combine outside and local knowledge in the search for more efficient and effective farming systems which can bring about a better nutritional balance for the family and increase family income.

A number of SAT groups in Mosquitia have carried out pig and poultry rearing projects but these have had mixed success. One lesson learned has been wariness in accepting material donations as opposed to financial loans. Several of the donations accepted involved breeds and feeding systems inappropriate for the area.

The importance of viewing nature as a source of life to be loved and cared for is also emphasized in SAT.

Bayán has also initiated the USAID-funded 'Management of the aquatic resources of the Bacalar Estuary' (PROLAB) project. This includes a botanical survey and the development of a community-based marine management programme. Future plans include a mangrove management and reforestation project linked to PROLAB, as well as a Centre for Environmental Studies at Palacios which would bring out the synergies between SAT and PROLAB.

Evolution of SAT in Honduras

Following agreements with the Ministry of Education in three departments (Colón, Atlántida and Gracias à Dios) the salaries of SAT tutors and coordinators are now being paid from regional government budgets. As of January 2002 more than three hundred students participate in some 20 SAT groups in Mosquitia. The development and expansion of SAT to new areas confirms the move towards national administration of the programme. The ultimate goal is for the SAT programme to be completely administered by the Honduran government, as has happened in Colombia.

Conclusion

SAT is tackling what is arguably the most important obstacle to sustainable development: the lack of appropriate skills, knowledge and attitudes for the development of individual and community capacity for self-reliance. It is truly empowering in that it provides a way for rural people to shape their development according to their own aspirations, rather than those of outsiders. Another important aspect of SAT is that sustainability is built into the programme, at least in terms of human resources: the most important output of the education process is a number of thinking and skilled young people who should themselves become community leaders.

Ineke Gijsbers has an MSc in Agroforestry from the University of Wageningen in the Netherlands. She worked for several years in a sustainable land use project in Mali, West Africa, before coming to England in 1997, where she became a Bahá'í in 2000. She is an officer of the Bahá'í Office for Social and Economic Development for the UK (BOSED) and editor of its newsletter Faith-in-Action. *She is also a member of the Task Force for the Tierra Santa Orphanage in Honduras which is financially supported by the British Bahá'í community and the Bahá'í Agency for Social and Economic Development UK (BASED-UK).*

Felin Gelli Rural Training Farm

Ineke Gijsbers

Background

Hidden in a valley near Peniel, north of Carmarthen in South Wales, is a Bahá'í-inspired treasure called Felin Gelli, meaning 'Mill in the Small Wood'. This 11-acre rural training farm is the home of Sheila and Richard Swann and their two sons, as well as long-term volunteer Clair Pope and her daughter. Its aim is to provide opportunities for young people with learning difficulties to acquire skills in a rural environment.

It all started 22 years ago when Sheila and Richard decided to combine their love of agricultural work with their teaching skills and interest in working with people who had learning difficulties. Felin Gelli, a 390-year-old farm – once an important mill on a huge estate – was purchased in 1979 under the ownership of the charity Stepping Stones Rural Training Association Ltd., which had been set up the year before.

Felin Gelli is a mixed farm with pigs, cows, sheep and chickens, and a small market garden with a poly-tunnel and a greenhouse. Produce is sold locally and most customers live within a ten mile radius. The farm is run on organic farming principles; however, it is not registered as an organic farm because the costs of organic feeds and the certification procedure on a small acreage are too high.

In September 1980 the first two students arrived, referred by the social services department. They stayed as residents, living with the Swann family. A planning application was made to convert the old mill into a residential building but objections from local people prevented this. Appeals were made and permission was finally granted in late 1981; however, at that time financial resources were insufficient to convert the building. Over the years, the focus has shifted to day provision, meaning that students live nearby (close enough to be picked up by the farm mini-bus).

In the late 1980s, government money was allocated to Wales to improve services for people with learning difficulties. This resulted in greater local interest in Felin Gelli and to date 12 students have resided there for periods ranging from several months to many years. Most students come for a few days each week during term times. They learn whatever is appropriate for them, including working with animals, organic fruit and vegetable production and general farm maintenance such as hedging and ditching. They are also taught social, cooking, literacy and numeracy skills.

One cannot talk about Felin Gelli without mentioning the volunteers who are as much part of the farm as the students. Twenty-eight people, from several countries and organizations such as International Voluntary Service, Land Use Volunteers, Community Service Volunteers (a British charity volunteer agency) and EcoAg Service have worked as volunteers. There have also been local as well as Bahá'í year-of-service volunteers.

Bahá'í Principles and Ideas

Bahá'í principles are so interwoven into daily life at Felin Gelli that Sheila and Richard find it difficult to distinguish them. Working at a farm is, of course, all about agriculture, which is regarded in the Bahá'í Faith as an activity 'conducive to the advancement of mankind and to the reconstruction of the world' (Bahá'u'lláh, *Tablets* 89). It is also 'the fundamental basis of the community' ('Abdu'l-Bahá, *Promulgation* 217). In one of his Tablets, 'Abdu'l-Bahá also indicates that should a person become proficient in the field of agriculture, he or she will become 'a means of providing for the comfort of untold numbers of people' ('Abdu'l-Bahá, in *Economics* no. 7).

Working with people with learning difficulties is directly linked to another Bahá'í principle: 'Regard man as a mine rich in gems of inestimable value. Education can, alone, cause it to reveal its treasures, and enable mankind to benefit therefrom' (Bahá'u'lláh, *Gleanings* 260). Felin Gelli is also concerned with improving the social image of people with learning difficulties as perceived by themselves, their families and the wider community. This accords with the Bahá'í principle of avoiding prejudice in any form and especially empowers families with children with learning difficulties. The volunteers also profit from the application of these principles: many of them have never worked at a farm or with people with learning difficulties or even in an English-speaking country.

Unity in diversity can be witnessed every day at the farm, with people from different backgrounds and cultures working as a team, each with responsibilities appropriate to their capacities. Talking and listening to each other and other consultation skills are basic tenets of life at the farm. Prejudices within the team and the wider community are fought and backbiting is not permitted. No one is considered better than another and with time students become responsible for increasingly difficult tasks. All current students are responsible for one chicken house each: this means they have to feed the birds, collect the eggs and clean the chicken house. They also have to clean, count and grade the eggs, thus improving their numeracy skills.

Respect for themselves, other people, the animals and the environment is very important. A respectful attitude for animals is particularly difficult to acquire because it so often contradicts a student's experiences away from Felin Gelli . It is also one reason behind the decision not to sell animals through the market, since by taking them straight to the abattoir animals are subjected to less stress. Getting a local butcher to cut and pack the meat not only addresses the ethical problem of transporting produce long distances from producer to consumer but also enables the farm to sell locally, directly to the consumer, thus attracting a higher income by cutting out the middle man.

Future Prospects

Funding problems are the main reason why Felin Gelli can still only accommodate three students. Up to now social services have not regarded Felin Gelli as a mainstream day service and therefore have not considered its funding a priority. This not only results in anxiety over monthly income and whether the students will have funding to cover the next term but also renders almost impossible the expansion of student numbers to six, considered the ideal number by Sheila and Richard. However, the relationship with social services is now improving. The whole property also requires major improvements. Fortunately, a donation of £5,000 to rebuild a derelict farm building as a storage and packaging unit for farm produce (vegetables, fruits and meat) has recently been received. It is hoped this will not only attract more customers for farm produce but also provide more learning opportunities for the students in the areas of numeracy, social skills and a better understanding of the production and processing chain for farm produce.

The renovation and development of existing buildings, which will be carried out in an environmentally sensitive way while maintaining the present external appearance, will be conducive to increased student numbers and an expanded curriculum. The building of a machinery shed and workshop will enable students to be involved in the routine repair and maintenance of farm and garden machinery. However, the small size of the farm will remain essential to the provision of the intense support that students require.

Looking further into the future, it may be possible to develop a sheltered employment scheme serving the local community by, for example, providing a gardening service as a natural extension of what the students are already doing.

Sheila, Richard and Clair see Felin Gelli as a first step in the development of the potential of people with learning difficulties and expect to continue to offer this unique mix of Bahá'í principles and love to the students, the volunteers and the local community.

EcoAg Service: Farm Apprenticeships for Youth
Nancy E. McIntyre

EcoAg Service began in 1993 as a youth agricultural apprenticeship programme working in cooperation with the Agriculture Special Interest Group of the Association for Bahá'í Studies, North America. Now a Bahá'í-inspired, non-profit organization, EcoAg offers agriculture-related educational programmes and links interested youth with farms that seek to grow food in ways that sustain the natural resource base and promote community. Its goals are to give young adults hands-on farming experience, to call attention to the emphasis that the Bahá'í writings place on the importance of agriculture and to help prepare youth for service.

In the Tablet of the World, Bahá'u'lláh said that giving special regard to agriculture was a prerequisite for the reconstruction of the world (Bahá'u'lláh, *Tablets* 89–90). While in New York City, 'Abdu'l-Bahá called agriculture 'the fundamental basis of the community' ('Abdu'l-Bahá, *Promulgation* 217) and elaborated on this topic with his description of the storehouse ('Abdu'l-Bahá, *Foundations* 39–41). Since 1983 the Universal House of Justice has enumerated guiding principles for Bahá'í-inspired social and economic development which includes agriculture (Bahá'í International Community, *Prosperity*).

With this guidance in mind, EcoAg Service has sponsored a number of educational workshops, many of them at the annual Rabbani Trust Social and Economic Development Seminar and Conference for the Americas. EcoAg also maintains an apprentice orientation programme and has produced a manual based on Bahá'í principles which serve as a preparation for service, agricultural or otherwise. Called 'Nine Points', this conceptual framework comprises:

- Apprenticeship as Quest/Investigation of Truth

- Gifts of Work in the Spirit of Service

- Unity of Creation/Issues of Sustainability

- Dynamic Coherence between Spiritual/Practical Matters

- Unity of Mankind/Grassroots Community-Building

- Unity in Diversity/Developing Trust in One's Capability

- Unity of Religions or Cultures/Attitude of Consultation

- Creativity and Authenticity/Relationship to Creator

- Sharing and Reflection/Coming to Know What It Is We Know
(McIntyre, *Nine Points*)

The number of EcoAg Service apprenticeships has risen from one or two in each of the first two years to five annually, with a total of 23 as of 2001. Early on, the scope of the programme became international. A dozen or more sites – some Bahá'í, some not – varying somewhat each year in number, are located on four continents. Apprentices have come from Africa and Europe as well as the Americas, with one Asian born. The Bádí' project in the Cape area of South Africa remains a favourite site; it places youth in traditional village settings and involves them in local agricultural efforts. Apprenticeships in Africa usually run from six months to two years. Those in the northern hemisphere are often for the summer only, though some may be longer or shorter. Eighteen is the minimum age requirement for apprenticeship unless a youth has had unusual experience away from home and seems ready to take on the responsibility expected of an EcoAg apprentice. These young adults forge their own agreement with the host site, accept liability for themselves and provide their own health insurance and transportation to and from the project site.

To honour Ben Levy, former director of the Rabbani Trust, for his recognition of the significance of agriculture in Bahá'í social and economic development activities and to encourage Latin American participation, EcoAg Service began in 2001 to award merit scholarships to attend the annual Social and Economic Development Seminar and Conference for the Americas. Nine scholarships were awarded that year.

The apprenticeship programme is, by the account of most EcoAg apprentices, a life-changing experience. Many of these young people serve an additional agricultural apprenticeship with EcoAg or through college programmes. Following are some of their comments, which attest to the value of their learning experiences:

Ron Whitmore, coordinator of the North West Lansing Healthy Communities Initiative and a Fellow with the Liberty Hyde Bailey scholars programme, is now a doctoral student in the Department of Resource Development at Michigan State University. 'I never expected to learn as much as I did about myself, my relationship to the rest of creation . . . how important [it is] . . . to nurture this connection through land stewardship . . . [I] never expected that my experience at the Land Stewardship Center (Michigan 1999) would be so thought-provoking and transformative. I learned far more than I expected . . . [and] have been inspired to continue enthusiastically in my development and agricultural work.'

Shiloh Moates, who learned to speak the Xhosa language and became a Bahá'í while an EcoAg apprentice in South Africa (1994), is now a graduate student in International Studies at the University of Maryland. 'It was through EcoAg that I was first sent on the road of anthropological study. My apprenticeship in South Africa . . . opened my eyes to the beautiful colours of human diversity . . . [and] introduced to me the community strengthening powers that agriculture can provide. It is my dream to incorporate agriculture and the application of appropriate technology . . .'

Lucy Greensmith Lodge from England, the first overseas apprentice to come to the United States (1997), is now coordinator of the EcoAg Service apprenticeship programme. 'Working directly with the earth – providing food for the local community . . . is an opportunity to learn lessons that cannot be learned in the classroom: how to work hard in a physical way, determination, constancy, attunement to the rhythms and cycles of nature, cooperation with fellow workers, service to the community and responsibility.'

Paula Posas, a 1997 EcoAg apprentice at Louis Gregory Baháʼí Institute in South Carolina, now works at the World Bank. 'I don't think people necessarily have to . . . be interested in agriculture *per se*. The EcoAgricultural apprenticeship can be seen as a one-time experience, not a life-long theme. It is an experience that is valuable in and of itself. That, however, does not mean that it won't become an important or guiding part of an apprentice's life.'

Laura Carter became an apprentice the year after she accompanied a friend to an EcoAg orientation weekend held at the Louis Gregory Baháʼí Institute (1997). She went on to serve several agricultural apprenticeships through other programmes. 'That weekend was an orientation for me, whether I knew it at the time or not . . . the fact that all of us young people were there, given that space and time to interact, experience the effort of community-building through agriculture, had lasting impacts, changed my life, who I am. I remember . . . not really being sure of why I was there, or even how I was connected to agriculture . . . [I] certainly was challenged to think and talk about it during that time. I love the diversity of the people that were there, young and old, of all degrees, from local and faraway places.'

The effect of the EcoAg Service programme seems to have extended beyond what the official numbers suggest. Many youth who do not serve an agricultural apprenticeship have participated in formal and informal EcoAg orientation sessions. Through workshops and conference displays, EcoAg has helped call attention to the Baháʼí writings on agriculture and to principles of grass-roots community-building which are part of social and economic development. The *American Baháʼí* has called EcoAg Service 'perhaps the granddaddy of Baháʼí mentoring projects' (Mennillo, 'Mandate' 15).

Until the recent widespread use of the Internet there were few ways for EcoAg to get word of the apprentice programme to Baháʼí youth. Now the number of applicants, both Baháʼís and non-Baháʼís, is rising. The farm sites have praised EcoAg apprentices and ask for more. Young adults who are studying agriculture in university – which the Baháʼí writings encourage ('Abduʼl-Bahá, *Selections* 144–5 and *Promulgation* 283) – say that apprenticeship is their only actual experience of growing food or fibre. Some individuals, such as a member of an agricultural village in Africa, have contacted EcoAg Service to consult on Baháʼí-inspired principles of social and economic development.

The diversity of the apprentices, of the sites and of those who work with and

otherwise take part in EcoAg programmes have added immeasurably to its richness. Increasing the complexity of the project gradually – step by step and with
limited resources – has also benefited the programme. Increasingly, EcoAg Service
has moved into educational activities and the 2002 board of directors is now planning to write curriculum modules. Another measure of the programme's success, in
addition to the testimony of the youth themselves, is that many former apprentices
choose to volunteer at EcoAg workshops and three now serve on its board. More
importantly, these young adults go forward to participate responsibly, with vision
and commitment, in jobs or other service opportunities that contribute to the
reconstruction of the world as envisioned by Bahá'u'lláh.

*Nancy McIntyre has worked as a small market farmer and as a registered lobbyist,
testifying at legislative, congressional and gubernatorial hearings on sustainable
agriculture issues. Over the past decade she volunteered on a daily basis, first with
the Association for Bahá'í Studies Agriculture Seminar and more recently with
EcoAg Service, started by John Bradley. She has been an active participant in the
International Society for Agriculture and Rural Development and in the Rabbani
Trust Annual Social and Economic Development Seminar and Conference for the
Americas. She now divides her time between a mountain farm in North Carolina and
rural Hawaii.*

Works Cited

'Abdu'l-Bahá. *Foundations of World Unity*. Wilmette, IL: Bahá'í Publishing Trust, 1945.
— *The Promulgation of Universal Peace*. Wilmette, IL: Bahá'í Publishing Trust, 1982.
— *Selections from the Writings of 'Abdu'l-Bahá*. Haifa: Bahá'í World Centre, 1978.
Bahá'í International Community. *The Prosperity of Humankind*. London: Bahá'í
    Publishing Trust, 1995.
Bahá'u'lláh. *Gleanings from the Writings of Bahá'u'lláh*. Wilmette, IL: Bahá'í Publishing
    Trust, 1983.
— *Tablets of Bahá'u'lláh*. Wilmette, IL: Bahá'í Publishing Trust, 1988.
Economics, Agriculture and Related Subjects. Compilation of the Research Department
    of the Universal House of Justice, 1 May 1997.
McIntyre, Nancy E. 'Nine Points – A Conceptual Framework to Prepare Youth for
    Service'. 2001.
Mennillo, Tom. 'Carrying Out a Mandate: EcoAg apprentices learn importance of
    farming'. *The American Bahá'í*, vol. 32–3 (2001), p. 15.
One Country, the newsletter of the Bahá'í International Community, volume 7, issue 3,
    October–December 1995; volume 12, issue 3, October–December 2000.

The Garden Terraces of the Shrine of the Báb:

An Interview with the Architect, Fariborz Sahba

Introduction: The Significance of the Mount Carmel Gardens

The magnificent terraced gardens of the Shrine of the Báb on Mount Carmel in Haifa, Israel are a tangible response by the Bahá'í world community to the recognition that our common home, the earth, belongs to its Creator, and that we honour God by caring for it. The construction of the gardens, which restore the deforested and eroded slopes of Carmel, symbolizes the ultimate goal of religion, that the earth should become a reflection of the divine world – a place of peace, unity, beauty, permanence and abundance. In this sense, the gardens epitomize the Bahá'í perspective on the physical world and humanity's relationship to it; they also epitomize, through the forms of horticulture and landscape architecture, Bahá'í views on agriculture.

The location of the gardens is particularly significant. Mount Carmel, held sacred by Jews, Christians, Muslims and Bahá'ís alike, has been at the crossroads of human history for millennia. Cro-Magnon skeletons were found in caves hollowed out of the limestone walls, while some of the earliest agricultural sites in the world are found in its vicinity. Pythagoras stayed in these hills on his way to Egypt; Jesus' family is said to have paused here on their way back from Egypt; and the Crusaders made pilgrimage to this holy mountain in 1150 CE. In 1891, the same year he revealed the Tablet of the World, which spoke to the vital importance of agriculture, Bahá'u'lláh pitched his tent at the foot of the mountain, making it a holy place for Bahá'ís.

Carmel's sacred nature is noted as early as the middle of the second millennium, when the mountain is referred to as 'the sacred promontory'. In the fourth century CE, the philosopher Iamblicus described Carmel as 'sacred above all mountains and forbidden of access to the vulgar'. It was on Carmel that Elijah, who lived in the mid-ninth century BCE, fought the Baal priests in order to maintain the integrity of monotheism.

In 1868 the German Templers relocated to Carmel to fulfil their dream of creating God's kingdom on earth. The north face of the mountain began to change from that time. The catalyst for this transformation was Bahá'u'lláh, who, one afternoon in 1891, pointed out to his son 'Abdu'l-Bahá the spot that should serve as the permanent resting-place for the remains of the Báb, his martyred forerunner. Following these instructions, 'Abdu'l-Bahá erected the initial structure of the mausoleum and interred the remains of the Báb there in 1909. Nine rudimentary terraces below the Shrine were constructed in the 1930s and throughout the years other parcels of land were purchased until all the necessary property had been acquired. The ornamental superstructure, which makes this Shrine one of

Haifa's best known landmarks, was constructed between 1949 and 1953 under the supervision of 'Abdu'l-Bahá's grandson and head of the Faith, Shoghi Effendi, who developed extensive formal gardens. Extending beyond the immediate area of the Shrine, the gardens transformed the barren mountain slope into a natural sanctuary in the middle of the growing city of Haifa. In the face of renewed persecution of the Bahá'ís in Iran during the 1980s and 1990s, the worldwide Bahá'í community gathered the necessary financial and human resources, and the mountain was reshaped. The terraces now stretch a kilometre up the mountain, reaching a height of 225 metres (738 feet), and their landscape spans the mountain from 60 metres (197 feet) to 400 metres (1,312 feet).

The terraced gardens magnify the spiritual significance of the Shrine of the Báb, who foretold the coming of Bahá'u'lláh and whose life and death marked the inception of the modern age. Designed as nine concentric circles, the terraces appear to radiate outwards from the Shrine, and all of their lines and curves direct attention towards the building at their heart. Harmony, symmetry and order are important aesthetic principles from which the gardens take their form, as an expression of 'Abdu'l-Bahá's words: 'It is natural for the heart and spirit to take pleasure and enjoyment in all things that show forth symmetry, harmony, and perfection.'

To achieve symmetry, a large section of the mountain was literally moved, as thousands of cubic metres of rock were excavated and relocated to even out the contours of its face. Throughout the length of the terraces, a sense of continuity is maintained and the noise of the city is masked by the gentle sound of water, which flows in runnels down the sides of the staircases and through a series of fountains. The Sajur and Jatt stone used on the terraces was chosen to reflect the ancient architectural heritage of the Holy Land. Unique hand-carved motifs and different designs of the paving stones used in the central area of each terrace add distinctiveness in the midst of a harmonious overall design. The entrance plaza at Ben Gurion Avenue is also distinctive, with its marble cascade, runnels and a unique star-shaped fountain at the heart of sixteen diamond-shaped silent, crystalline pools of water that create two levels of glassy surfaces. On the ninth terrace, just below the Shrine, stand two young orange trees propagated from seeds taken from a tree in the courtyard of the Báb's house in Shiraz, Iran, before it was destroyed by Islamic revolutionary authorities.

While designing gardens to enhance the beauty of the Shrine, convey some of the richness of its history and symbolize its essential spiritual truths, the architect also paid close attention to the ecology of the area. Each terrace has three garden zones. The central area is formal in layout, with lawns of Zoysia grass, annual flowerbeds, santolina and duranta hedges, bushes and carefully pruned trees. The side zone is more informal, with flowering trees and perennial bushes characteristic of the Middle East, including drought-tolerant, low-maintenance succulents, oleanders, rosemary, lantana, olive, jacaranda, coral and plumeria. Wildflowers and bulbs blossom in profusion from December to April, while flowering trees and shrubs assume prominence during the spring and summer. The third zone has been left free to develop into natural forests that serve as wildlife corridors. Native animals such as mongooses, hedgehogs, land tortoises and reptiles have returned to the wildlife corridors created on the border of the terraces. Birds native to the area, including blue kingfishers, ravens, Palestinian sunbirds, finches, quail, hoopoe birds, hawks, owls, doves, bulbuls and jays, have also found a home there. Beneficial birds and insects such as ladybugs, praying mantises and spiders, which eat other insects, have been introduced to provide natural pest control and reduce the use of pesticides. On the steeper slopes, drought-resistant groundcovers such as ivy, juniper and lippia minimize erosion during the rains and preserve slope geometry with minimal maintenance.

The mountain has now come full circle, from the fertile, forested mountain known to the ancient Hebrews as a symbol of fruitfulness and prosperity, to a dry, rocky landscape caused by mass deforestation during the Ottoman occupation, to terraced gardens and informal landscaping that recall and amplify Carmel's former beauty. Once again, she embodies her Hebrew name 'kerem', meaning vineyard or fruitful garden. The completion of the Gardens in 2001 fulfils 'Abdu'l-Bahá's vision that 'A person standing on the summit of Mount Carmel will look upon the most sublime and majestic spectacle of the whole world'.

> It shall blossom abundantly, and rejoice even with joy and singing:
> the glory of Lebanon shall be given unto it, the excellency of Carmel and Sharon,
> they shall see the glory of the LORD, and the excellency of our God.
> Isaiah 35:2

Interview with Fariborz Sahba, Architect of the Terraces of the Shrine of the Báb and Project Manager of the Mount Carmel Bahá'í Projects

Fariborz Sahba, a Canadian citizen, was born in 1948 in Iran. He received a Master's degree in architecture in 1972 from the Faculty of Fine Arts at Tehran University. In Iran Mr Sahba was involved in the design of a wide range of prestigious buildings. In 1976 he was selected to design the Bahá'í House of Worship for the Indian subcontinent in New Delhi, India. This project, on which he worked for ten years as architect and project manager, was described by Canadian architect Arthur Erickson as 'one of the most remarkable achievements of our time, proving that the drive and vision of spirit can achieve miracles'. With over 3.5 million visitors a year, this building, commonly known as the 'Lotus of Bahapur', is one of the most visited sites in the world. In 1987 Mr Sahba was selected to design 18 terraces as a majestic approach to the Shrine of the Báb. He was also appointed project manager to execute the Bahá'í World Centre building projects on Mount Carmel. The terraces of the Shrine of the Báb received the 1998 Ephraim Lifshitz Award from the Municipality of Haifa and the 1999 Magshim Award from the Council for a Beautiful Israel. Mr Sahba has received many international awards, among them the First Honour Award 1987 for 'Excellence in Architecture' from the Interfaith Forum on Religion, Art and Architecture, an affiliate of the American Institute of Architects. Articles about his work have been published in almost 400 magazines and newspapers throughout the world.

Interviewer: Can you elaborate on the inspiration of the design you created for the terraces of the Shrine of the Báb?

Sahba: The greatest inspiration for me has been the life of the Báb himself. The story of his life is so tragic and moving, in particular the last seven years of his life, between his declaration and his martyrdom. The whole history of this period, the execution of thousands of his followers, their heroic and dramatic martyrdom, is something that will remain the source of inspiration for artists for centuries to come. In my room I have a photograph of the prison of Mákú, where the Báb spent several months of his life, which he poignantly described in a letter to the shah of Iran. It is so moving to look at this picture, this bleak, sad castle at the top of a rocky cliff with no greenery, where the Báb spent the days of his life with a few prisoners and a dog. It is such a contrast when you look at this picture and compare it with his shrine on Mount Carmel. They imprisoned this spiritual Sun in such a dark dungeon in the hope that his light would be extinguished. But that Sun rose from the other side of the world on this magnificent and beautiful Mount Carmel, in such a colourful and dramatic landscape, in such a heavenly garden, so appropriately named 'Vineyard of the Lord'. It is in memory of those dark nights in the prison of Mákú, during which the Báb said he did not have even one lamp in his presence, that this mountain has been flooded with light.

Another source of inspiration has been the design of the Shrine of the Báb itself, designed by the outstanding Canadian architect William Sutherland Maxwell, under the direction of Shoghi Effendi, the Guardian of the Bahá'í religion. It is so elegant and special. It has blended the architecture of the East and the West in such a unique and extraordinary manner that it really touches the heart of the visitor. The Shrine is now very appropriately known as the 'Bride of Carmel' and the 'Queen of Carmel'. Because of its unique character it has become the symbol of the city of Haifa and has grown very close to the heart of its people.

The gardens around the Shrine of the Báb, originally designed by Shoghi Effendi, are also most inspiring because of their simplicity, elegance and order. All these elements together create a very spiritual atmosphere. This is the place to discover colours, lights, the contrasts of emerald green of the grass and the deep, cold green of the cypress, with the beautiful duranta hedges blending the light emerald green and the dark cold green in a wonderful display of perfection of the green colour. Green, in fact, was the colour of the Báb himself, the colour he always dressed in. The gardens are also such a magnificent blend of the landscape of the East and the West. They bring the fragrance of the gardens of Shiraz, where the Báb was born, the symbol of which is cypress trees and orange blossoms, the magnificent geometry and order of the gardens of Kashmir and at the same time reflect the beautiful English gardens, all in one place. Anyone looking at this mountain, the Shrine and the gardens feels something very extraordinary in this space, even if he does not know the whole history of the Báb and his extraordinary spiritual mission.

Interviewer: What is the spiritual significance behind these terraces? Why 18 terraces?

Sahba: The terraces are in fact a tribute to the Shrine of the Báb, a prelude and approach to it. They are supposed to complement and enhance the Shrine and direct one towards it. If the Shrine can be considered a jewel, a diamond, the terraces are supposed to provide the most beautiful golden ring that will bring the beauty of the diamond to the fore and provide a perfect setting for it.

The terraces are 18 in number in memory of the first 18 disciples of the Báb, whom he called the Letters of Hai. The word Hai means life in both Arabic and Hebrew. These 18 disciples were known as the 'Letters of the Living'. So, symbolically, here is the Báb surrounded by his 18 disciples. The word 'Hai' – 'Living', made much more sense when I read the description that the Universal House of Justice once used to describe the terraces:

> The beauty and magnificence of the Gardens and Terraces now under development are symbolic of the nature of the transformation which is destined to occur both within the hearts of the world's peoples and in the physical environment of the planet.

I consider the terraces a symbol of beauty, perfection and hope, the way the Báb described and wished life to be for the people of the world.

Interviewer: The way these terraces have been designed on the steep slopes of Mount Carmel, it appears they have been created to inhibit people from visiting them and not inviting them. Can this be said to be correct?

Sahba: On the contrary. The extraordinary landscape of the Shrine, its location in the heart of the mountain provided a unique landscape and extraordinary challenges for the design. This is a very special place where the sea, the mountain and the sky merge in such a dramatic way. I have not seen many landscapes like it, where the elements of the sea, land, mountain and sky are so closely harmonized together and display their utmost beauty in the most extraordinary way. To me, the location of the Shrine and the 18 terraces each on a different level provide a ladder for ascent to pilgrims for their spiritual encounter with the Shrine during their pilgrimage. It is symbolic of the ascent of the soul to heaven. These are not supposed to be only beautiful gardens, they are supposed to be spiritual gardens. The spirit goes through the process of different stages. The same can be said of a pilgrim ascending the different levels of the terraced gardens.

Interviewer: What features can you highlight which would come to the fore in your design when the terraces are seen during the day and then again during the night?

Sahba: This is an important observation because the whole concept of the design is around light. As such, day and night make two important aspects of the design. The main concept is that the Shrine is the centre of nine concentric circles. If you look at the mountain from the sky you will find that the Shrine is the centre and then nine concentric circles create the basic geometric pattern for the nine terraces above and nine terraces below the Shrine. At night, it is as if waves of light are emanating from the Shrine, which is the centre of illumination. During the day these movements are created by sunlight filtering through the lines of cypress trees and reflecting on the curved parallel surfaces of the emerald green lawns. During the different hours of the day these surfaces reflect and display different shades of light and the green colour, in sharp contrast with the cold dark green of cypress and silver grey green of olive trees, becomes more prominently displayed. The deliberate order and rhythm that has been used in all parallel concentric circles, provide the comfort and relaxation that will contribute to the creation of that spiritual feeling. While walking towards the terraces all the lines appear to accompany the visitor. They are all in agreement with the visitor; there is no argument, no resistance, only continuity of space. One space merges with another and there is no end to the space. The same principle of order and rhythm is created by the lights at night. Waves of light emanating from the Shrine at night make them appear as 'terraces of light, light upon light'.

The Shrine itself, and the dome of the Shrine, has a magnificent relationship with the sky and with light and this combination provides at every hour of the day a different display of light, generating different feelings. There are special hours of the day when you look at the Shrine and the surrounding gardens, and they remind you of the Garden of Eden.

Interviewer: Water, I believe, plays a significant role in the terraces. Can you elaborate on this and on the subject of irrigation?

Sahba: Water has been used intensively along the entire length of the terraces, from the top to the bottom of the mountain. As you walk down the terraces, water accompanies you. The oasis of water attracts birds and, in harmony with the song of the birds, creates the best camouflage for the noise of the city, gives space for the tranquillity that you need to be separated from the day-to-day reality of life. When you are in the gardens you feel you are in a different world. The environment enables you to become detached from your mundane activities.

A very important factor in the choice of plants and trees in these gardens is water conservation. Israel is a dry country and water conservation is of great importance for the people of Israel. Intensive study has been made of plants that are drought resistant and if you look carefully you will find only the central terraces are designed with the more decorative plants that need water. The majority of the areas of the mountain moving away from the centre line of the terraces turns to drought resistant ground covers and then merges with forested areas that do not require any irrigation at all.

Israel is acknowledged for its state-of-the-art irrigation technology. All over the world people are interested to know about the experience and scientific studies carried out in this country on this subject. We have availed ourselves of the expertise of many outstanding leaders in the field of horticulture and irrigation and we have used the most advanced technology available in the country. The total requirement of water in our fountains is insignificant and limited to a couple of cubic metres of water during the day, mainly lost through evaporation. The entire volume of water is recycled; and while giving the impression that the water flows from the top to the bottom of the mountain, in fact, at the end of each terrace the water is recycled to the top of the terrace and there is no wastage of water. The system of irrigation used is intelligent and state-of-the-art; it avoids any wastage of water and uses the amount that is absolutely essential for the plants.

Many publications in Israel have stated that these gardens are exemplary for water conservation.

Interviewer: Have flowers and plants been chosen at random or is there a definite pattern in the landscape of the terraces and the colours which appear in every season?

Sahba: Nothing in the entire landscape of the terraces has been done randomly. Attention to detail is the essence of this design. Extensive experiments were carried out for years in an experimental garden that was developed on the mountain. We collected the most beautiful species of plants in Israel in order to determine those best suited for the type of soil, the direction of the sun, proximity of the sea and the direction of the wind on this mountain.

Colour has been of primary concern in the design of the landscape and the choice of plants. I have already spoken about light. Light and colours are very much related in that colour is an expression of light. We have carried out a special study of colour combinations of seasonal flowers. For example, when jacaranda trees are in bloom, convolvulus has been chosen to complement it as ground cover. This creates a purple season for the mountain and the most beautiful display of purple combines with other colours that are in harmony or in decided contrast with purple. In the same way we have a red season, a yellow and pink season. There is full coordination between the choice of seasonal flowers, permanent ground covers and flowering trees. The two colours used most intensively in the gardens are red and green. Red symbolizes the martyrdom of the Báb and green was, as I mentioned before, the colour that the Báb always used. The other colours are complementary.

Interviewer: What is the rationale behind the choice of different ornaments on the terraces?

Sahba: The ornaments used on the terraces are of no particular religious significance. They are just ornaments which have been used to enhance and to complement the gardens. In general, we have used the same type of ornaments that the Guardian of the Bahá'í religion, Shoghi Effendi, used in the gardens that he established in Haifa and 'Akká. However, there are thousands of ornamental details, from balustrades to gates and fountains, that have been designed in harmony with the architecture of the Shrine of the Báb. For example, if you look at the balustrades you will find that although they are very innovative, they are a reflection of the ornamental windows of the dome of the Shrine, so that in the overview they are complementary.

The landscape and the ornaments again reflect the concept of harmony of the East and the West. They are neither Eastern nor Western, at the same time they bring the fragrance of both these cultures. They cannot be classified as either Modern or Classic, for though they may be seen as modern and innovative, nevertheless they are old and familiar.

Interviewer: Can you comment on the choice of stone which has been used elaborately in the terraces?

Sahba: I have been very particular to use materials that are familiar in this environment and native to the mountain. All the stones used on the terraces are local, from the Galilee areas. It was with great effort that we found the best quality of local stone. When some parts of the ornaments, owing to their complex design or large numbers, were required to be carved with computerized equipment not available in Israel, we sent the stone from here to Italy to be carved and then returned it back to Israel. This is perhaps the first time that somebody has exported stone from Israel to Italy in this way. The beige coloured stone is in harmony with the Shrine of the Báb as well as the entire landscape of Haifa. The yellowish cream stone on the steps is darker and more comfortable and soothing for the eyes when ascending or descending, as it does not fully reflect light.

Interviewer: As the architect, what would you consider to be the unique features of the design of the terraces?

Sahba: First of all, it was a challenging and dramatic landscape. Secondly, the design had to be in harmony with the Shrine of the Báb and blend the architectural styles of the East and the West. Third, the way it addresses the challenge of the slope. The choice of concave terraces provides the most appropriate solution to this challenge. In other words, while resolving the 225 metres height difference from the bottom to the top of the mountain, minimum architectural features and walls have been produced, with the concept of building into the mountain rather than projecting upwards on the mountain.

This interview formed the basis for the text of Bahá'í Shrine and Gardens on Mount Carmel, Haifa, Israel – A Visual Journey, *edited and compiled by the Haifa Tourist Board and published by Haifa Municipality, Haifa Tourist Board and MOD Publishing House. It is used with the kind permission of Fariborz Sahba and the Haifa Municipality.*

George Ronald Bahá'í Studies Series

Bahá'í Studies is a challenging series developed for students of the Bahá'í Faith and those teaching courses on the religion. Subjects to be covered by the series include the history and development of the religion, its sociology, theology and literature, as well as the religious, social and cultural contexts of its birth and growth.

Bahá'í Studies will be especially interesting to those with an academic interest in the Bahá'í Faith, those who wish to undertake a serious study of the religion and those who want to study it at a level deeper than is possible with introductory books. Libraries and academic institutions will find the series a particularly useful addition to their collections.

CPSIA information can be obtained
at www.ICGtesting.com
Printed in the USA
FSHW020914130120
65895FS